McDougal Littell

GEORGIA HIGH SCHOOL
MATHEMATICS 2

McDougal Littell
A DIVISION OF HOUGHTON MIFFLIN COMPANY

Evanston, Illinois • Boston • Dallas

ISBN-10: 0-618-92021-8
ISBN-13: 978-0-618-92021-1   5 6 7 8 9-0918-11 10 09

Internet Web Site: http://www.mcdougallittell.com

About This Book

McDougal Littell Georgia High School Mathematics 2

The Georgia High School Mathematics 2 book covers all of the Georgia Performance Standards for Mathematics 2. Its content has been organized into a convenient sequence that corresponds to the strands of the Georgia Performance Standards. Georgia standards that correlate to the content of each lesson are given at point of use in the Student Edition and Teacher's Edition of *Georgia High School Mathematics 2*.

At the front of this book, you will find a complete listing of all the Georgia Performance Standards for Mathematics 2, along with a correlation of these standards to appropriate lessons in *Georgia High School Mathematics 2*.

Advisers and Reviewers

Curriculum Advisers and Reviewers

Michele Borror Long
Mathematics Teacher
LaGrange High School
LaGrange, GA

Sandye Ashley
Mathematics Teacher
Rome Middle School
Rome, GA

Georgia Panel

Ernest Adams
Mathematics Teacher,
    Department Chair
Northview High School
Duluth, GA

Salvatore Angelica
Mathematics Teacher
Luella High School
Locust Grove, GA

Sandra Campagnone
Mathematics Teacher
Pebblebrook High School
Mableton, GA

Mack Graham
Mathematics Teacher
Benjamin E. Mays High School
Atlanta, GA

Debra Hodge
Mathematics Teacher
Dunwoody High School
Dunwoody, GA

Carletta Malcom
Mathematics Teacher,
    Department Chair
Cedar Grove High School
Ellenwood, GA

Yvonne Pringle
Mathematics Teacher,
    Department Chair
North Atlanta High School
Atlanta, GA

Maria Travitz
Mathematics Teacher
Kennesaw Mountain High School
Kennesaw, GA

Melissa Walker
Mathematics Teacher,
    Department Chair
Martin Luther King, Jr. High School
Lithonia, GA

Contents

Student Resources

Correlation to Standards

Correlation of *McDougal Littell Georgia High School Mathematics 2* to the Georgia Performance Standards for Mathematics 2

NUMBER AND OPERATIONS

Students will use the complex number system.

Georgia Performance Standard		Lesson/Activity
MM2N1	**Students will represent and operate with complex numbers.**	
MM2N1a	Write square roots of negative numbers in imaginary form.	Lesson 1.1
MM2N1b	Write complex numbers in the form $a + bi$.	Lesson 1.1, Lesson 1.2, Problem Solving Workshop 1.2, Lesson 1.3, Technology Activity 1.3, Lesson 1.4, Investigating Math Activity 1.4
MM2N1c	Add, subtract, multiply, and divide complex numbers.	Lesson 1.2, Problem Solving Workshop 1.2, Lesson 1.3, Technology Activity 1.3
MM2N1d	Simplify expressions involving complex numbers.	Lesson 1.2, Problem Solving Workshop 1.2, Lesson 1.3, Technology Activity 1.3, Lesson 1.4, Investigating Math Activity 1.4

ALGEBRA

Students will investigate piecewise, exponential, and quadratic functions, using numerical, analytical, and graphical approaches, focusing on the use of these functions in problem-solving situations. Students will solve equations and inequalities and explore inverses of functions.

MM2A1	**Students will investigate step and piecewise functions, including greatest integer and absolute value functions.**	
MM2A1a	Write absolute value functions as piecewise functions.	Lesson 2.5
MM2A1b	Investigate and explain characteristics of a variety of piecewise functions including domain, range, vertex, axis of symmetry, zeros, intercepts, extrema, points of discontinuity, intervals over which the function is constant, intervals of increase and decrease, and rates of change.	Lesson 2.4, Investigating Math Activity 2.4, Lesson 2.5
MM2A1c	Solve absolute value equations and inequalities analytically, graphically, and by using appropriate technology.	Lesson 2.2, Problem Solving Workshop 2.2, Technology Activity 2.4

Georgia Performance Standard		Lesson/Activity
MM2A2	**Students will explore exponential functions.**	
MM2A2a	Extend properties of exponents to include all integer exponents.	Lesson 4.1, Investigating Math Activity 4.1
MM2A2b	Investigate and explain characteristics of exponential functions, including domain and range, asymptotes, zeros, intercepts, intervals of increase and decrease, rates of change, and end behavior.	Lesson 4.4, Lesson 4.5
MM2A2c	Graph functions as transformations of $f(x) = a^x$.	Lesson 4.4, Lesson 4.5
MM2A2d	Solve simple exponential equations and inequalities analytically, graphically, and by using appropriate technology.	Lesson 4.6, Technology Activity 4.6
MM2A2e	Understand and use basic exponential functions as models of real phenomena.	Lesson 4.4, Lesson 4.5
MM2A2f	Understand and recognize geometric sequences as exponential functions with domains that are whole numbers.	Lesson 4.9
MM2A2g	Interpret the constant ratio in a geometric sequence as the base of the associated exponential function.	Lesson 4.9
MM2A3	**Students will analyze quadratic functions in the forms** $f(x) = ax^2 + bx + c$ **and** $f(x) = a(x - h)^2 + k$.	
MM2A3a	Convert between standard and vertex form.	Lesson 3.2, Lesson 3.7
MM2A3b	Graph quadratic functions as transformations of the function $f(x) = x^2$.	Lesson 3.1, Lesson 3.2, Investigating Math Activity 3.2
MM2A3c	Investigate and explain characteristics of quadratic functions, including domain, range, vertex, axis of symmetry, zeros, intercepts, extrema, intervals of increase and decrease, and rates of change.	Lesson 3.1, Lesson 3.2, Lesson 3.3, Lesson 3.4
MM2A3d	Explore arithmetic series and various ways of computing their sums.	Lesson 4.7, Lesson 4.8, Investigating Math Activity 4.8, Problem Solving Workshop 4.8
MM2A3e	Explore sequences of partial sums of arithmetic series as examples of quadratic functions.	Lesson 4.8
MM2A4	**Students will solve quadratic equations and inequalities in one variable.**	
MM2A4a	Solve equations graphically using appropriate technology.	Problem Solving Workshop 3.8
MM2A4b	Find real and complex solutions of equations by factoring, taking square roots, and applying the quadratic formula.	Lesson 3.4, Lesson 3.5, Lesson 3.6, Lesson 3.7, Lesson 3.8
MM2A4c	Analyze the nature of roots using technology and using the discriminant.	Lesson 3.8, Investigating Math Activity 3.8
MM2A4d	Solve quadratic inequalities both graphically and algebraically, and describe the solutions using linear inequalities.	Lesson 3.9, Technology Activity 3.9

Georgia Performance Standard		Lesson/Activity
MM2A5	Students will explore inverses of functions.	
MM2A5a	Discuss the characteristics of functions and their inverses, including one-to-oneness, domain, and range.	Lesson 2.3, Lesson 4.3
MM2A5b	Determine inverses of linear, quadratic, and power functions and functions of the form $f(x) = \frac{a}{x}$, including the use of restricted domains.	Lesson 4.3
MM2A5c	Explore the graphs of functions and their inverses.	Lesson 4.3
MM2A5d	Use composition to verify that functions are inverses of each other.	Lesson 4.2, Lesson 4.3

GEOMETRY

Students will explore right triangles and right-triangle trigonometry. They will understand and apply properties of circles and spheres, and use them in determining related measures.

MM2G1	Students will identify and use special right triangles.	
MM2G1a	Determine the lengths of sides of 30°-60°-90° triangles.	Lesson 5.1, Investigating Math Activity 5.1
MM2G1b	Determine the lengths of sides of 45°-45°-90° triangles.	Lesson 5.1, Investigating Math Activity 5.1
MM2G2	Students will define and apply sine, cosine, and tangent ratios to right triangles.	
MM2G2a	Discover the relationship of the trigonometric ratios for similar triangles.	Lesson 5.2, Lesson 5.3, Technology Activity 5.3
MM2G2b	Explain the relationship between the trigonometric ratios of complementary angles.	Lesson 5.2, Lesson 5.3, Investigating Math Activity 5.4
MM2G2c	Solve application problems using the trigonometric ratios.	Lesson 5.2, Lesson 5.3, Lesson 5.4, Problem Solving Workshop 5.4
MM2G3	Students will understand properties of circles.	
MM2G3a	Understand and use properties of chords, tangents, and secants as an application of triangle similarity.	Lesson 6.1, Lesson 6.3, Lesson 6.6
MM2G3b	Understand and use properties of central, inscribed, and related angles.	Lesson 6.2, Investigating Math Activity 6.2, Problem Solving Workshop 6.2, Lesson 6.4, Lesson 6.5, Investigating Math Activity 6.5
MM2G3c	Use the properties of circles to solve problems involving the length of an arc and the area of a sector.	Lesson 6.7, Lesson 6.8
MM2G3d	Justify measurements and relationships in circles using geometric and algebraic properties.	Lesson 6.1, Lesson 6.2, Lesson 6.3, Lesson 6.4, Lesson 6.5, Lesson 6.6, Lesson 6.8, Technology Activity 6.8

Georgia Performance Standard		Lesson/Activity
MM2G4	Students will find and compare the measures of spheres.	
MM2G4a	Use and apply surface area and volume of a sphere.	Lesson 6.9
MM2G4b	Determine the effect on surface area and volume of changing the radius or diameter of a sphere.	Lesson 6.9

DATA ANALYSIS AND PROBABILITY

Students will demonstrate understanding of data analysis by posing questions to be answered by collecting data. Students will organize, represent, investigate, interpret, and make inferences from data. They will use regression to analyze data and to make inferences.

MM2D1	Using sample data, students will make informal inferences about population means and standard deviations.	
MM2D1a	Pose a question and collect sample data from at least two different populations.	Lesson 7.5, Technology Activity 7.5, Lesson 7.6
MM2D1b	Understand and calculate the means and standard deviations of sets of data.	Lesson 7.3, Problem Solving Workshop 7.3
MM2D1c	Use means and standard deviations to compare data sets.	Lesson 7.3
MM2D1d	Compare the means and standard deviations of random samples with the corresponding population parameters including those population parameters for normal distribution. Observe that the different sample means vary from one sample to the next. Observe that the distribution of the sample means has less variability than the population distribution.	Lesson 7.4, Lesson 7.6
MM2D2	Students will determine an algebraic model to quantify the association between two quantitative variables.	
MM2D2a	Gather and plot data that can be modeled with linear and quadratic functions.	Lesson 7.1, Investigating Math Activity 7.1, Lesson 7.2, Investigating Math Activity 7.2, Lesson 7.7
MM2D2b	Examine the issues of curve fitting by finding good linear fits to data using simple methods such as the median-median line and "eyeballing."	Lesson 7.1, Investigating Math Activity 7.1
MM2D2c	Understand and apply the processes of linear and quadratic regression for curve fitting using appropriate technology.	Lesson 7.2, Investigating Math Activity 7.2, Lesson 7.7
MM2D2d	Investigate issues that arise when using data to explore the relationship between two variables, including confusion between correlation and causation.	Lesson 7.1

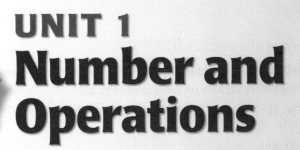

UNIT 1
Number and Operations

Write Complex Numbers

Georgia Performance Standards: MM2N1a, MM2N1b

Goal Use the imaginary unit i to write complex numbers.

Vocabulary

A number r is a **square root** of a number s if $r^2 = s$.

The expression $\sqrt{s}$ is called a **radical**. The symbol $\sqrt{}$ is a radical sign and the number s beneath the radical sign is the **radicand** of the expression.

$\sqrt{a \cdot b} = \sqrt{a} \cdot \sqrt{b}$ Product property of radicals

$\sqrt{\dfrac{a}{b}} = \dfrac{\sqrt{a}}{\sqrt{b}}$ Quotient property of radicals

The **imaginary unit i** is defined as $i = \sqrt{-1}$ where $i^2 = -1$.

By adding real numbers to real multiples of this imaginary unit, the set of complex numbers is obtained. A **complex number** written in standard form is a number $a + bi$ where a and b are real numbers. The number a is the real part of the complex number, and the number bi is the imaginary part.

If $b \neq 0$, then $a + bi$ is an **imaginary number**. If $a = 0$ and $b \neq 0$, then $a + bi$ is a **pure imaginary number**. The diagram below shows how different types of complex numbers are related.

Two complex numbers $a + bi$ and $c + di$ are equal if and only if $a = c$ and $b = d$. For example, if $x + yi = 5 - 3i$, then $x = 5$ and $y = -3$.

Complex Numbers ($a + bi$)

Real Numbers ($a + 0i$)	Imaginary Numbers ($a + bi, b \neq 0$)
-1 $\quad$ $\dfrac{9}{2}$ π $\quad$ $\sqrt{3}$	$2 + 3i$ $\qquad\qquad$ $5 - 5i$ **Pure Imaginary Numbers** ($0 + bi, b \neq 0$) $-4i$ $\qquad$ $6i$

Example 1   **Use properties of square roots**

Simplify the expression.

a. $\sqrt{8} \cdot \sqrt{6} = \sqrt{48} = \sqrt{16} \cdot \sqrt{3} = 4\sqrt{3}$ Product property

b. $\sqrt{\dfrac{5}{36}} = \dfrac{\sqrt{5}}{\sqrt{36}} = \dfrac{\sqrt{5}}{6}$ Quotient property

Georgia Performance Standards

MM2N1a Write square roots of negative numbers in imaginary form. ☑

MM2N1b Write complex numbers in the form $a + bi$. ☑

Example 2 Write complex numbers in standard form

a. $\sqrt{-9} = \sqrt{9(-1)} = \sqrt{9} \cdot \sqrt{-1} = 3i$

b. $\sqrt{-5} = \sqrt{5(-1)} = \sqrt{5} \cdot \sqrt{-1} = i\sqrt{5}$

c. $\sqrt{-12} = \sqrt{12(-1)} = \sqrt{12} \cdot \sqrt{-1} = 2i\sqrt{3}$

d. $4 + \sqrt{-16} = 4 + \sqrt{16(-1)} = 4 + \sqrt{16} \cdot \sqrt{-1} = 4 + 4i$

Guided Practice for Examples 1 and 2

Simplify the expression.

1. $\sqrt{300}$

2. $\sqrt{98}$

3. $\sqrt{\dfrac{19}{144}}$

4. $\sqrt{\dfrac{20}{81}}$

Write the complex number in standard form.

5. $\sqrt{-1}$

6. $\sqrt{-25}$

7. $\sqrt{-2}$

8. $\sqrt{-20}$

9. $1 + \sqrt{-36}$

10. $7 - \sqrt{-27}$

Example 3 Equality of complex numbers

Find real numbers x and y to make the equation true.

a. $2x + 2yi = 6 + 4i$ **b.** $3x + 5yi = 9 - 15i$

Solution

Because the numbers are equal, their real parts must be equal and their imaginary parts must be equal.

a. $2x = 6$ Set the real parts equal to each other.

     $x = 3$ Divide each side by 2 to solve for x.

     $2y = 4$ Set the imaginary parts equal to each other.

     $y = 2$ Divide each side by 2 to solve for y.

b. $3x = 9$ Set the real parts equal to each other.

     $x = 3$ Divide each side by 3 to solve for x.

     $5y = -15$ Set the imaginary parts equal to each other.

     $y = -3$ Divide each side by 5 to solve for y.

Guided Practice for Example 3

Find real numbers x and y to make the equation true.

11. $6x + 3yi = 24 + 48i$

12. $3x - 4yi = -21 - 32i$

Exercise
Set A

MM2N1a   Write square roots of negative numbers in
         imaginary form.

MM2N1b   Write complex numbers in the form $a + bi$.

Simplify the expression.

1. $\sqrt{500}$ **2.** $\sqrt{108}$ **3.** $\sqrt{242}$ **4.** $\sqrt{128}$

5. $\sqrt{125}$ **6.** $\sqrt{343}$ **7.** $\sqrt{\dfrac{25}{169}}$ **8.** $\sqrt{\dfrac{16}{36}}$

9. $\sqrt{\dfrac{23}{121}}$ **10.** $\sqrt{\dfrac{6}{9}}$ **11.** $\sqrt{\dfrac{27}{4}}$ **12.** $\sqrt{\dfrac{32}{25}}$

Match the complex number with the correct standard form.

13. $10 + \sqrt{-16}$ **A.** $4i$

14. $\sqrt{-16}$ **B.** $10 + 4i$

15. $10 - \sqrt{-16}$ **C.** $10 - 4i$

Write the complex number in standard form.

16. $\sqrt{-4}$ **17.** $\sqrt{-64}$ **18.** $\sqrt{-100}$

19. $\sqrt{-32}$ **20.** $\sqrt{-17}$ **21.** $\sqrt{-75}$

22. $\sqrt{-45}$ **23.** $\sqrt{\dfrac{108}{49}}$ **24.** $\sqrt{-\dfrac{68}{81}}$

25. $3 + \sqrt{-2}$ **26.** $5 - \sqrt{-21}$ **27.** $9 + \sqrt{-81}$

28. $-2 + \sqrt{-18}$ **29.** $-4 - \sqrt{49}$ **30.** $8 - \sqrt{-48}$

31. $\sqrt{-11} + 6$ **32.** $-\sqrt{-25} + 12$ **33.** $\sqrt{144} - 11$

Error Analysis *Describe* and correct the error in writing the complex number
in standard form.

34.

$$5 - \sqrt{-9} = 5 - (\sqrt{-9})$$
$$= 5 - (-3)$$
$$= 5 + 3$$
$$= 8$$

$\times$

35.

$$3 + \sqrt{-8} = 3 + \sqrt{8(-1)}$$
$$= 3 + \sqrt{8}\sqrt{-1}$$
$$= 3 + 2i\sqrt{2}$$
$$= 5i\sqrt{2}$$

$\times$

Find real numbers *x* and *y* to make the equation true.

36. $2x - 4yi = 8 + 12i$ **37.** $5x + yi = 10 + i$ **38.** $-3x + 2yi = 15 - 4i$

39. $-2x + 6yi = 14 - 24i$ **40.** $4x + 3i = 16 - yi$ **41.** $11 - 5yi = x + 10i$

42. $x + 7yi = -6 + 21i$ **43.** $-4x - 4yi = 4 + 48i$ **44.** $22 - 8i = 11x + 4yi$

45. The complex numbers $-2xi + 8$ and $6 + 4yi$ are equal. Find the values of x and y.

Exercise Set B

MM2N1a Write square roots of negative numbers in imaginary form.

MM2N1b Write complex numbers in the form $a + bi$.

Simplify the expression.

1. $\sqrt{52}$

2. $\sqrt{99}$

3. $\sqrt{175}$

4. $\sqrt{392}$

5. $\sqrt{375}$

6. $\sqrt{270}$

7. $\sqrt{\dfrac{76}{225}}$

8. $\sqrt{\dfrac{200}{49}}$

9. $\sqrt{\dfrac{405}{4}}$

10. $\sqrt{\dfrac{75}{256}}$

11. $\sqrt{\dfrac{216}{625}}$

12. $\sqrt{\dfrac{140}{196}}$

Match the complex number with the correct standard form.

13. $-4 + \sqrt{-50}$

14. $-\sqrt{-25}$

15. $-4 - \sqrt{-76}$

A. $-4 - 2i\sqrt{19}$

B. $-5i$

C. $-4 + 5i\sqrt{2}$

Write the complex number in standard form.

16. $\sqrt{-121}$

17. $\sqrt{-169}$

18. $\sqrt{-225}$

19. $\sqrt{-78}$

20. $\sqrt{-\dfrac{63}{121}}$

21. $\sqrt{-\dfrac{208}{25}}$

22. $\sqrt{-180}$

23. $\sqrt{-(-128)}$

24. $\sqrt{-168}$

25. $8 + \sqrt{-8}$

26. $-15 + \sqrt{-28}$

27. $1 - \sqrt{-400}$

28. $-21 + \sqrt{-52}$

29. $4 - \sqrt{17 - 49}$

30. $18 - \sqrt{97 - 48}$

31. $\sqrt{-161} - 4$

32. $-\sqrt{-\dfrac{125}{9}} - 15$

33. $\sqrt{-\dfrac{120}{169}} + 29$

Find real numbers x and y to make the equation true.

34. $x - 3yi = 5 + 15i$

35. $-5x - yi = 20 - 9i$

36. $-6x + 7yi = 18 + 28i$

37. $-4x + 5yi = -2 - 35i$

38. $4x - 7i = 22 - 2yi$

39. $\dfrac{3}{4} - 2yi = 2x + 5i$

40. $5x - 7yi = -\dfrac{7}{10} - 56i$

41. $-2x - \dfrac{1}{3}yi = 26 + 4i$

42. $27 - 8i = -13x + 3yi$

43. $-14 + 12i = 7x - 6yi$

44. The complex numbers $\dfrac{2}{5}xi + 3$ and $-4 - \dfrac{1}{4}yi$ are equal. Find the values of x and y.

UNIT 1

Add and Subtract Complex Numbers

Georgia Performance Standards: MM2N1b, MM2N1c, MM2N1d

Goal Add and subtract complex numbers.

Vocabulary

To add (or subtract) two complex numbers, add (or subtract) their real parts and their imaginary parts separately.

Sum of complex numbers:

$$(a + bi) + (c + di) = (a + c) + (b + d)i$$

Difference of complex numbers:

$$(a + bi) - (c + di) = (a - c) + (b - d)i$$

Example 1 Add complex numbers

Write the expression as a complex number in standard form.

a. $(7 - i) + (5 + 3i)$

b. $(3 + 2i) + (7 + 6i)$

c. $(-5 + 3i) + (-2 - 8i)$

Solution

a. $(7 - i) + (5 + 3i) = (7 + 5) + (-1 + 3)i$ Complex addition

$= 12 + 2i$ Write in standard form.

b. $(3 + 2i) + (7 + 6i) = (3 + 7) + (2 + 6)i$ Complex addition

$= 10 + 8i$ Write in standard form.

c. $(-5 + 3i) + (-2 - 8i) = (-5 - 2) + (3 - 8)i$ Complex addition

$= -7 - 5i$ Write in standard form.

Guided Practice for Example 1

Write the expression as a complex number in standard form.

1. $(5 - 2i) + (2 + 7i)$ **2.** $(-1 + i) + (6 - 3i)$ **3.** $(3 + 2i) + (-5 - i)$

Example 2 Subtract complex numbers

Write the expression as a complex number in standard form.

a. $(6 - 5i) - (1 + 2i)$

b. $(4 + 2i) - (5 - i)$

c. $(-6 + 5i) - (-3 + 9i)$

Georgia Performance Standards

MM2N1b Write complex numbers in the form $a + bi$. ✓

MM2N1c Add, subtract, multiply, and divide complex numbers. ✓

MM2N1d Simplify expressions involving complex numbers. ✓

Example 2   Subtract complex numbers *(continued)*

Solution

a. $(6 - 5i) - (1 + 2i) = (6 - 1) + (-5 - 2)i$ Complex subtraction

$= 5 - 7i$ Write in standard form.

b. $(4 + 2i) - (5 - i) = (4 - 5) + (2 + 1)i$ Complex subtraction

$= -1 + 3i$ Write in standard form.

c. $(-6 + 5i) - (-3 + 9i) = (-6 + 3) + (5 - 9)i$ Complex subtraction

$= -3 - 4i$ Write in standard form.

Example 3   Add and subtract complex numbers

Write the expression as a complex number in standard form.

a. $11 - (8 + 7i) + 3i$

b. $9 - (10 + 2i) - 5i$

c. $5i + (-4 + 4i) + 17$

Solution

a. $11 - (8 + 7i) + 3i = [(11 - 8) - 7i] + 3i$ Complex subtraction

$= (3 - 7i) + 3i$ Simplify.

$= 3 + (-7 + 3)i$ Complex addition

$= 3 - 4i$ Write in standard form.

b. $9 - (10 + 2i) - 5i = [(9 - 10) - 2i] - 5i$ Complex subtraction

$= (-1 - 2i) - 5i$ Simplify.

$= -1 + (-2 - 5)i$ Complex subtraction

$= -1 - 7i$ Write in standard form.

c. $5i + (-4 + 4i) + 17 = [-4 + (5 + 4)i] + 17$ Complex addition

$= (-4 + 9i) + 17$ Simplify.

$= (-4 + 17) + 9i$ Complex addition

$= 13 + 9i$ Write in standard form.

Guided Practice for Examples 2 and 3

Write the expression as a complex number in standard form.

4. $(9 - 4i) - (-2 + 3i)$ **5.** $(6 + 2i) - (5 - 4i)$ **6.** $(-3 + 7i) - (-3 - i)$

Write the expression as a complex number in standard form.

7. $8 - (2 + 4i) + 3i$ **8.** $2 - (7 + 2i) - 4i$ **9.** $-7i + (9 + i) + 6$

Exercise Set A

MM2N1b Write complex numbers in the form $a + bi$.

MM2N1c Add, subtract, multiply, and divide complex numbers.

MM2N1d Simplify expressions involving complex numbers.

Match the expression with the correct standard form.

1. $(3 + 5i) - (-2 + 5i)$

2. $(5 + 2i) + (8 - i)$

3. $(2 + i) + (-2 - 3i)$

4. $(3 + 4i) - (7 - 9i)$

A. $13 + i$

B. $-4 + 13i$

C. $-2i$

D. 5

5. **Multiple Choice** What is the standard form of the expression $(3 + 2i) - (8 + 3i)$?

A. -4 **B.** $-5 + 7i$ **C.** $-5 - i$ **D.** $5 + i$

Write the expression as a complex number in standard form.

6. $(-3 + 3i) + (2 - i)$

7. $(8 + 2i) + (2 - 3i)$

8. $(1 - i) + (1 - i)$

9. $(5 + 4i) - (4 + 2i)$

10. $(7 + 3i) - (1 + 7i)$

11. $(-6 + 2i) + (2 - i)$

12. $(14 + 19i) + (-16 - 11i)$

13. $(-8 + 4i) + (-1 + 13i)$

14. $(-1 + 19i) - (4 - i)$

15. $(-18 - 11i) + (-14 + 17i)$

16. $(-20 + 4i) - 16i$

17. $6 - (-11 + 9i)$

18. $18 + (-2 + 18i)$

19. $(1 - 17i) + (12 - i)$

20. $-14 + (-17 + 7i) - 20i$

21. $14 - (6 - 12i) + 8i$

22. $-7i + (-6 - 19i) + 5$

23. $3 + (12 + 15i) - 7i$

24. $-8i + (9 + 16i) - 16$

25. $-18i + (-8 - 4i) - 6$

26. $9 + (-10 + 5i) + 14i$

27. $-12 - (7 - 5i) + 4i$

Error Analysis *Describe* and correct the error in writing the expression as a complex number in standard form.

28.

$$(2 + 4i) - (-1 + 9i) = (2 - 1) + (4 - 9)i$$
$$= 1 - 5i$$

✗

29.

$$6 - (3 + 4i) + (-4i) = 6 - (3 + 4i - 4i)$$
$$= 6 - 3$$
$$= 3$$

✗

MM2N1b Write complex numbers in the form $a + bi$.

MM2N1c Add, subtract, multiply, and divide complex numbers.

MM2N1d Simplify expressions involving complex numbers.

Match the expression with the correct standard form.

1. $6 - (-3 + 8i) + 5i$

2. $-8 + (-18 - 20i) + 12i$

3. $10i + (6 + 4i) - 2$

4. $-i - (14 - 4i) - 10$

A. $-24 + 3i$

B. $4 + 14i$

C. $-26 - 8i$

D. $9 - 3i$

5. **Multiple Choice** What is the standard form of the expression $10 - (26 + 5i) - 18i$?

   A. -16 **B.** $-16 - 13i$ **C.** $-16 - 23i$ **D.** $16 + 23i$

Write the expression as a complex number in standard form.

6. $(-6 - 29i) + (8 - 12i)$

7. $(8 + 11i) + (25 + 28i)$

8. $(16 - 26i) + (-3 + 27i)$

9. $(-14 - 6i) - (28 + 13i)$

10. $(17 - 21i) + (16 + 2i)$

11. $(9 + 20i) - (14 + 11i)$

12. $(-8 + 9i) - (-17 - 9i)$

13. $(25 - i) + (-22 + 22i)$

14. $(-7 + 13i) - (4 + 6i)$

15. $(-5 + i) - (-21 - 23i)$

16. $(-30 + 4i) - 17i$

17. $13 - (29 + 13i)$

18. $-4 + (-9 - 8i)$

19. $(1.5 - 4.2i) + (1.2 - 2.6i)$

20. $(6.3 + 1.5i) - (2.5 - 7.1i)$

21. $(-2.7 + 7.8i) + (0.6 + 5.3i)$

22. $-27i + (-27 - 26i) + 9$

23. $13 - (23 + 7i) - 25i$

24. $-10i + (-17 + 16i) - 23$

25. $12i + (1 - 4i) - 25$

26. $20 + (-23 - 8i) + 7i$

27. $-13 - (25 - 3i) + 25i$

28. **Multiple Representations** Every complex number corresponds to a point in the complex plane. (You will learn more about the complex plane in Lesson 1.4.) The complex plane has a horizontal axis called the real axis and a vertical axis called the imaginary axis. The graph shows how you can geometrically add two complex numbers (in this case, $3 + i$ and $2 + 4i$) to find their sum (in this case, $5 + 5i$). Use the definition of complex addition to find each of the following sums and then find the sums by drawing a graph.

   a. $(3 + i) + (1 + 3i)$

   b. $(-5 + 2i) + (6 - 3i)$

   c. $(4 - 4i) + (-3 - i)$

   d. $(8 + 2i) + (-4 - 6i)$

LESSON 1.2

Problem Solving Workshop

Problem Circuit components such as resistors, inductors, and capacitors all oppose the flow of current. This opposition is called *resistance* for resistors and *reactance* for inductors and capacitors. A circuit's total opposition to current flow is *impedance*. All of these quantities are measured in ohms (Ω).

Component and symbol	Resistor —⋀⋀—	Inductor —⬚⬚⬚—	Capacitor —⊣⊢—
Resistance or reactance	R	L	C
Impedance	R	Li	$-Ci$

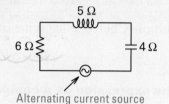

Alternating current source

The table shows the relationship between a component's resistance or reactance and its contribution to impedance. A *series circuit* is also shown with the resistance or reactance of each component labeled.

The impedance for a series circuit is the sum of the impedances for the individual components. Find the impedance of the circuit shown above.

STEP 1 Read and Understand

What do you know? The resistance or reactance of each component in the circuit and how it is related to impedance

What do you want to find out? The impedance of the circuit

STEP 2 Make a Plan Use what you know to find the impedance of the circuit by adding the contribution to impedance of each component.

STEP 3 Solve the Problem The resistor has a resistance of 6 ohms, so its impedance is 6 ohms. The inductor has a reactance of 5 ohms, so its impedance is $5i$ ohms. The capacitor has a reactance of 4 ohms, so its impedance is $-4i$ ohms.

$$\text{Impedance of circuit} = 6 + 5i + (-4i) \qquad \text{Add the individual impedances.}$$
$$= 6 + i \qquad\qquad\qquad \text{Simplify.}$$

The impedance of the circuit is $6 + i$ ohms.

STEP 4 Look Back Double-check to make sure that you converted the resistance or reactance of each component to the correct impedance.

Practice

1. **What If?** Suppose the series circuit above has a resistor with a resistance of 10 ohms, an inductor with a reactance of 7 ohms, and a capacitor with a reactance of 5 ohms. What is the impedance of the circuit?

2. **Circuits** A series circuit has a resistor with a resistance of 14 ohms, an inductor with a reactance of 8 ohms, and a capacitor with a reactance of 8 ohms. What is the impedance of the circuit?

UNIT 1

Multiply and Divide Complex Numbers

Georgia Performance Standards: MM2N1b, MM2N1c, MM2N1d

Goal Multiply and divide complex numbers.

Vocabulary

To multiply two complex numbers, use the distributive property or the FOIL method just as you do when multiplying real numbers or algebraic expressions.

Two complex numbers of the form $a + bi$ and $a - bi$ are called **complex conjugates**. The product of complex conjugates is always a real number. For example, $(2 + 4i)(2 - 4i) = 4 - 8i + 8i + 16 = 20$. You can use this fact to divide complex numbers. When a quotient has an imaginary number in the denominator, rewrite the denominator as a real number so you can express the quotient in standard form.

Example 1   Multiply complex numbers

Write the expression as a complex number in standard form.

a. $3i(-7 + i)$ **b.** $(8 - 2i)(-6 + 5i)$

c. $(-3 + i)(8 + 5i)$ **d.** $(4 + 3i)(4 - 3i)$

Solution

a. $3i(-7 + i) = -21i + 3i^2$ Distributive property

$\quad\quad\quad\quad\quad = -21i + 3(-1)$ Use $i^2 = -1$.

$\quad\quad\quad\quad\quad = -21i - 3$ Simplify.

$\quad\quad\quad\quad\quad = -3 - 21i$ Write in standard form.

b. $(8 - 2i)(-6 + 5i) = -48 + 40i + 12i - 10i^2$ Multiply using FOIL.

$\quad\quad\quad\quad\quad\quad\quad\quad = -48 + 52i - 10(-1)$ Simplify and use $i^2 = -1$.

$\quad\quad\quad\quad\quad\quad\quad\quad = -48 + 52i + 10$ Simplify.

$\quad\quad\quad\quad\quad\quad\quad\quad = -38 + 52i$ Write in standard form.

c. $(-3 + i)(8 + 5i) = -24 - 15i + 8i + 5i^2$ Multiply using FOIL.

$\quad\quad\quad\quad\quad\quad\quad = -24 - 7i + 5(-1)$ Simplify and use $i^2 = -1$.

$\quad\quad\quad\quad\quad\quad\quad = -24 - 7i - 5$ Simplify.

$\quad\quad\quad\quad\quad\quad\quad = -29 - 7i$ Write in standard form.

d. $(4 + 3i)(4 - 3i) = 16 - 12i + 12i - 9i^2$ Multiply using FOIL.

$\quad\quad\quad\quad\quad\quad\quad = 16 - 9(-1)$ Simplify and use $i^2 = -1$.

$\quad\quad\quad\quad\quad\quad\quad = 25$ Simplify.

Guided Practice for Example 1

Write the expression as a complex number in standard form.

1. $-2i(1 + 4i)$ **2.** $(-5 + i)(2 - 7i)$ **3.** $(3 - 2i)(-5 - 9i)$

Example 3 | Divide complex numbers

Write the expression as a complex number in standard form.

a. $\dfrac{8 + 3i}{1 - 2i}$ **b.** $\dfrac{5 - 2i}{3 + 8i}$ **c.** $\dfrac{4 + 3i}{5i}$

Solution

a. $\dfrac{8 + 3i}{1 - 2i} = \dfrac{8 + 3i}{1 - 2i} \times \dfrac{1 + 2i}{1 + 2i}$ Multiply numerator and denominator by $1 + 2i$.

$= \dfrac{8 + 16i + 3i + 6i^2}{1 + 2i - 2i - 4i^2}$ Multiply using FOIL.

$= \dfrac{8 + 19i + 6(-1)}{1 - 4(-1)}$ Simplify and use $i^2 = 1$.

$= \dfrac{2 + 19i}{5}$ Simplify.

$= \dfrac{2}{5} + \dfrac{19}{5}i$ Write in standard form.

b. $\dfrac{5 - 2i}{3 + 8i} = \dfrac{5 - 2i}{3 + 8i} \times \dfrac{3 - 8i}{3 - 8i}$ Multiply numerator and denominator by $3 - 8i$.

$= \dfrac{15 - 40i - 6i + 16i^2}{9 - 24i + 24i - 64i^2}$ Multiply using FOIL.

$= \dfrac{15 - 46i + 16(-1)}{9 - 64(-1)}$ Simplify and use $i^2 = 1$.

$= \dfrac{-1 - 46i}{73}$ Simplify.

$= -\dfrac{1}{73} - \dfrac{46}{73}i$ Write in standard form.

c. $\dfrac{4 + 3i}{5i} = \dfrac{4 + 3i}{5i} \times \left(\dfrac{-5i}{-5i}\right)$ Conjugate of $5i$ is $-5i$.

$= \dfrac{-20i - 15i^2}{-25i^2}$ Distributive property

$= \dfrac{-20i - 15(-1)}{-25(-1)}$ Simplify and use $i^2 = 1$.

$= \dfrac{15 - 20i}{25} = \dfrac{3}{5} - \dfrac{4}{5}i$ Write in standard form.

Guided Practice for Example 2

Write the expression as a complex number in standard form.

4. $\dfrac{5}{1 + i}$ **5.** $\dfrac{5 + 2i}{3 - 2i}$ **6.** $\dfrac{2 - 6i}{4i}$

Exercise Set A

MM2N1b Write complex numbers in the form $a + bi$.

MM2N1c Add, subtract, multiply, and divide complex numbers.

MM2N1d Simplify expressions involving complex numbers.

1. What is the complex conjugate of $a - bi$?

Match the expression with the correct standard form.

2. $(-8 - 2i)(1 + 2i)$

3. $10i(2 + i)$

4. $(1 - 4i)^2$

A. $-10 + 20i$

B. $-4 - 18i$

C. $-15 - 8i$

Write the expression as a complex number in standard form.

5. $-6(8 - 2i)$

6. $11i(5 + 8i)$

7. $6i(-3 - 7i)$

8. $(1 - 6i)(2 + 3i)$

9. $(2 + 4i)(2 - 6i)$

10. $(-4 - 10i)(6 - 5i)$

11. $(1 - i)(1 + 2i)$

12. $(9 + 2i)(4 + 11i)$

13. $(-8 + 9i)(-7 - i)$

14. $(5 - i)(-2 + 12i)$

15. $(-7 + 3i)(4 + 6i)$

16. $(-5 + i)(-5 - i)$

17. $(2 + 8i)(-2 + i)$

18. $(-7 - 5i)(2 - 4i)$

19. $(-3 + 4i)7i$

20. $(2 + 3i)2i$

21. $(-2 - 5i)^2$

22. $(1 - 4i)(2 - 6i)$

23. $-(3 + i)(2 - 7i)$

24. $(-2 + 3i)^2$

25. $2i(5 + i)(-2 + 7i)$

26. $3i(4 - 2i)(1 - 4i)$

27. $\dfrac{4}{5 - 2i}$

28. $\dfrac{5}{3 - 2i}$

29. $\dfrac{2 - i}{3 + 4i}$

30. $\dfrac{-2 + 4i}{6 + 3i}$

31. $\dfrac{7 - 4i}{6i}$

32. $\dfrac{2 + 9i}{-7i}$

33. $\dfrac{-4 - 5i}{9 + i}$

34. $\dfrac{7 + 4i}{-2 - 5i}$

35. $\dfrac{1 + 2i}{\sqrt{2} + i}$

36. $\dfrac{1 - 3i}{\sqrt{3} - i}$

37. $\dfrac{5 + 6i}{-2 - 3i} + 4 - i$

38. $\dfrac{3}{2 - 4i} - (3 + 2i)$

39. Using the fact that $i^2 = -1$, make a table that shows the powers of i from i^1 to i^8 in the first row and the simplified forms of these powers in the second row. *Describe* the pattern you observe in the table. Verify that the pattern continues by evaluating the next four powers of i.

MM2N1b Write complex numbers in the form $a + bi$.

MM2N1c Add, subtract, multiply, and divide complex numbers.

MM2N1d Simplify expressions involving complex numbers.

Match the expression with the correct standard form.

1. $\dfrac{6 + 2i}{5i}$

   A. $-5 + 12i$

2. $7i(2 - i)$

   B. $\dfrac{2}{5} - \dfrac{6}{5}i$

3. $(-2 - 3i)^2$

   C. $7 + 14i$

Write the expression as a complex number in standard form.

4. $(6 - 3i)(4 + 2i)$

5. $(4 - i)(2 + 5i)$

6. $(2 - 3i)(7 + 3i)$

7. $(-5 + 2i)(4 - 10i)$

8. $(-8 + 4i)(-5 - 7i)$

9. $(5 - 5i)(-5 + 5i)$

10. $(6 + 3i)(4 - 6i)$

11. $(-3 + 4i)(-4 + 3i)$

12. $(2 + 5i)(-2 - 9i)$

13. $(7 - 4i)(6 - 8i)$

14. $(-7 + 5i)2i$

15. $-7i(5 - 6i)$

16. $(3 - 2i)^2$

17. $(2 - 2i)(3 - 5i)$

18. $3i(2 - i)(4 + 2i)$

19. $(2 + i)(3 - i)(2 - 3i)$

20. $-(2 + i)(6 - 5i) + (-4 + 2i)$

21. $-i(1 + i)^2(2 + i)$

22. $\dfrac{7}{3 + i}$

23. $\dfrac{8}{5 - 2i}$

24. $\dfrac{3 + i}{-2 - 5i}$

25. $\dfrac{6 - 4i}{2 - i}$

26. $\dfrac{-6 + i}{2 + 4i}$

27. $\dfrac{4 - 6i}{-2 + 2i}$

28. $\dfrac{4 - i}{6i}$

29. $\dfrac{-9 + 2i}{-3i}$

30. $\dfrac{1 + i\sqrt{2}}{\sqrt{2} - i}$

31. $\dfrac{1 + i\sqrt{3}}{\sqrt{3} + i}$

32. $\dfrac{2 + 3i}{4 - i} \times \dfrac{1 - 3i}{4 + i}$

33. $\dfrac{4 + 7i}{3 + 2i} \times \dfrac{1 - i}{3 - 2i}$

34. $\dfrac{(8 + 2i) - (3 - 2i)}{(-6 + 7i) + (4 - 5i)}$

35. $\dfrac{(6 - 2i) + (3 - 7i)}{(2 + 6i) - (8 - 2i)}$

36. $\dfrac{(9 - 4i) + (3 + 8i)}{4i(6 - 3i)}$

37. $\dfrac{1 - 5i}{3 - 5i} - (4 - 5i)$

38. Using the fact that $i^2 = -1$, find the product $(i^4)(i^3)(i^2)(i)$.

39. Show that the complex conjugate of the product of two complex numbers $a_1 + b_1i$ and $a_2 + b_2i$ is the product of their complex conjugates.

Georgia Performance Standards

MM2N1b   Write complex numbers in the form $a + bi$.

MM2N1c   Add, subtract, multiply, and divide complex numbers.

MM2N1d   Simplify expressions involving complex numbers.

Technology Activity

Operations with Complex Numbers

Use after Lesson 1.3

Question

How can you use a graphing calculator to perform operations with complex numbers?

Change the mode of the calculator to handle complex numbers by pressing **MODE** and highlighting $a + bi$.

To insert the imaginary unit i in an expression, press **2nd** [i].

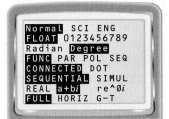

Example 1

Write $(-4 - 8i) + (5 - 3i)$ as a complex number in standard form.

STEP 1   **Enter** the expression.

STEP 2   **Press** the **ENTER** key.

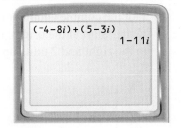

Example 2

Write the expression $\dfrac{7 + 4i}{2 - 3i}$ as a complex number in standard form.

STEP 1   **Enter** the expression.

STEP 2   **Select** the **MATH** menu and choose *Frac* to display the answer using fractions. Press the **ENTER** key.

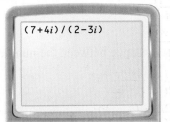

Practice

Use a graphing calculator to write the expression in standard form.

1. $(6 + 2i) - (2 - 3i)$ **2.** $(-4 + 5i)(1 - 4i)$ **3.** $\dfrac{2 + i}{3 - i}$

UNIT 1

Georgia Performance Standards

MM2N1b   Write complex numbers in the form $a + bi$. ☑

MM2N1d   Simplify expressions involving complex numbers. ☑

Investigating Math Activity
Numbers in the Complex Plane

Use before Lesson 1.4

Question

How can you find the absolute value of a complex number?

The absolute value of a real number is the distance between the number and zero on a number line. Likewise, the absolute value of a complex number is the distance between the number and the origin in the complex plane. The complex plane has a horizontal axis called the *real* axis and a vertical axis called the *imaginary* axis.

Explore

Find the absolute value of $4 + 2i$.

STEP 1   Plot the number

Plot the complex number in the complex plane. Start at the origin, move 4 units to the right and 2 units up.

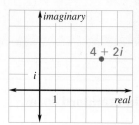

STEP 2   Observe the graph

Notice that a right triangle can be formed with legs of 4 units and 2 units. The hypotenuse is the distance from the origin to the complex number.

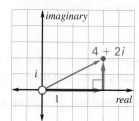

STEP 3   Find the distance

Use the Pythagorean Theorem to find the distance between the complex number and the origin.

$$\text{Distance} = \sqrt{4^2 + 2^2} = \sqrt{16 + 4} = \sqrt{20} = 2\sqrt{5}$$

Because the absolute value of a complex number is the distance between the number and the origin, $|4 + 2i| = 2\sqrt{5}$.

Draw Conclusions

Find the absolute value of the complex number.

1. $6 + 8i$ **2.** $-3 + 6i$ **3.** $-5 - 12i$

4. **Reasoning** Plot the complex number $3 + i$ in the complex plane. Plot the conjugate of the number. Find the absolute values of both numbers. Will the absolute values of a complex number and its conjugate always be equal? *Explain.*

UNIT 1

Use the Complex Plane

Georgia Performance Standards: MM2N1b, MM2N1d

Goal Use the complex plane and find the absolute value of a complex number.

Vocabulary

Just as every real number corresponds to a point on the real number line, every complex number corresponds to a point in the **complex plane**. The complex plane has a horizontal axis called the *real axis* and a vertical axis called the *imaginary axis*.

The **absolute value of a complex number** $z = a + bi$, denoted by $|z|$, is a nonnegative real number defined as $|z| = \sqrt{a^2 + b^2}$. This is the distance between z and the origin in the complex plane.

Example 1   Plot complex numbers

Plot the complex numbers in the same complex plane.

    a. $3 - 2i$ **b.** $-2 + 4i$

    c. $3i$ **d.** $-4 - 3i$

    e. $6 + 5i$ **f.** $-6 + 6i$

Solution

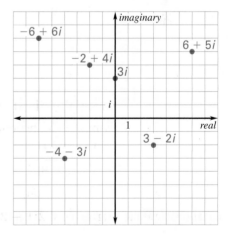

    a. To plot $3 - 2i$, start at the origin, move 3 units right, and then move 2 units down.

    b. To plot $-2 + 4i$, start at the origin, move 2 units left, and then move 4 units up.

    c. To plot $3i$, start at the origin and move 3 units up.

    d. To plot $-4 - 3i$, start at the origin, move 4 units left, and then move 3 units down.

    e. To plot $6 + 5i$, start at the origin, move 6 units right, and then move 5 units up.

    f. To plot $-6 + 6i$, start at the origin, move 6 units left, and then move 6 units up.

Guided Practice for Example 1

Plot the complex numbers in the same complex plane.

    1. $1 + 4i$ **2.** $2 - 2i$ **3.** $-3 + 3i$

    4. $-5i$ **5.** $-5 - 6i$ **6.** $6 - 4i$

Example 2 Find absolute values of complex numbers

Find the absolute value of the complex number.

a. $4 - i$

b. $-3 + 4i$

c. $3i$

d. $2 + 6i$

Solution

a. $\begin{aligned} |4 - i| &= \sqrt{4^2 + (-1)^2} && \text{Definition of absolute value} \\ &= \sqrt{16 + 1} && \text{Evaluate powers.} \\ &= \sqrt{17} && \text{Simplify.} \end{aligned}$

b. $\begin{aligned} |-3 + 4i| &= \sqrt{(-3)^2 + 4^2} && \text{Definition of absolute value} \\ &= \sqrt{9 + 16} && \text{Evaluate powers.} \\ &= \sqrt{25} && \text{Simplify.} \\ &= 5 && \text{Evaluate square root.} \end{aligned}$

c. $\begin{aligned} |3i| &= \sqrt{0^2 + 3^2} && \text{Definition of absolute value} \\ &= \sqrt{0 + 9} && \text{Evaluate powers.} \\ &= \sqrt{9} && \text{Simplify.} \\ &= 3 && \text{Evaluate square root.} \end{aligned}$

d. $\begin{aligned} |2 + 6i| &= \sqrt{2^2 + 6^2} && \text{Definition of absolute value} \\ &= \sqrt{4 + 36} && \text{Evaluate powers.} \\ &= \sqrt{40} && \text{Simplify.} \\ &= 2\sqrt{10} && \text{Evaluate square root.} \end{aligned}$

Guided Practice for Example 2

Find the absolute value of the complex number.

7. $15 + 8i$

8. $7 - 24i$

9. $-5 + 6i$

10. $9i$

11. $-2 - 4i$

12. $4 - 9i$

Exercise Set A

MM2N1b   Write complex numbers in the form $a + bi$.

MM2N1d   Simplify expressions involving complex numbers.

Match the complex number with the correct letter on the graph.

1. $2 + i$ **2.** $-3 - 6i$ **3.** $1 - 4i$ **4.** -5

5. $4 + 5i$ **6.** $-6 + 3i$ **7.** $6 + 2i$ **8.** $7 - 5i$

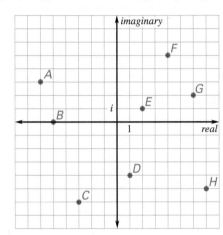

Find the absolute value of the complex number.

9. $5 - 2i$ **10.** $5 + 12i$

11. $-3 - 4i$ **12.** $2 + 3i$

13. $2 - 6i$ **14.** $6 - 5i$

15. $1 + 2i$ **16.** $9 + 40i$

17. $5i$ **18.** $-2 + 12i$

19. $4 + 6i$ **20.** $-5 - i$

21. $-2 + i$ **22.** $-7 - 5i$

23. $-3 - 11i$ **24.** $2i$

25. $-2 - 5i$ **26.** $1 - 4i$

27. $2 - 7i$ **28.** $-2 + 3i$

29. $5 + 4i$ **30.** $4 - 2i$

31. $\sqrt{5} + 2i$ **32.** $\sqrt{11} + 5i$

33. $2 - i\sqrt{21}$ **34.** $-\sqrt{23} + i\sqrt{26}$

35. What is the absolute value of $a - bi$?

36. Is every complex number an imaginary number? *Explain.*

Exercise Set B

MM2N1b   Write complex numbers in the form $a + bi$.

MM2N1d   Simplify expressions involving complex numbers.

Match the complex number with the correct letter on the graph.

1. $6 + 4i$
2. $3 - 2i$
3. $-2 + 6i$
4. $-i\sqrt{26}$

5. $\sqrt{17} - 5i$
6. $-6 - i$
7. $\sqrt{29} + 2i$
8. $-\sqrt{42} - 2i\sqrt{7}$

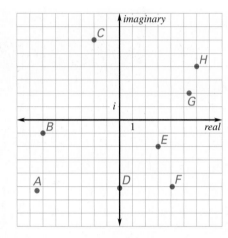

Find the absolute value of the complex number.

9. $24 - 10i$
10. $4 - i$
11. $-3i$

12. $-9 + 12i$
13. $-5 - 7i$
14. $5 - 5i$

15. $4 - 6i$
16. $-11 + 60i$
17. $-2 - 9i$

18. $7 + 4i$
19. $-2 + 2i$
20. $5 - 6i$

21. $4 + 2i$
22. $12 - 16i$
23. $1 - i\sqrt{3}$

24. $\sqrt{5} + 2i\sqrt{2}$
25. $2 - \dfrac{\sqrt{3}}{4}i$
26. $\sqrt{7} + \dfrac{2\sqrt{5}}{9}i$

Determine whether *a* and *b* are *greater than zero, less than zero*, or *equal to zero* for the given complex number $a + bi$.

27. $a + bi$ lies in the first quadrant of the complex plane.

28. $a + bi$ lies in the second quadrant of the complex plane.

29. $a + bi$ lies in the third quadrant of the complex plane.

30. $a + bi$ lies in the fourth quadrant of the complex plane.

31. $a + bi$ lies on the negative real axis of the complex plane.

32. $a + bi$ lies on the positive imaginary axis of the complex plane.

TEST | for Unit 1

Simplify the expression.

1. $\sqrt{525}$
2. $\sqrt{567}$
3. $\sqrt{192}$
4. $\sqrt{\dfrac{49}{81}}$
5. $\sqrt{\dfrac{128}{25}}$
6. $\sqrt{\dfrac{53}{9}}$

Write the complex number in standard form.

7. $\sqrt{-99}$
8. $\sqrt{-196}$
9. $\sqrt{-80}$
10. $2 + \sqrt{-27}$
11. $6 - \sqrt{-162}$
12. $-3 + \sqrt{-44}$

Write the expression as a complex number in standard form.

13. $6i + (-2 - 7i)$
14. $(1 - 4i) - (1 + 3i)$
15. $(2 + 5i) + (5 - 2i)$
16. $(-7 - 12i) + (4 + 5i)$
17. $(1 - i) - (6 + i)$
18. $(9 - 8i) - (4 - 13i)$
19. $(-2 + 3i) + (2 - 3i)$
20. $(4 - i) - (-6 + 7i)$
21. $6i + (-7 + i) - 2$
22. $7 - (-10 + i) + 4i$
23. $(1 + 3i)(-2 + i)$
24. $(-2 - 5i)(2 - 2i)$
25. $(3 - 2i)7i$
26. $(7 + i)5i$
27. $(-2 + 2i)^2$
28. $(1 - i)(2 - 6i)$
29. $-(2 + 3i)(1 - 4i)$
30. $(3 + 5i)^2$
31. $4i(3 - i)(-2 + 8i)$
32. $-3i(2 - i)(4 - 5i)$
33. $\dfrac{3i}{4 - i}$
34. $\dfrac{6 + 2i}{4 + 8i}$
35. $\dfrac{1 + 2i}{2 - 4i} \times \dfrac{2 + 4i}{1 - 2i}$
36. $\dfrac{-3 + i}{5 + 2i} + (2 + 2i)$

Identify the complex numbers plotted in the complex plane. Then find the absolute value of each complex number.

37.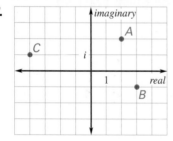

38.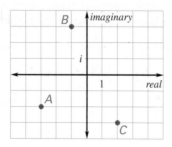

TEST | for Unit 1 *(continued)*

Determine whether the complex number is *real, imaginary, pure imaginary,* or *neither*.

39. The sum of a complex number and its conjugate

40. The difference of a complex number and its conjugate

41. The product of a complex number and its conjugate

42. The quotient of a complex number and its conjugate

Determine whether the statement is *true* or *false*.

43. There is no complex number that is equal to its complex conjugate.

44. The sum of two imaginary numbers is always an imaginary number.

45. The absolute values of a complex number and its complex conjugate are always equal.

Performance Task

Fractals

Fractals are extremely irregular lines or surfaces formed from an infinite number of similarly irregular sections. To construct a fractal, a pattern needs to be replicated, or iterated, over and over. Often these patterns can be represented by a function. To iterate a function, input a starting value and solve the function. Then input the solution into the same function and solve.

For example, to iterate the function $f(x) = 5x - 1$ for the starting value $x = i$, begin by replacing x with i in the function. The answer is $5i - 1$. This completes the first iteration. Use the answer from the first iteration $5i - 1$ to find the second iteration. Using the same function, replace x with $5i - 1$. The answer to the second iteration is $25i - 6$.

Usually the iteration is written as an ordered pair. Using the example above, the first iteration would be $(i, 5i - 1)$ and the second iteration would be $(5i - 1, 25i - 6)$. Repeating this process and plotting the points would create a fractal. A computer is typically used to accomplish this task.

Find the first and second iterations of the function for the given starting value. Write your answers as ordered pairs.

a. $f(x) = x + 7$ for $x = 3i$

b. $f(x) = x^2$ for $x = 1 + i$

c. $f(x) = 2x^2 - 1$ for $i + 4$

d. Find the first, second, and third iterations of $f(x) = x^2 + 3$ for the starting value $x = 2 - i$. Write your answers as ordered pairs.

UNIT 1

UNIT 2
Algebra: Functions and Absolute Value

Use Problem Solving Strategies and Models

Georgia Performance Standards: MM2P1d, MM2P3a

Goal Solve problems using verbal models.

Vocabulary

When solving real-life problems, write an equation called a **verbal model** in words before you write the equation in mathematical symbols.

Example 1 **Use a formula**

A rectangular flower garden has an area of 125 square feet. If the length of the garden is 12 feet, what is the width of the garden?

You can use the formula for the area of a rectangle as a verbal model.

Area (square feet)	=	Length (feet)	·	Width (feet)
125	=	12	·	w

An equation for this situation is $125 = 12 \cdot w$. Solve for w.

$125 = 12 \cdot w$ Write equation.

$10.4 \approx w$ Divide each side by 12.

The width of the garden is about 10.4 feet.

Guided Practice for Example 1

1. The perimeter of a rectangular city park is 1080 yards. The width of the park is 240 yards. What is the length of the park?

2. A train travels at a speed of 44 miles per hour. How long will it take the train to travel 154 miles?

Example 2 **Look for a pattern**

Look for a pattern in the table. Then write an equation that represents the table.

x	0	1	2	3
y	0	3	6	9

Solution

Each y-value is 3 times the corresponding x-value. You can use this pattern to write an equation $y = 3x$.

Georgia Performance Standards

| MM2P1d | Monitor and reflect on the process of mathematical problem solving. | |
| MM2P3a | Organize and consolidate mathematical thinking through communication. | ☑ |

Guided Practice for Example 2

Look for a pattern in the table. Then write an equation that represents the table.

3.

x	0	1	2	3
y	0	−2	−4	−6

4.

x	0	1	2	3
y	1	5	9	13

Example 3 Draw a diagram

You are designing a square flower garden surrounded by a brick sidewalk of uniform width. The garden has a side length of 6 yards. The side length of the outside square is 10 yards. Draw a diagram to find the width of the sidewalk.

Solution

Begin by drawing and labeling a diagram, as shown below.

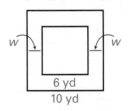

From the diagram, you can write and solve an equation to find w.

$w + 6 + w = 10$	Write equation.
$2w + 6 = 10$	Combine like terms.
$2w = 4$	Subtract 6 from each side.
$w = 2$	Divide each side by 2.

The width of the sidewalk is 2 yards.

Guided Practice for Example 3

5. You want to create an open rectangular box from a rectangular piece of cardboard. The cardboard has a length of 14 inches and you will cut 2 inch squares from each corner. Draw a diagram to find the length of the box.

6. A piece of fabric is 52 inches long. You cut the fabric into two pieces. The first piece is x inches long. The second piece is 14 inches longer than the first piece. Draw and label a diagram of the fabric. Then write and solve an equation to find x.

7. You want to create an open rectangular box from a square piece of cardboard. The cardboard is 20 inches by 20 inches and you will cut 3 inch squares from each corner. Draw a diagram to find the length of the box.

UNIT 2

Exercise Set A

| MM2P1d | Monitor and reflect on the process of mathematical problem solving. |
| MM2P3a | Organize and consolidate mathematical thinking through communication. |

Use the formula $d = rt$ for distance traveled to solve for the missing variable.

1. $d = $ _?_ , $r = 55$ mi/h, $t = 3$ h

2. $d = 240$ mi, $r = 60$ mi/h, $t = $ _?_

3. $d = 552$ mi, $r = $ _?_ , $t = 8$ h

4. $d = 247.5$ mi, $r = 45$ mi/h, $t = $ _?_

Use the formula $A = bh$ for the area of a parallelogram to solve for the missing variable.

5. $A = $ _?_ , $b = 6$ ft, $h = 3$ ft

6. $A = 34$ ft^2, $b = $ _?_ , $h = 4$ ft

7. $A = 175$ m^2, $b = 25$ m, $h = $ _?_

8. $A = $ _?_ , $b = 23$ cm, $h = 15$ cm

Look for a pattern in the table. Then write an equation that represents the table.

9.
x	0	1	2	3
y	5	10	15	20

10.
x	0	1	2	3
y	22	25	28	31

11.
x	0	1	2	3
y	17	16	15	14

12.
x	0	1	2	3
y	89	82	75	68

13. **Error Analysis** *Describe* and correct the error in writing the equation.

x	0	1	2	3
y	65	55	45	35

An equation that represents the table is $y = 65x - 10$.

14. **Fastest Solar Powered Vehicle** The highest speed reached by a solar powered vehicle is 48.71 miles per hour. This record was set by a car called Sunraycer on June 24, 1988, in Mesa, Arizona. How far could Sunraycer travel in 2.5 hours at this speed?

15. **Cable Bill** Your local cable company charges $29.99 per month for basic cable service. Premium channels are available for a surcharge of $5.95 per channel. You have $70 per month budgeted for cable. How many premium channels can you purchase?

16. **Sharing the Drive** You and a friend take turns driving on a 450 mile trip. Your friend drives for 3.5 hours at an average speed of 60 miles per hour. What must your average speed be for the remainder of the trip if you want to reach your hotel in 4 more hours?

17. **Parking Lot** A five gallon bucket of tar can seal 3500 square feet of blacktop. If a parking lot is 15,000 square feet, how many buckets of tar must be purchased in order to seal it?

Exercise Set B

MM2P1d Monitor and reflect on the process of mathematical problem solving.

MM2P3a Organize and consolidate mathematical thinking through communication.

Look for a pattern in the table. Then write an equation that represents the table.

1.

x	0	1	2	3
y	18	26	34	42

2.

x	0	3	6	9
y	28	22	16	10

3. **Multiple Representations** You pay $7.50 a year to belong to a music club that allows you to download songs for $.75 per song. So far this year you have spent $24.

    a. **Making a Table** Copy and complete the table below. Use the table to estimate how many songs you have downloaded.

Songs	0	20	40	60	80	100
Yearly Cost	$7.50	?	?	?	?	?

    b. **Writing a Model** Write an equation for the situation. Solve it to find the number of songs you have downloaded.

    c. **Comparing Answers** Is your estimate from part (a) compatible with the exact answer from part (b)? *Explain.*

4. **Fastest One Mile Run** Svetlana Masterkova of Russia set the female world record for the fastest mile run with a time of 4 minutes 12.56 seconds in 1996. What was her speed in miles per hour? Round to 2 significant digits.

5. **Commission** A furniture salesman earns a base salary of $14,000 per year. The salesman also receives a 7% commission on his sales. If his total sales exceed $500,000 for the year, a bonus of $5000 is paid in December. Last year the salesman reported an income of $55,771 to the IRS. What were his total sales?

6. **House Painting** The local painters union received an unusual and urgent request to paint 2 houses in 4 hours. If each painter can paint one house in 10 hours, how many painters will it take to accommodate this request?

7. **Lighting Configuration** You want to install 3 ceiling lights in a row to improve the visibility in your garage. Each light is 3 feet long and your garage is 27 feet long. The distance between each light should be the same. Also, the distance between the group of lights and the walls should be half of the distance between any 2 consecutive lights. Draw a diagram to help solve this problem. What is the distance between successive lights?

8. **Packing Weight** A moving company weighs 25 boxes you have packed that contain either books or clothes and says the total weight is 414 pounds. You know that a box of books weighs 30 pounds and a box of clothes weighs 6 pounds. How many boxes of books and how many boxes of clothes did you pack?

UNIT 2

Solve Absolute Value Equations and Inequalities

Georgia Performance Standards: MM2A1c

Goal Solve absolute value equations and inequalities.

Vocabulary

An **extraneous solution** is an apparent solution that must be rejected because it does not satisfy the original equation.

Example 1   Solve an absolute value equation

Solve $|8 - 4x| = 12$.

$|8 - 4x| = 12$		Write original equation.
$8 - 4x = 12$ or $8 - 4x = -12$		Expression can equal 12 or -12.
$-4x = 4$ or $-4x = -20$		Subtract 8 from each side.
$x = -1$ or $x = 5$		Divide each side by -4.

The solutions are -1 and 5.

Guided Practice for Example 1

Solve the equation.

1. $|x + 3| = 7$ **2.** $|x - 2| = 6$ **3.** $|2x - 5| = 9$ **4.** $|2x + 1| = 9$

Example 2   Check for extraneous solutions

Solve $|2x + 6| = 4x$. Check for extraneous solutions.

$|2x + 6| = 4x$		Write original equation.
$2x + 6 = 4x$ or $2x + 6 = -4x$		Expression can equal $4x$ or $-4x$.
$6 = 2x$ or $6 = -6x$		Subtract $2x$ from each side.
$3 = x$ or $-1 = x$		Solve for x.

Check the apparent solutions to see if either is extraneous.

$$|2x + 6| = 4x \qquad\qquad\qquad |2x + 6| = 4x$$
$$|2(3) + 6| \overset{?}{=} 4(3) \qquad\qquad |2(-1) + 6| \overset{?}{=} 4(-1)$$
$$|12| \overset{?}{=} 12 \qquad\qquad\qquad\quad |4| \overset{?}{=} -4$$
$$12 = 12 \;\checkmark \qquad\qquad\qquad 4 \neq -4 \;\textbf{X}$$

The solution is 3. Reject -1 because it is an extraneous solution.

Georgia Performance Standards

MM2A1c Solve absolute value equations and inequalities analytically, graphically, and by using appropriate technology. ☑

Guided Practice for Example 2

Solve the equation. Check for extraneous solutions.

5. $|x - 1| = 2x$ **6.** $|x + 2| = 3x$ **7.** $|3x + 3| = 6x$

Example 3 **Solve an inequality of the form $|ax + b| > c$**

Solve $|2x - 1| > 5$. Then graph the solution.

Solution

The absolute value inequality is equivalent to $2x - 1 < -5$ or $2x - 1 > 5$.

First Inequality		**Second Inequality**
$2x - 1 < -5$	Write inequalities.	$2x - 1 > 5$
$2x < -4$	Add 1 to each side.	$2x > 6$
$x < -2$	Divide each side by 2.	$x > 3$

The solutions are all real numbers less than -2 or greater than 3. The graph is shown below.

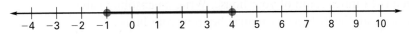

Example 4 **Solve an inequality of the form $|ax + b| \le c$**

Solve $|2x - 3| \le 5$. Then graph the solution.

Solution

$|2x - 3| \le 5$	Write original inequality.
$-5 \le 2x - 3 \le 5$	Write equivalent compound inequality.
$-2 \le 2x \le 8$	Add 3 to each expression.
$-1 \le x \le 4$	Divide each expression by 2.

The solution is all real numbers greater than or equal to -1 and less than or equal to 4. The graph is shown below.

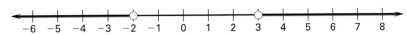

Guided Practice for Examples 3 and 4

Solve the inequality. Then graph the solution.

8. $|x - 3| > 5$ **9.** $|x + 7| > 2$ **10.** $|2x + 1| \ge 5$

11. $|x - 6| \le 4$ **12.** $|x + 7| < 2$ **13.** $|3x + 5| \ge 10$

Georgia Performance Standards

MM2A1c Solve absolute value equations and inequalities analytically, graphically, and by using appropriate technology.

LESSON 2.2

Problem Solving Workshop

Problem A professional hockey puck should weigh 5.75 ounces, with a tolerance of 0.25 ounce. (*Tolerance* is the maximum acceptable deviation of an item from some ideal or mean measurement.) Write and solve an absolute value inequality that describes the acceptable weights for a hockey puck.

STEP 1 Read and Understand
What do you know? You know that a professional hockey puck should weigh 5.75 ounces. You also know that the maximum acceptable deviation of the weight of the hockey puck is 0.25 ounce.

What do you want to find out? You want to find out the acceptable weights for a hockey puck.

STEP 2 Make a Plan
Use what you know to write a verbal model that represents what you want to find out. Then write an inequality and solve it.

STEP 3 Solve the Problem
Write a verbal model. Then write an inequality. Let w be the actual weight of a hockey puck.

Actual weight (ounces)		Ideal weight (ounces)		Tolerance (ounces)
	$-$		$\leq$	
$|w$	$-$	$5.75|$	$\leq$	0.25

The inequality is $|w - 5.75| \leq 0.25$. Solve the inequality.

$|w - 5.75| \leq 0.25$	Write inequality.
$-0.25 \leq w - 5.75 \leq 0.25$	Write equivalent compound inequality.
$5.5 \leq w \leq 6$	Add 5.75 to each expression.

So, a hockey puck should weigh between 5.5 ounces and 6 ounces, inclusive. The graph is shown below.

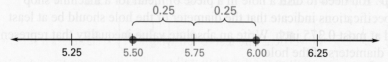

STEP 4 Look Back
Because the tolerance is 0.25 ounce, the minimum acceptable weight of a hockey puck is $5.75 - 0.25 = 5.5$ ounces and the maximum acceptable weight is $5.75 + 0.25 = 6$ ounces. So, a hockey puck can weigh between 5.5 and 6 ounces, inclusive. The solution in Step 3 is correct.

Practice

1. **Gymnastics** The horizontal bar used in gymnastics should be placed 110.3 inches above the ground, with a tolerance of 0.39 inch. Write and solve an absolute value inequality for the acceptable bar heights.

2. **Soil pH Levels** Cucumbers grow in soil having a pH level of 6.45, with a tolerance of 0.99 point on the pH scale. Write and solve an absolute value inequality describing the pH of soil in which cucumbers can grow.

Represent Relations and Functions

Georgia Performance Standards: MM2A5a

Goal Represent relations and graph linear functions.

Vocabulary

A **relation** is a mapping, or pairing, of input values with output values.

The **domain** of a relation is the set of input values and the **range** of a relation is the set of output values.

A **function** is a relation for which each input value has exactly one output value. By the *vertical line test* a relation is a function if and only if no vertical line intersects the graph of the relation at more than one point.

An **equation in two variables** has an **independent variable**, or input variable, and a **dependent variable**, or output variable, that depends on the value of the independent variable.

An ordered pair (x, y) is a **solution of an equation in two variables** if substituting x and y into the equation produces a true statement. The **graph of an equation in two variables** is the set of all points (x, y) that represent solutions of the equation.

A **linear function** can be written in the form $y = mx + b$ where m and b are constants, or in function notation as $f(x) = mx + b$.

A function is **one-to-one** if no two values in the domain have the same value in the range.

Example 1 Represent relations and identify functions

Consider the relation given by the ordered pairs $(-1, 0)$, $(0, -3)$, $(-3, 3)$, and $(2, 1)$.

  a. Identify the domain and range.

  b. Represent the relation using a graph.

  c. Use the vertical line test to tell whether the relation is a function.

  d. If the relation is a function, tell whether it is a one-to-one function.

Solution

  a. The domain consists of all the x-coordinates: $-3, -1, 0,$ and 2. The range consists of all the y-coordinates: $-3, 0, 1,$ and 3.

  b. See the graph at the right.

  c. The relation is a function because no single vertical line intersects more than one point of the graph.

  d. The function is a one-to-one function because no two values in the domain have the same value in the range.

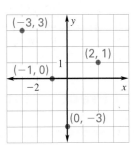

Georgia Performance Standards

MM2A5a Discuss the characteristics of functions and their inverses, including one-to-oneness, domain, and range.

Example 2 Graph an equation in two variables

Graph the equation $y = 3x + 2$.

STEP 1 **Construct** a table of values.

x	−2	−1	0	1	2
y	−4	−1	2	5	8

STEP 2 **Plot** the points.

STEP 3 **Connect** the points with a line.

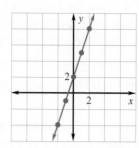

Guided Practice for Examples 1 and 2

Identify the domain and range of the given relation. Represent the relation using a graph. Use the vertical line test to tell whether the relation is a function. If the relation is a function, tell whether it is a one-to-one function. *Explain.*

1. $(-2, -2), (-1, 3), (0, 2), (2, 3)$ **2.** $(4, 1), (-1, 3), (-3, 2), (4, -2)$

Graph the equation.

3. $y = x + 3$ **4.** $y = 2x - 1$ **5.** $y = -3x + 1$

Example 3 Classify and evaluate functions

Tell whether the function $f(x) = 6x + 1$ is linear. Evaluate when $x = -3$ and when $x = 3$.

Solution

The function $f(x) = 6x + 1$ is linear because it has the form $f(x) = mx + b$.

$f(-3) = 6(-3) + 1 = -17$ Substitute -3 for x and simplify.

$f(3) = 6(3) + 1 = 19$ Substitute 3 for x and simplify.

Guided Practice for Example 3

Tell whether the function is linear. Evaluate when $x = -1$ and when $x = 1$.

6. $f(x) = x^2 + 2$ **7.** $f(x) = -4x - 1$ **8.** $h(x) = 5x - 5$

LESSON 2.3

Exercise Set A

MM2A5a   Discuss the characteristics of functions and their inverses, including one-to-oneness, domain, and range.

Identify the domain and range of the given relation. Then tell whether the relation is a function. If the relation is a function, tell whether it is a one-to-one function.

1. $(0, 3), (1, 1), (2, 2), (3, 4), (4, 2)$

2. $(-2, -3), (-1, -1), (0, 1), (0, 3), (1, 5)$

3. $(1, -5), (2, -4), (3, 0), (4, 2), (5, 1)$

4. $(-2, 0), (-3, 2), (-4, 4), (-3, 6), (-2, 8)$

5. $(-5, -5), (-3, -4), (1, -1), (2, 3), (4, 6)$

6. $(4, 3), (2, 3), (0, 3), (-2, 3), (-6, 3)$

Use the vertical line test to determine whether the relation is a function.

7.
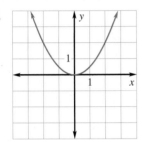

8.
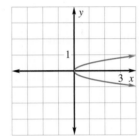

9.
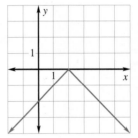

10. Multiple Choice The relation given by the ordered pairs

$$(-7, 4), (-3, 5), (0, 6), \text{ and } (3, 1)$$

is a function. Which ordered pair can be included with this relation to form a new relation that is also a function?

A. $(0, -6)$ **B.** $(5, 4)$ **C.** $(-3, 20)$ **D.** $(3, 5)$

Match the equation with its graph.

11. $y = 3x + 2$

12. $y = -2x - 2$

13. $y = -x$

A.
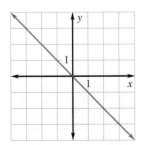

B.
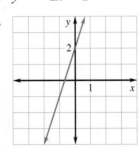

C.
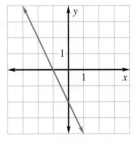

Graph the equation.

14. $y = -x + 3$

15. $y = \frac{1}{2}x + 2$

16. $y = 2x - 5$

17. $y = x + 2$

18. $y = -1$

19. $y = -\frac{1}{4}x - 1$

20. $y = -3x$

21. $y = -2x + 3$

22. $y = 1 - x$

Exercise Set A *(continued)*

Tell whether the function is linear and evaluate the function for the given values of *x*.

23. $f(x) = x + 5; f(-2), f(2)$ **24.** $f(x) = x^2 + x - 2; f(-2), f(1)$ **25.** $f(x) = 3 - 3x; f(0), f(2)$

26. $f(x) = |x + 2|; f(-4), f(0)$ **27.** $f(x) = \dfrac{2}{x - 2}; f(0), f(6)$ **28.** $f(x) = \dfrac{2}{3}x - 5; f(-9), f(9)$

In Exercises 29–31, use the following information.

LPGA Money List The table below shows the top five players on the 2006 LPGA Tour money list along with the number of wins for each player.

Player	Lorena Ochoa	Karrie Webb	Annika Sorenstam	Cristie Kerr	Mi Hyun Kim
Wins, x	6	5	3	3	2
Dollars, y (in millions)	2.5	2.1	2.0	1.6	1.3

29. What is the domain of the relation?

30. What is the range of the relation?

31. Is the amount of money earned a function of the number of wins?

In Exercises 32–34, use the following information.

Furniture Assembly At the beginning of your 8 hour shift, there were 42 units of furniture that needed to be assembled. The number of units *n* that still need to be assembled during your shift can be modeled by $n(t) = -3t + 42$ where *t* is the time in hours.

32. Graph the model.

33. What is a reasonable domain and range of the model?

34. How many units still need to be assembled after you have worked 5 hours of your shift?

35. Electoral Votes The table shows the populations of several states and their electoral votes in the 2004 and 2008 U.S. presidential elections. The figures are based on U.S. census data for the year 2000.

State	Population (millions), *p*	Electoral votes, *v*
California	33.9	55
Illinois	12.4	21
New York	19.0	31
Ohio	11.4	20
Pennsylvania	12.3	21

   a. Identify the domain and range of the relation given by the ordered pairs (p, v).

   b. Is the relation from part (a) a function? *Explain.*

   c. Is the relation given by the ordered pairs (v, p) a function? *Explain.*

Identify the domain and range of the given relation. Then tell whether the relation is a function. If the relation is a function, tell whether it is a one-to-one function.

1. $(-1, 5), (-2, 4), (-3, 0), (-4, 2), (-5, 1)$

2. $(2, 5), (-3, 6), (4, 7), (-3, 8), (-2, 9)$

3. $(1.1, 2.5), (2.5, 3.6), (3.6, 2.5), (4.8, 1.1)$

4. $(0.1, 1.5), (0.2, 1.5), (0.3, 1.4), (0.3, 1.6)$

5. $\left(\frac{2}{3}, \frac{2}{3}\right), \left(\frac{1}{4}, \frac{3}{4}\right), \left(\frac{3}{4}, \frac{1}{4}\right), \left(-\frac{2}{3}, \frac{1}{3}\right)$

6. $\left(-\frac{1}{3}, \frac{1}{3}\right), \left(-\frac{5}{3}, \frac{1}{3}\right), \left(\frac{1}{3}, \frac{1}{3}\right), \left(\frac{2}{3}, \frac{1}{3}\right)$

Tell whether the relation is a function. If the relation is a function, tell whether it is a one-to-one function.

7.

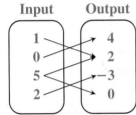

Input   Output

8.

x	−2	−1	4	0	2
y	1	1	1	1	1

9.

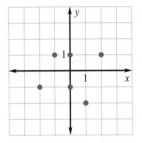

10. **Multiple Choice** The relation given by the ordered pairs $(-5, 2), (-1, 3), (0, 5)$, and $(3, -1)$ is a function. Which ordered pair can be included with this relation to form a new relation that is also a function?

A. $(0, -6)$ **B.** $(-1, 18)$ **C.** $(5, 3)$ **D.** $(3, 3)$

Match the equation with its graph.

11. $y = 5x + 3$

12. $y = 2$

13. $y = 3 - 6x$

A.

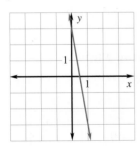

B.

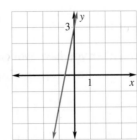

C.

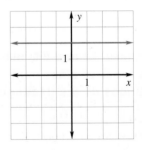

Graph the equation.

14. $y = \frac{2}{3}x + 1$

15. $y = 4 - \frac{1}{2}x$

16. $y = -\frac{3}{2}x$

17. $y = 0.6x + 0.7$

18. $y = 3\left(\frac{1}{6}x + 1\right)$

19. $y = 0$

20. $y = 2\left(\frac{3}{4}x - 2\right)$

21. $y = 7x + 2$

22. $y = |x| + 1$

UNIT 2

Exercise Set B (continued)

Tell whether the function is linear and then evaluate the function for the given values of x.

23. $f(x) = 5 - 3x; f(-2), f(2)$

24. $f(x) = 3x^2 - 10x + 7; f(1), f\left(\frac{7}{3}\right)$

25. $f(x) = |x + 1| - 2; f(-5), f(3)$

26. $f(x) = 2x\left(3 - \frac{1}{2}x\right); f(0), f(6)$

27. $f(x) = \frac{x - 1}{x - 2}; f(0), f(4)$

28. $f(x) = \frac{1}{x^2 + 1}; f(-3), f(3)$

29. Watermelons For the period 1999–2004, the average number of acres w (in thousands) used to grow watermelons in the United States can be modeled by the function $w(t) = -6.30t + 170$ where t is the number of years since 1999. Determine a reasonable domain and range for $w(t)$. *Explain* the meaning of the range.

In Exercises 30–32, use the table which shows the year completed x and the length in feet y of various suspension bridges in the United States.

30. What is the domain and range of the relation?

31. Graph the relation.

32. Is the length of the bridge a function of the year it was completed?

Bridge	Year	Length
Golden Gate	1937	4200
Mackinac	1957	3800
George Washington	1931	3500
Bronx–Whitestone	1939	2300
Delaware Memorial	1968	2150
Seaway Skyway	1960	2150
Walt Whitman	1957	2000

In Exercises 33 and 34, use the table which shows the postage rates r in dollars for first class mail in 2007 and the corresponding maximum weight w in ounces of the package.

Weight, w	1	2	3	4	5	6	7	8	9	10	11	12	13
Rate, r	0.39	0.63	0.87	1.11	1.35	1.59	1.83	2.07	2.31	2.55	2.79	3.03	3.27

33. Is the postage rate a function of the weight of the package being mailed? *Explain.*

34. How much does it cost to mail a package that weighs 5.1 ounces?

Georgia Performance Standards

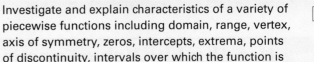

MM2A1b Investigate and explain characteristics of a variety of piecewise functions including domain, range, vertex, axis of symmetry, zeros, intercepts, extrema, points of discontinuity, intervals over which the function is constant, intervals of increase and decrease, and rates of change.

Investigating Math Activity
Exploring Transformations

Use before Lesson 2.4

Question How are graphs of absolute value functions related?

You can investigate families of *absolute value functions* with equations of the form $y = a|x - h| + k$ by varying the values of a, h, and k and then graphing. The *vertex* (h, k) of an absolute value graph is the highest or lowest point of the graph. The *axis of symmetry* of an absolute value graph is the vertical line that passes through the vertex.

Explore Graph and describe functions of the form $y = |x| + k$.

STEP 1 Vary the value of k

Enter $y = |x|$, $y = |x| + 1$, $y = |x| + 4$ and $y = |x| - 2$.

STEP 2 Display graphs

Graph the equations in the standard viewing window by pressing **ZOOM** **6**.

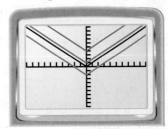

STEP 3 Describe graphs

Describe how the domain, range, vertex, and axis of symmetry of the graph of $y = |x| + k$ change as the value of k changes.

> The domain (all real numbers) and the axis of symmetry ($x = 0$) remain the same. The range changes to $y \geq k$ and the vertex shifts vertically k units.

Draw Conclusions

1. **Writing** Graph $y = |x - h|$ for $h = 0, 1, 3$, and -4. *Describe* how the domain, range, vertex, and axis of symmetry of the graph of $y = |x - h|$ change as the value of h changes.

2. **Writing** Graph $y = a|x|$ for $a = 1, 3, 4$, and $\frac{1}{3}$. *Describe* how the domain, range, vertex, and axis of symmetry of the graph of $y = a|x|$, where $a > 0$, change as the value of a changes.

3. **Writing** Graph $y = a|x|$ for $a = 1, -1, -2$, and $-\frac{1}{3}$. *Describe* how the domain, range, vertex, and axis of symmetry of the graph of $y = a|x|$, where $a < 0$, change as the value of a changes.

Use Absolute Value Functions and Transformations

Georgia Performance Standards: MM2A1b

Goal Graph and write absolute value functions.

Vocabulary

The function $f(x) = |x|$ is an **absolute value function**. The highest or lowest point on the graph of an absolute value function is called the **vertex of an absolute value graph**. An **axis of symmetry** of the graph of a function is a vertical line that divides the graph into mirror images. An absolute value graph has one axis of symmetry that passes through the vertex.

The **zeros** of a function $f(x)$ are the values of x that make the value of $f(x)$ zero.

A **transformation** changes a graph's size, shape, position, or orientation. A **translation** is a transformation that shifts a graph horizontally and/or vertically, but does not change its size, shape, or orientation. When $a = -1$, the graph of $y = a|x|$ is a **reflection** in the x-axis of the graph of $y = |x|$.

Example 1   Graph a function of the form $y = a|x - h| + k$

Graph $y = 3|x + 2| - 3$. Identify the intercepts, zeros, and intervals of increase and decrease. Compare the graph with the graph of $y = |x|$.

The graph of $y = a|x - h| + k$ is the graph of $y = |x|$ translated h units horizontally and k units vertically with its vertex at (h, k). The factor a stretches or shrinks the graph.

STEP 1 **Identify** and plot the vertex, $(h, k) = (-2, -3)$.

STEP 2 **Plot** another point $(-1, 0)$ on the graph. The axis of symmetry is the vertical line $x = -2$. Use symmetry to plot a third point $(-3, 0)$.

STEP 3 **Connect** the points with a V-shaped graph.

STEP 4 **Examine** the graph. The x-intercepts are -1 and -3, which are also the zeros of the function, and the y-intercept is 3. The function is increasing when $x > -2$ and decreasing when $x < -2$.

STEP 5 **Compare** with $y = |x|$. The graph of $y = 3|x + 2| - 3$ is the graph of $y = |x|$ first stretched vertically by a factor of 3, then translated left 2 units and down 3 units.

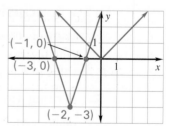

Guided Practice for Example 1

Graph the function. Identify the intercepts, zeros, and intervals of increase and decrease. *Compare* the graph with the graph of $y = |x|$.

1. $y = |x - 1| + 2$

2. $y = 2|x + 3| - 1$

3. $y = -|x - 2| + 1$

Georgia Performance Standards

MM2A1b Investigate and explain characteristics of a variety of piecewise functions including domain, range, vertex, axis of symmetry, zeros, intercepts, extrema, points of discontinuity, intervals over which the function is constant, intervals of increase and decrease, and rates of change.

Example 2 Write an absolute value function

Membership y (in tens) in a charitable organization decreased steadily then increased steadily, as shown in the graph where x is the time in months. Write an equation for the membership y.

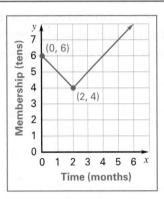

The vertex of the membership function is (2, 4).
The equation has the form $y = a|x - 2| + 4$.
Substitute the coordinates of the point (0, 6) into the equation and solve for a.

$6 = a|0 - 2| + 4$ Substitute 0 for x and 6 for y.

$1 = a$ Solve for a.

An equation for the membership is $y = |x - 2| + 4$.

Example 3 Apply transformations to a graph

The graph of a function y = f(x) is shown. Sketch the graph of y = −f(x + 1) − 3.

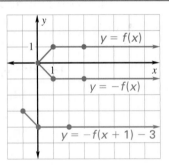

The graph of $y = -f(x + 1) - 3$ is the graph of $y = f(x)$ reflected in the x-axis, then translated 1 unit left and 3 units down. To draw the graph, first reflect the plotted points and connect their images. Then translate and connect these points to form the final image.

Guided Practice for Examples 2 and 3

4. Sales y (in thousands of dollars) decreased steadily then increased steadily, as shown in the graph where x is the time in months. Write an equation for the sales y.

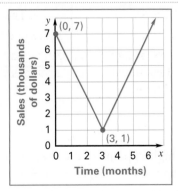

Use the graph of y = f(x) in Example 3 to sketch the graph of the given function.

5. $y = f(x + 2)$ 6. $y = f(x - 3) + 2$ 7. $y = 2 \cdot f(x)$

UNIT 2

Exercise Set A

MM2A1b Investigate and explain characteristics of a variety of piecewise functions including domain, range, vertex, axis of symmetry, zeros, intercepts, extrema, points of discontinuity, intervals over which the function is constant, intervals of increase and decrease, and rates of change.

For the function (a) tell whether the graph *opens up* or *opens down*, (b) identify the vertex, and (c) tell whether the graph is *wider*, *narrower*, or the *same width* as the graph of $y = |x|$.

1. $y = -|x + 1|$

2. $f(x) = 7|x - 3| - 4$

3. $y = -4|x + 2| + 2$

4. $f(x) = 2|x + 2| + 8$

5. $y = -\frac{2}{3}|x + 1|$

6. $f(x) = -|x| - 5$

7. $y = \frac{5}{2}|x + 9| - 1$

8. $f(x) = \frac{7}{8}|x + 3| - 9$

9. $y = -\frac{7}{5}|x - 1| + 1$

10. **Error Analysis** *Describe* and correct the error in graphing $y = |x + 4|$.

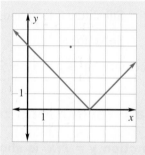

Graph the function.

11. $y = 3|x|$

12. $f(x) = -\frac{2}{3}|x|$

13. $y = -3|x + 1|$

14. $y = 2|x + 1| - 1$

15. $f(x) = \frac{1}{2}|x - 3| + 2$

16. $y = -\frac{3}{2}|x - 4| + 2$

Write an equation of the graph shown. Identify the intercepts, zeros, and intervals of increase and decrease.

17.

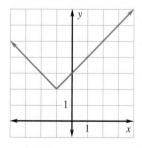

18.

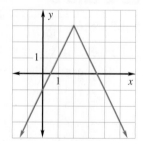

19.

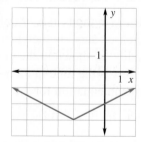

20. **Multiple Choice** The highest point on the graph of $y = f(x)$ is $(0, 7)$. What is the highest point on the graph of $y = 3 \cdot f(x - 2) + 4$?

   A. $(-5, 4)$ **B.** $(6, 5)$ **C.** $(-2, 25)$ **D.** $(2, 25)$

21. Multiple Choice Which equation has the graph shown?

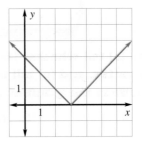

  A. $y = |x| + 3$

  B. $y = |x| - 3$

  C. $y = |x + 3|$

  D. $y = |x - 3|$

Let $f(x) = x + 2$. Graph $f(x)$. Then graph the given function by applying a transformation to the graph of $f(x)$.

22. $y = f(x) + 1$ **23.** $y = f(x - 2)$ **24.** $y = -2 \cdot f(x)$

25. $y = \dfrac{1}{4} \cdot f(x)$ **26.** $y = 3 \cdot f(x + 2) - 1$ **27.** $y = -f(x - 1) + 3$

28. Multiple Representations The diagram shows a truck driving toward a radio station transmitter that has a broadcasting range of 60 miles.

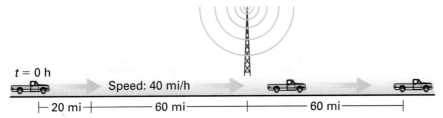

a. **Making a Table** Make a table that shows the truck's distance d (in miles) from the transmitter after $t = 0, 0.5, 1, 1.5, 2, 2.5, 3, 3.5,$ and 4 hours.

b. **Drawing a Graph** Use your table from part (a) to draw a graph that shows d as a function of t.

c. **Writing an Equation** Write an equation that gives d as a function of t. During what driving times is the truck within range of the transmitter?

In Exercises 29–31, use the following information.

Speedboats The number of boats B a boat dealer sells in each month of the year can be modeled by the function $B = -15|t - 5| + 120$ where t is the time in months and $t = 1$ represents January.

29. Graph the function for $1 \le t \le 12$.

30. What is the maximum number of sales in one month? In what month is the maximum reached?

31. What is the minimum number of sales in one month? In what month is the minimum reached?

UNIT 2

MM2A1b Investigate and explain characteristics of a variety of piecewise functions including domain, range, vertex, axis of symmetry, zeros, intercepts, extrema, points of discontinuity, intervals over which the function is constant, intervals of increase and decrease, and rates of change.

For the function (a) tell whether the graph *opens up* or *opens down*, (b) identify the vertex, and (c) tell whether the graph is *wider, narrower*, or the *same width* as the graph of $y = |x|$.

1. $y = -2|x - 4|$

2. $f(x) = 2|x - 1| - 3$

3. $y = 2 - |x - 10|$

4. $f(x) = 5 + \frac{1}{2}|x - 2|$

5. $y = 8 - \frac{2}{3}|x - 4|$

6. $f(x) = -\frac{8}{5}|x - 2| - 5$

7. $y = -3 - \frac{5}{9}|x + 4|$

8. $f(x) = \frac{7}{6}|x + 3|$

9. $y = 14 - \frac{7}{5}|x - 7|$

Match the function with its graph.

10. $y = 3\left|x + \frac{1}{2}\right| - 2$

11. $y = \frac{1}{5}|x + 2| - 1$

12. $f(x) = 4 - \frac{7}{3}|x|$

A.

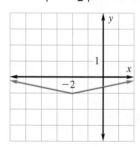

B.

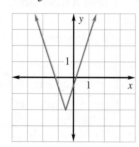

C.

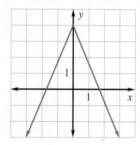

Graph the function.

13. $y = 1 - |x|$

14. $y = 1 + |x + 3|$

15. $y = 2\left|x + \frac{1}{2}\right| - 3$

16. $f(x) = 4 - 3|x - 4|$

17. $f(x) = 0.5|x - 1.6| + 2.2$

18. $y = -2.5|x + 3.6| - 1.4$

Write an equation of the graph shown. Identify the intercepts, zeros, and intervals of increase and decrease.

19.

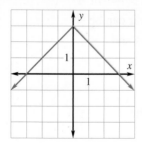

20.

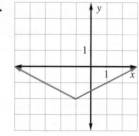

21.

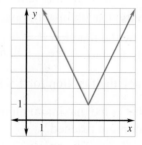

Exercise Set B (continued)

Let $f(x) = 2x - 1$. Graph $f(x)$. Then graph the given function by applying a transformation to the graph of $f(x)$.

22. $y = \dfrac{1}{4} \cdot f(x)$ **23.** $y = 3 \cdot f(x + 2) - 1$ **24.** $y = -f(x - 1) + 3$

25. Multiple Choice The highest point on the graph of $y = f(x)$ is $(-2, -1)$. What is the highest point on the graph of $y = 5 \cdot f(x + 2) - 8$?

   A. $(-4, -13)$ **B.** $(-22, -1)$ **C.** $(-20, 22)$ **D.** $(-10, -13)$

In Exercises 26–27, use the following information.

Pool On the pool table shown, you bank the five ball off the side at $(-2.5, 10)$. You want the ball to go in the pocket at $(-10, 0)$.

26. Write an equation for the path of the ball.

27. Do you make the shot? *Explain* how you found your answer.

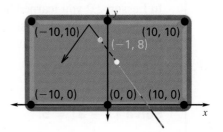

In Exercises 28–30, use the following information.

Raincoats A raincoat retailer has modeled the number of raincoats sold from January through May by the function $R_1 = -30\left| t - 3 \right| + 80$ and May through December by the function $R_2 = -10\left| t - 9 \right| + 60$. Let t be the time in months and $t = 1$ represent January.

28. Graph the function for the entire year, $1 \le t \le 12$.

29. What is the maximum number of raincoats sold in one month? In what month(s) is the maximum reached?

30. What is the minimum number of raincoats sold in one month? In what month(s) is the minimum reached?

31. Pyramids of Egypt The Great Pyramid of Giza, Khufu, is the first wonder of the ancient world. It stands 450 feet tall and its base is 755 feet long. Imagine a coordinate plane is placed flat over a side of the pyramid. In the coordinate plane, each unit is one foot and the origin is at the center of the pyramid's base. Write an absolute value function for the outline of the pyramid.

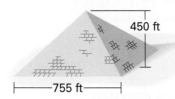

450 ft

755 ft

32. Challenge The graph of $y = a\left| x - h \right| + k$ passes through $(-1, 6)$ and $(3, 6)$. *Describe* the possible values of h and k.

UNIT 2

Georgia Performance Standards

MM2A1c Solve absolute value equations and inequalities analytically, graphically, and by using appropriate technology.

☑

Technology Activity

Solving Absolute Value Equations and Inequalities

Use after Lesson 2.4

Question

How can you use technology to solve absolute value equations and inequalities?

In Lesson 2.2 you learned how to solve absolute value equations and inequalities algebraically, and in Lesson 2.4 you learned how to graph absolute value functions. In this activity, you will use a graphing calculator to solve absolute value equations and inequalities.

Example 1

Solve $|x - 3| = 5$.

STEP 1 Enter the functions $y = |x - 3|$ and $y = 5$ into a graphing calculator.

STEP 2 Display the graphs of the two functions.

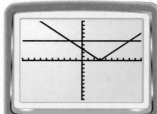

STEP 3 Find the points of intersection of the graphs using the *intersect* feature. The x-coordinates of these points will be the solutions of the equation.

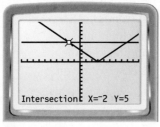

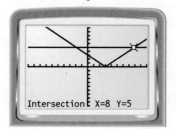

The solutions of $|x - 3| = 5$ are -2 and 8.

Practice

Use a graphing calculator to solve the absolute value equation.

1. $|x - 4| = 1$

2. $|x + 2| = 3$

3. $|2x + 1| = 5$

4. $|3x - 9| = 0$

Example 2

Solve $|x + 2| > 4$.

The solutions of $|x + 2| > 4$ are the values of x for which the graph of $y = |x + 2|$ lies above the graph of $y = 4$. Identify these values of x by graphing $y = |x + 2|$ and $y = 4$ in the same coordinate plane.

STEP 1 **Enter** the functions $y = |x + 2|$ and $y = 4$ into a graphing calculator.

STEP 2 **Display** the graphs of the two functions.

STEP 3 **Find** the values of x for which the graph of $y = |x + 2|$ lies above the graph of $y = 4$. These values of x appear to be $x < -6$ or $x > 2$. Use the *intersect* feature to check these values.

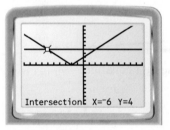

The solution of $|x + 2| > 4$ is $x < -6$ or $x > 2$.

Practice

In Exercises 5 and 6, solve the absolute value inequality algebraically.

5. $|x| < 4$ **6.** $|x| > 4$

7. Use a graphing calculator to verify your solutions to Exercises 5 and 6.

Use a graphing calculator to solve the absolute value inequality.

8. $|x - 4| > 3$ **9.** $|x - 4| < 3$

10. $|2x - 3| > 7$ **11.** $|2x - 3| < 7$

Use Piecewise Functions

Georgia Performance Standards: MM2A1a, MM2A1b

Goal Evaluate, graph, and write piecewise functions.

Vocabulary

A **piecewise function** is defined by at least two equations, each of which applies to a different part of the function's domain.

Points on the graph of a function in which there is a break, hole, or gap are called **points of discontinuity**.

A **step function** is a piecewise function that is defined by a constant value over each part of its domain. Its graph resembles a set of stairs.

Extrema are the maximums or minimums of a function. Extrema can be local (within a given part of the domain) or global (within the entire domain).

The **average rate of change** of a function between two points (x_1, y_1) and (x_2, y_2) on its graph is the slope of the line through the two points:

$$\text{average rate of change} = \frac{y_2 - y_1}{x_2 - x_1}.$$

Example 1   Evaluate a piecewise function

Evaluate the function when (a) $x = 0$ and (b) $x = 4$.

$$g(x) = \begin{cases} 3x - 1, & \text{if } x \le 0 \\ 2x + 1, & \text{if } x > 0 \end{cases}$$

Solution

a. $g(x) = 3x - 1$ Because $0 \le 0$, use first equation.

     $g(0) = 3(0) - 1$ Substitute 0 for x.

         $= -1$ Simplify.

b. $g(x) = 2x + 1$ Because $4 > 0$, use second equation.

     $g(4) = 2(4) + 1$ Substitute 4 for x.

         $= 9$ Simplify.

Guided Practice for Example 1

Evaluate the function for the given value of x.

$$f(x) = \begin{cases} 8x + 3, & \text{if } x > 2 \\ \frac{1}{2}x - 1, & \text{if } x \le 2 \end{cases}$$

1. $f(-6)$ **2.** $f(2)$ **3.** $f(3)$ **4.** $f(4)$

Example 2   Graph a piecewise function

Graph the function $f(x) = \begin{cases} -\dfrac{1}{2}x - 1, & \text{if } x < -2 \\ x, & \text{if } -2 \le x \le 1. \\ 2, & \text{if } x > 1 \end{cases}$

Find the *x*-coordinates for which there are points of discontinuity.

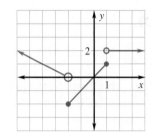

STEP 1 To the left of $x = -2$, graph $y = -\dfrac{1}{2}x - 1$. Use an open dot at $(-2, 0)$ because the equation $y = -\dfrac{1}{2}x - 1$ does not apply when $x = -2$.

STEP 2 From $x = -2$ to $x = 1$, inclusive, graph $y = x$. Use solid dots at $(-2, -2)$ and $(1, 1)$ because the equation $y = x$ applies to both $x = -2$ and $x = 1$.

STEP 3 To the right of $x = 1$, graph $y = 2$. Use an open dot at $(1, 2)$ because the equation $y = 2$ does not apply when $x = 1$.

STEP 4 Examine the graph. Because there are gaps in the graph at $x = -2$ and $x = 1$, these are the *x*-coordinates for which there are points of discontinuity.

Example 3   Write a piecewise function

Write a piecewise function for the step function shown. Describe any intervals over which the function is constant.

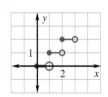

For x between 0 and 1, including $x = 0$, the graph is the line segment given by $y = 0$.

For x between 1 and 2, including $x = 1$, the graph is the line segment given by $y = 1$.

For x between 2 and 3, including $x = 2$, the graph is the line segment given by $y = 2$. So, a piecewise function for the graph is as follows:

$$f(x) = \begin{cases} 0, & \text{if } 0 \le x < 1 \\ 1, & \text{if } 1 \le x < 2 \\ 2, & \text{if } 2 \le x < 3 \end{cases}$$

The intervals over which the function is constant are $0 \le x < 1$, $1 \le x < 2$, and $2 \le x < 3$.

Guided Practice for Examples 2 and 3

5. Graph the function $g(x) = \begin{cases} 5, & \text{if } x \le -2 \\ -x + 1, & \text{if } -2 < x < 1 \\ -\frac{1}{2}x + \frac{7}{2}, & \text{if } x \ge 1 \end{cases}$.

Find the x-coordinates for which there are points of discontinuity.

6. Repeat Exercise 5 if $-x + 1$ is replaced by $-x + 3$.

7. Write a piecewise function for the step function shown. *Describe* any intervals over which the function is constant.

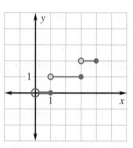

Example 4 Write and analyze a piecewise function

Write the function $f(x) = 2|x + 4| - 3$ as a piecewise function. Find any extrema as well as the rate of change of the function to the left and to the right of the vertex.

STEP 1 **Graph** the function. Find and label the vertex, one point to the left of the vertex, and one point to the right of the vertex. The graph shows one minimum value of -3, located at the vertex, and no maximum.

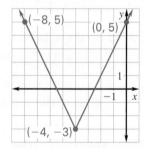

STEP 2 **Find** linear equations that represent each piece of the graph.

Left of vertex:	*Right of vertex:*	
$m = \dfrac{5 - (-3)}{-8 - (-4)} = -2$	$m = \dfrac{5 - (-3)}{0 - (-4)} = 2$	Formula for slope
$y - 5 = -2(x - (-8))$	$y - 5 = 2(x - 0)$	Point-slope form
$y = -2x - 11$	$y = 2x + 5$	Solve for y.

So, the function may be written as $f(x) = \begin{cases} -2x - 11, & \text{if } x < -4 \\ 2x + 5, & \text{if } x \ge -4 \end{cases}$.

The extremum is a minimum located at the vertex $(-4, -3)$. The rate of change of the function is -2 when $x < -4$, and 2 when $x > -4$.

Guided Practice for Example 4

8. Write the function $f(x) = 3|x - 2| + 1$ as a piecewise function. Find any extrema as well as the rate of change of the function to the left and to the right of the vertex.

MM2A1a   Write absolute value functions as piecewise functions.

MM2A1b   Investigate and explain characteristics of a variety of piecewise functions including domain, range, vertex, axis of symmetry, zeros, intercepts, extrema, points of discontinuity, intervals over which the function is constant, intervals of increase and decrease, and rates of change.

Evaluate the piecewise function when (a) $x = -2$, (b) $x = 0$, and (c) $x = 1$.

1. $f(x) = \begin{cases} 3x + 2, & \text{if } x < 1 \\ 2x + 3, & \text{if } x \geq 1 \end{cases}$

2. $g(x) = \begin{cases} 1 - 4x, & \text{if } x \leq -2 \\ 1 + 4x, & \text{if } x > -2 \end{cases}$

3. $g(x) = \begin{cases} 1, & \text{if } x \leq -1 \\ x, & \text{if } -1 < x \leq 0 \\ 2 - x, & \text{if } x > 0 \end{cases}$

4. $f(x) = \begin{cases} x + 2, & \text{if } x \leq -2 \\ x - 2, & \text{if } -2 < x < 1 \\ \frac{1}{2}x - \frac{3}{2}, & \text{if } x \geq 1 \end{cases}$

Graph the piecewise function. Find the x-coordinates for which there are points of discontinuity.

5. $f(x) = \begin{cases} 3x + 2, & \text{if } x \geq 0 \\ -x + 2, & \text{if } x < 0 \end{cases}$

6. $g(x) = \begin{cases} x, & \text{if } x \leq 1 \\ 3x - 1, & \text{if } x > 1 \end{cases}$

7. $f(x) = \begin{cases} 4, & \text{if } x \leq 2 \\ 2, & \text{if } 2 < x \leq 4 \\ 6, & \text{if } x > 4 \end{cases}$

8. $h(x) = \begin{cases} 2, & \text{if } x < -2 \\ x + 1, & \text{if } -2 \leq x \leq 2 \\ 2x, & \text{if } x > 2 \end{cases}$

Write a piecewise function for the step function shown. *Describe* any intervals over which the function is constant.

9.

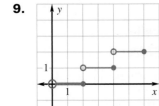

10.

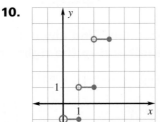

11.

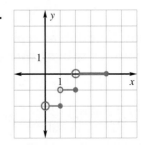

Write the function as a piecewise function. Find any extrema as well as the function's rate of change to the left and to the right of the vertex.

12. $f(x) = |x| + 1$

13. $f(x) = |x - 3| + 3$

14. $f(x) = 2|x + 4| - 12$

15. **Greatest Integer Function** A function in which the output $f(x)$ is the greatest integer less than or equal to the input x is called the *greatest integer function*. Write the greatest integer function as a piecewise function and graph it using the domain $-4 \leq x \leq 4$.

UNIT 2

MM2A1a   Write absolute value functions as piecewise functions.

MM2A1b   Investigate and explain characteristics of a variety of
piecewise functions including domain, range, vertex,
axis of symmetry, zeros, intercepts, extrema, points
of discontinuity, intervals over which the function is
constant, intervals of increase and decrease, and rates
of change.

Evaluate the piecewise function when (a) $x = -2$, (b) $x = 0$, and (c) $x = 1$.

1. $g(x) = \begin{cases} x^2 + 2x + 1, & \text{if } x \le -2 \\ 1 - x^2, & \text{if } x > -2 \end{cases}$

2. $f(x) = \begin{cases} x(x^2 + 1), & \text{if } x \le -2 \\ 4x + 5, & \text{if } -2 < x < 1 \\ \dfrac{1}{2x + 3}, & \text{if } x \ge 1 \end{cases}$

Graph the piecewise function. Find the x-coordinates for which there are points of discontinuity.

3. $h(x) = \begin{cases} 0, & \text{if } x \le 2 \\ x, & \text{if } 2 < x \le 4 \\ -x, & \text{if } x > 4 \end{cases}$

4. $g(x) = \begin{cases} 2, & \text{if } x < -2 \\ 0, & \text{if } x = -2 \\ -\dfrac{3}{2}x + \dfrac{3}{2}, & \text{if } x > -2 \end{cases}$

Write a piecewise function for the step function shown. *Describe* any intervals over which the function is constant.

5.

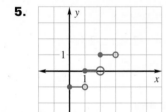

6.

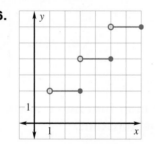

7.

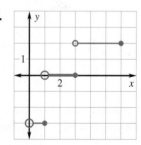

Write the function as a piecewise function. Find any extrema as well as the function's rate of change to the left and to the right of the vertex.

8. $f(x) = |x - 1| + 1$

9. $f(x) = 2 - 2|x + 2|$

10. $f(x) = -0.5|x - 1.4| + 3.6$

11. Postal Rates In 2007 the cost C (in dollars)
to send U.S. Postal Service Express Mail up to
5 pounds depended on the weight w (in ounces)
according to the function at the right. Graph
the function. What is the cost to send a parcel
weighing 3 pounds 8 ounces?

$C(w) = \begin{cases} 14.40, & \text{if } 0 < w \le 8 \\ 18.80, & \text{if } 8 < w \le 32 \\ 22.20, & \text{if } 32 < w \le 48 \\ 25.50, & \text{if } 48 < w \le 64 \\ 28.75, & \text{if } 64 < w \le 80 \end{cases}$

12. Rounding Function The *rounding function* is a function in which the output $f(x)$
is the input x rounded to the nearest integer. If the decimal part of x is 0.5, then x is
rounded up when x is positive and x is rounded down when x is negative. Write the
rounding function as a piecewise function and graph it using the domain $-4 \le x \le 4$.

UNIT 2

TEST | for Unit 2

Use the formula $A = \ell w$ for the area of a rectangle to solve for the missing variable.

1. $A = \underline{\ ?\ }$, $\ell = 6$ in., $w = 16$ in.

2. $A = 169$ cm^2, $\ell = \underline{\ ?\ }$, $w = 13$ cm

Look for a pattern in the table. Then write an equation that represents the table.

3.

x	1	2	3	4	5
y	7	8	9	10	11

4.

x	−2	−1	0	1	2
y	−5	−3	−1	1	3

Solve the equation or inequality.

5. $|x + 1| = 1$

6. $|x - 3| = \dfrac{7}{2}$

7. $|3x + 2| = 5$

8. $|x - 2| < 4$

9. $|2x + 3| > 1$

10. $\left|\dfrac{1}{4}x + 3\right| \leq 1$

Identify the domain and range of the given relation. Then tell whether the relation is a function. If the relation is a function, tell whether it is a one-to-one function.

11. $(1, 0), (−2, −1), (2, −1)$

12.

x	1	2	3	2	1
y	0	1	2	3	4

13. $(1, 3), (2, 2), (3, 1), (0, 0)$

Graph the equation.

14. $y = \dfrac{1}{2} - x$

15. $y = 2x - 6$

16. $y = 3x + 3$

Tell whether the function is linear and evaluate the function when $x = -2$, $x = 0$, and $x = 1$.

17. $f(x) = x + 16$

18. $f(x) = |x + 0.5|$

19. $f(x) = x(x - 1)$

Let $f(x) = x - 5$. Graph $f(x)$. Then graph the given function by applying a transformation to the graph of $f(x)$.

20. $y = f(x + 1)$

21. $y = 2 \cdot f(x)$

22. $y = 3 \cdot f(x - 2) + 1$

Graph the function.

23. $f(x) = -|x + 6|$

24. $f(x) = 3|x| + 2$

25. $f(x) = -10|x - 1| + 2$

26. $f(x) = \begin{cases} x + 5, & \text{if } x < -5 \\ -5 - x, & \text{if } x \geq -5 \end{cases}$

27. $f(x) = \begin{cases} x + 2, & \text{if } x < -2 \\ x - \dfrac{1}{2}, & \text{if } -2 \leq x \leq 2 \\ \dfrac{1}{2}x - \dfrac{3}{2}, & \text{if } x > 2 \end{cases}$

28. Multiple Representations Your cell phone plan costs $30 per month plus $.10 per text message. You receive a bill for $43.80.

    a. Making a Table Copy and complete the table below. Use the table to estimate how many text messages you sent.

Text messages	0	50	100	150	200
Monthly bill	$30	?	?	?	?

    b. Writing a Model Write an equation for the situation. Solve it to find exactly how many text messages you sent.

    c. Comparing Answers Is your estimate from part (a) compatible with the exact answer from part (b)? *Explain*.

29. Baseball A baseball has a cushioned cork center called the *pill*. The pill must weigh 0.84 ounce, with a tolerance of 0.04 ounce.

    a. Write an absolute value inequality that describes the acceptable weights for the pill.

    b. Solve the inequality to find the acceptable weights for the pill.

30. Mountain Climbing A climber on Mount Ranier in Washington climbs from an elevation of 5200 feet above sea level to an elevation of 10,100 feet. The elevation h (in feet) as the climber ascends can be modeled by $h(t) = 1000t + 5200$ where t is the time (in hours). Graph the function. Determine a reasonable domain and range. What is the climber's elevation after climbing 2.5 hours?

Performance Task

Road Trip

You are driving to visit your cousin who lives in a different state. It takes you 3 days to get there by car. You drive for 8 hours each day.

    a. You drive at an average speed of 60 miles per hour the first day, 68 miles per hour the second day, and 64 miles per hour the third day. Make a table which shows the number of miles you drive each day. How far away does your cousin live?

    b. Write the number of miles you drive as a function of total time spent driving (in hours) as a piecewise function.

    c. Determine the domain and range of the function you found in part (b) and explain the meaning of each.

    d. Graph the function you found in part (b).

    e. Before you go on your trip, you research the prices of gasoline along the way. You find that the lowest price is $2.34 per gallon and the highest price is $2.96 per gallon. Write an absolute value inequality that represents the range of prices.

UNIT 3
Algebra: Quadratic Functions

Graph Quadratic Functions in Standard Form

Georgia Performance Standards: MM2A3b, MM2A3c

Goal Graph quadratic functions.

Vocabulary

A **quadratic function** is a function that can be written in the **standard form**
$y = ax^2 + bx + c$ where $a \neq 0$. The graph of a quadratic equation is a **parabola**.
The lowest or highest point on a parabola is the **vertex**. The axis of symmetry
divides the parabola into mirror images and passes through the vertex.

The minimum(s) and maximum(s) of a function on a certain interval are the extreme
values, or **extrema**, of the function. For $y = ax^2 + bx + c$, the vertex's y-coordinate
is the **minimum value** of the function if $a > 0$ and the **maximum value** if $a < 0$.

Example 1 | **Graph a function of the form $y = ax^2 + c$**

Graph $y = -x^2 + 2$. Identify the domain and range of the function.

STEP 1 **Make** a table of values for $y = -x^2 + 2$.

x	−2	−1	0	1	2
y	−2	1	2	1	−2

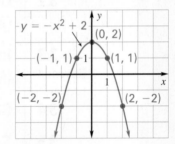

STEP 2 **Plot** the points from the table.

STEP 3 **Draw** a smooth curve through the points.

STEP 4 **Identify** the domain and range. The domain is all real numbers and
the range is $y \leq 2$.

Example 2 | **Graph a function of the form $y = ax^2 + bx + c$**

Graph $y = x^2 - 6x + 8$.

STEP 1 **Identify** the coefficients of the function: $a = 1$, $b = -6$, $c = 8$.

STEP 2 **Find** the vertex. To find the x-coordinate, use
$x = -\dfrac{b}{2a} = -\dfrac{-6}{(2)1} = 3$. The y-coordinate is
$(3)^2 - 6(3) + 8 = -1$. Plot the vertex $(3, -1)$.

STEP 3 **Draw** the axis of symmetry $x = 3$.

STEP 4 **Identify** the y-intercept $(0, 8)$ and reflect the
point in the axis of symmetry to plot $(6, 8)$.

STEP 5 **Evaluate** the function for $x = 1$. Plot the
point $(1, 3)$ and its reflection $(5, 3)$.

STEP 6 **Draw** a parabola through the plotted points.

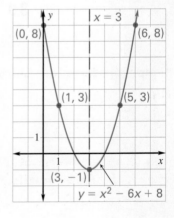

UNIT 3

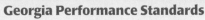

Georgia Performance Standards

MM2A3b Graph quadratic functions as transformations of the function $f(x) = x^2$.

MM2A3c Investigate and explain characteristics of quadratic functions, including domain, range, vertex, axis of symmetry, zeros, intercepts, extrema, intervals of increase and decrease, and rates of change.

Example 3 Find the minimum or maximum value

Tell whether the function $y = -2x^2 + 8x - 7$ has a *minimum value* or a *maximum value*. Find the minimum or maximum value.

Because $a < 0$, the function has a maximum value. The coordinates of the vertex are $x = -\dfrac{b}{2a} = -\dfrac{8}{(-4)} = 2$ and $y = -2(2)^2 + 8(2) - 7 = 1$. The maximum value is $y = 1$.

Example 4 Find the maximum value of a quadratic function

Revenue A street vendor sells about 20 shirts each day when she charges $8 per shirt. If she decreases the price by $1, she sells about 10 more shirts each day. How can she maximize daily revenue?

STEP 1 Define the variables. Let x represent the price reduction and $R(x)$ represent the daily revenue.

STEP 2 Write a verbal model. Then write and simplify a quadratic function.

Revenue (dollars)	=	Price (dollars/shirt)	•	Number of shirts

$$R(x) = (8 - x) \cdot (20 + 10x)$$
$$R(x) = 160 + 80x - 20x - 10x^2$$
$$R(x) = -10x^2 + 60x + 160$$

STEP 3 Find the coordinates $(x, R(x))$ of the vertex.

$$x = -\frac{b}{2a} = -\frac{60}{2(-10)} = 3 \qquad \text{Find } x\text{-coordinate.}$$

$$R(3) = -10(3)^2 + 60(3) + 160 = 250 \qquad \text{Evaluate } R(3).$$

The vertex is $(3, 250)$. The vendor should reduce the price by $3 to maximize daily revenue.

Guided Practice for Examples 1, 2, 3, and 4

Graph the function. Label the vertex and axis of symmetry.

1. $y = 6x^2$

2. $y = -x^2 + 1$

3. $y = -4x^2 - 1$

4. $y = x^2 + 4x + 4$

5. $y = 2x^2 - 8x + 6$

6. $y = x^2 - 4x - 4$

Tell whether the function has a *minimum value* or a *maximum value*. Then find the minimum or maximum value.

7. $y = 2x^2 + 8x - 3$

8. $y = -x^2 + 6x - 8$

9. $y = -x^2 - 4x - 12$

UNIT 3

LESSON
3.1

Exercise Set A

MM2A3b Graph quadratic functions as transformations of the function $f(x) = x^2$.

MM2A3c Investigate and explain characteristics of quadratic functions, including domain, range, vertex, axis of symmetry, zeros, intercepts, extrema, intervals of increase and decrease, and rates of change.

Copy and complete the table of values for the function.

1. $y = 2x^2$

x	−2	−1	0	1	2
y	?	?	?	?	?

2. $y = -3x^2$

x	−2	−1	0	1	2
y	?	?	?	?	?

3. $y = -\dfrac{1}{2}x^2$

x	−4	−2	0	2	4
y	?	?	?	?	?

4. $y = \dfrac{1}{3}x^2$

x	−6	−3	0	3	6
y	?	?	?	?	?

For the following functions (a) tell whether the graph _opens up_ or _opens down_, (b) find the vertex, and (c) find the axis of symmetry.

5. $y = -3x^2 + 1$

6. $y = -2x^2 - 1$

7. $y = 3x^2 - 2x$

8. $y = -4x^2 - 2x + 9$

9. $y = 5x^2 - 5x + 7$

10. $y = -2x^2 - 3x + 3$

Match the equation with its graph.

11. $y = \dfrac{1}{4}x^2 - 2x + 3$

12. $y = x^2 + 1$

13. $y = -\dfrac{1}{2}x^2 + 4x - 4$

14. $y = -x^2 + 5x - 2$

15. $y = -x^2 - 5x - 2$

16. $y = -\dfrac{1}{4}x^2 + 2$

A.

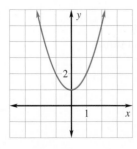

B.

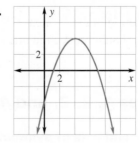

C.

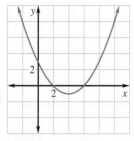

D.

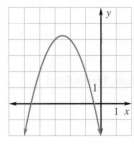

E.

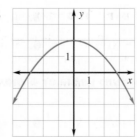

F.

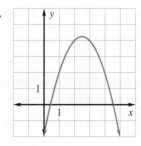

Exercise Set A *(continued)*

Graph the function. Identify the domain and range.

17. $y = 2x^2 + 3$

18. $y = -3x^2 - 4$

19. $y = -x^2 + 2x - 1$

20. $y = 4x^2 + 4x + 1$

21. $y = \frac{1}{2}x^2 - 2$

22. $y = -\frac{1}{4}x^2 + 2$

Graph the function. Label the vertex and axis of symmetry.

23. $y = x^2 - 3$

24. $y = -2x^2 + 4x$

25. $y = 2x^2 + 6x + 1$

26. $y = 4x^2 - 16x + 3$

27. $y = -3x^2 - 12x + 1$

28. $y = \frac{1}{3}x^2 + 2x - 1$

29. $y = x^2 + 5x - 1$

30. $y = 3x^2 + 3x - 2$

31. $y = -5x^2 + 4x + 2$

32. $y = -\frac{1}{2}x^2 + 3x - 1$

33. $y = -2x^2 - 4x + 3$

34. $y = 2x^2 - 4x - 2$

35. **Calculators** A department store is selling Brand X calculators for $90 each at a rate of 30 per month. The marketing department determines that for every $5 decrease in price, 5 more calculators would be sold per month. Write a quadratic equation in standard form that models the revenue R from calculator sales.

In Exercises 36–39, use the following information.

Minimize Cost A baker has modeled the monthly operating costs for making wedding cakes by the function $y = 0.5x^2 - 12x + 150$ where y is the total cost in dollars and x is the number of cakes prepared.

36. Find the domain and range of the function in the context of the situation.

37. Find the vertex and axis of symmetry.

38. What is the minimum monthly operating cost?

39. How many cakes should be prepared each month to yield the minimum operating cost?

In Exercises 40 and 41, use the following information.

Maximize Revenue A sports store sells about 50 mountain bikes per month at a price of $220 each. For each $20 decrease in price, about 10 more bikes per month are sold.

40. Write a quadratic function in standard form that models the revenue from bike sales.

41. What price produces the maximum revenue?

MM2A3b   Graph quadratic functions as transformations of the function $f(x) = x^2$.

MM2A3c   Investigate and explain characteristics of quadratic functions, including domain, range, vertex, axis of symmetry, zeros, intercepts, extrema, intervals of increase and decrease, and rates of change.

Copy and complete the table of values for the function.

1. $y = -6x^2 - 3$

x	−2	−1	0	1	2
y	?	?	?	?	?

2. $y = 2x^2 + x - 2$

x	−2	−1	0	1	2
y	?	?	?	?	?

3. $y = -\frac{1}{4}x^2 + 1$

x	−8	−4	0	4	8
y	?	?	?	?	?

4. $y = \frac{1}{7}x^2 - 2x + 6$

x	−14	−7	0	7	14
y	?	?	?	?	?

For the following functions (a) tell whether the graph *opens up* or *opens down*, (b) find the vertex, and (c) find the axis of symmetry.

5. $y = 5x^2 + 1$

6. $y = -x^2 - 1$

7. $y = -2x^2 - 4$

8. $y = -x^2 - 2x - 1$

9. $y = \frac{1}{2}x^2 + x - 2$

10. $y = -2x^2 - 6x + 3$

Match the equation with its graph.

11. $y = 2x^2 - 2$

12. $y = \frac{1}{2}x^2 - 2$

13. $y = \frac{1}{10}x^2 + x - 2$

A.
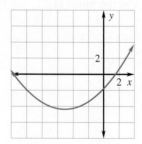

B.
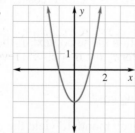

C.
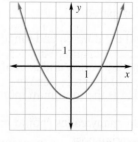

Error Analysis *Describe* and correct the error in analyzing the graph of $y = 2x^2 + 3x - 4$.

14.
The x-coordinate of the vertex is:
$$x = \frac{b}{2a} = \frac{3}{2(2)} = \frac{3}{4}$$

15.
The y-intercept of the graph is the value of c, which is 4.

Exercise Set B (continued)

Graph the function. Identify the domain and range.

16. $y = \frac{1}{2}x^2 - \frac{3}{4}$

17. $y = -\frac{1}{4}x^2 + 3$

18. $y = -\frac{1}{2}x^2 - 2x$

19. $y = \frac{1}{3}x^2 + \frac{1}{2}x$

20. $y = \frac{1}{2}x^2 + 2x - \frac{3}{8}$

21. $y = -\frac{1}{3}x^2 - 4x + 1$

Graph the function. Label the vertex and axis of symmetry.

22. $y = -4x^2 - 1$

23. $y = x^2 + 2x$

24. $y = 2x^2 + 4x - 3$

25. $y = 2x^2 - 5x + 3$

26. $y = -6x^2 - 4x + 1$

27. $y = \frac{1}{3}x^2 + 3x - 2$

28. $y = 2x^2 + 4x + 1$

29. $y = \frac{1}{2}x^2 + 4x + 10$

30. $y = -\frac{4}{3}x^2 + \frac{8}{3}x + \frac{8}{3}$

31. $y = 2x^2 - x - 1$

32. Visual Thinking Use a graphing calculator to graph $y = ax^2 - 4x + 6$ where $a = 8, 4,$ and $\frac{1}{2}$. Use the same viewing window for all three graphs. How do the graphs change as a decreases?

33. Challenge Find a, b, and c so that the parabola whose equation is $y = ax^2 + bx + c$ has its vertex at $\left(\frac{3}{2}, \frac{15}{2}\right)$ and passes through the point $(-1, -5)$. Graph the parabola.

In Exercises 34 and 35, use the following information.

Maximize Revenue A grocery store sells about 36 packs of bubble gum per day at a price of $.45 each. For each $.05 increase in price, the store expects to sell two less packs per day.

34. Write a quadratic function in standard form that models the revenue from bubble gum sales.

35. Should the store change the price of bubble gum to maximize revenue? *Explain.*

In Exercises 36–39, use the following information.

Minimize Cost An outdoor sign maker has modeled the monthly operating costs for making signs by the function $y = 0.4x^2 - 16x + 250$ where y is the total cost in dollars and x is the number of signs made.

36. Find the domain and the range of the function in the context of the situation.

37. Find the vertex and axis of symmetry.

38. What is the minimum monthly operating cost?

39. How many signs should be made each month to yield a minimum operating cost?

UNIT 3

Investigating Math Activity
Graph Quadratic Functions

Use before Lesson 3.2

Materials
graphing calculator

Question

How can the vertex form of a quadratic function help you graph the function quickly?

Explore

Graph quadratic functions.

Using a graphing calculator, graph the parent function $y = x^2$, and compare its graph to the graphs of the given quadratic functions.

a. $y = (x - 2)^2$
$y = (x + 3)^2$

b. $y = x^2 + 2$
$y = x^2 - 3$

c. $y = (x - 2)^2 + 3$
$y = (x + 3)^2 - 2$

STEP 1
Enter equations
Enter the parent function $y = x^2$ as Y_1, $y = (x - 2)^2$ as Y_2, and $y = (x + 3)^2$ as Y_3.

STEP 2
Graph equations
View the equations in the standard viewing window.

STEP 3
Find vertex
Use the *zoom* feature to help determine the vertex of each function.

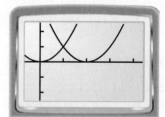

Repeat Steps 1–3 for the functions given in (b) and (c).

Draw Conclusions

1. Look at the graphs for the functions given in parts (a) and (b). What happens to the parent function $y = x^2$ when you add or subtract a number from x before squaring? when you add or subtract a number from x after squaring?

2. **Writing** Use your answers to Exercise 1 and the graphs of the functions given in part (c) to explain how you would shift the parent function $y = x^2$ to graph the function $y = (x - 4)^2 + 5$.

3. **Reasoning** *Explain* how you can use the vertex form $y = (x - h)^2 + k$ of a quadratic function to quickly graph the function.

Graph Quadratic Functions in Vertex or Intercept Form

Georgia Performance Standards: MM2A3a, MM2A3b, MM2A3c

Goal Graph quadratic functions in vertex form or intercept form.

Vocabulary

The **vertex form** of a quadratic function is given by $y = a(x - h)^2 + k$. The graph of the vertex form is the parabola $y = ax^2$ translated horizontally h units and vertically k units. The vertex is (h, k). The axis of symmetry is $x = h$. The graph opens up if $a > 0$ and down if $a < 0$.

If the graph of a quadratic function has at least one x-intercept, then the function can be represented in **intercept form**, $y = a(x - p)(x - q)$. The graph of the intercept form has x-intercepts at p and q. The axis of symmetry is halfway between $(p, 0)$ and $(q, 0)$. Its equation is $x = \dfrac{p + q}{2}$. The graph opens up if $a > 0$ and down if $a < 0$. Because the function's value is zero when $x = p$ and when $x = q$, the numbers p and q are also called zeros of the function.

Example 1   **Graph quadratic functions**

a. Graph $y = 2(x - 1)^2 + 3$, a quadratic function in vertex form.

STEP 1 **Identify** $a = 2$, $h = 1$, and $k = 3$. Because $a > 0$, the parabola opens up.

STEP 2 **Plot** the vertex $(1, 3)$ and draw $x = 1$, the axis of symmetry.

STEP 3 **Evaluate** y for $x = 0$ and $x = 2$. Plot the points $(0, 5)$ and $(2, 5)$.

STEP 4 **Draw** a parabola through the points.

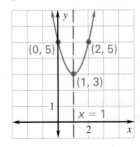

b. Graph $y = 3(x - 4)(x + 2)$, a quadratic function in intercept form.

STEP 1 **Identify** the x-intercepts. Because $p = 4$ and $q = -2$, $(4, 0)$ and $(-2, 0)$ are the x-intercepts.

STEP 2 **Find** the coordinates of the vertex.

$$x = \frac{p + q}{2} = \frac{4 + (-2)}{2} = \frac{2}{2} = 1$$

$$y = 3(1 - 4)(1 + 2) = -27$$

The vertex is $(1, -27)$.

STEP 3 **Draw** a parabola through the vertex and the points where the x-intercepts occur.

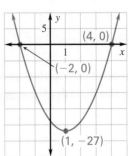

UNIT 3

Georgia Performance Standards

MM2A3a   Convert between standard and vertex form.   ☑

MM2A3b   Graph quadratic functions as transformations of the   ☑
         function $f(x) = x^2$.

MM2A3c   Investigate and explain characteristics of quadratic   ☑
         functions, including domain, range, vertex, axis of
         symmetry, zeros, intercepts, extrema, intervals of
         increase and decrease, and rates of change.

Example 2 Use a quadratic model in vertex form

Bridges A bridge is designed with cables that connect two towers that rise above
a roadway. The ends of each cable are the same height above the roadway. Each
cable is modeled by

$$y = \frac{(x - 1600)^2}{6800} + 30$$

where x is the horizontal distance (in feet) from the left tower and y is the
corresponding height (in feet) of the cable. Find the distance between the towers.

Solution

The vertex of the parabola is (1600, 30). The cable's lowest point is 1600 feet from
either tower. The distance between the towers is $d = 2(1600) = 3200$ feet.

Example 3 Change quadratic functions to standard form

Write the quadratic function in standard form.

   a. $y = 3(x - 1)(x + 2)$ **b.** $y = (x + 1)^2 + 2$

Solution

   a. $y = 3(x - 1)(x + 2)$ Write original function in intercept form.

       $= 3(x^2 + 2x - x - 2)$ Multiply using FOIL.

       $= 3(x^2 + x - 2)$ Combine like terms.

       $= 3x^2 + 3x - 6$ Distributive property

   b. $y = (x + 1)^2 + 2$ Write original function in vertex form.

       $= (x + 1)(x + 1) + 2$ Rewrite $(x + 1)^2$.

       $= (x^2 + x + x + 1) + 2$ Multiply using FOIL.

       $= x^2 + 2x + 3$ Combine like terms.

Guided Practice for Examples 1, 2, and 3

**Graph the function. Label the vertex and axis of symmetry.
Then write the quadratic function in standard form.**

  1. $y = (x + 1)^2$ **2.** $y = -(x - 1)^2$ **3.** $y = 2(x + 2)^2$

  4. $y = (x + 1)(x - 1)$ **5.** $y = 2(x - 2)(x - 3)$ **6.** $y = -(x + 3)^2 + 1$

  7. Rework Example 2 where $y = \dfrac{(x - 1500)^2}{6500} + 28$.

MM2A3a Convert between standard and vertex form.

MM2A3b Graph quadratic functions as transformations of the function $f(x) = x^2$.

MM2A3c Investigate and explain characteristics of quadratic functions, including domain, range, vertex, axis of symmetry, zeros, intercepts, extrema, intervals of increase and decrease, and rates of change.

For the following functions (a) tell whether the graph *opens up* or *opens down*, (b) find the vertex, and (c) find the axis of symmetry.

1. $y = -(x + 1)(x - 3)$

2. $y = (x + 2)(x - 1)$

3. $y = -2(x - 4)(x + 6)$

4. $y = -4(x - 2)^2 + 2$

5. $y = (x + 5)^2 - 1$

6. $y = 2(x - 1)^2 - 6$

Match the equation with its graph.

7. $y = 2(x - 2)^2 + 1$

8. $y = -(x - 3)(x - 1)$

9. $y = -(x + 1)^2 + 2$

10. $y = (x + 2)(x - 2)$

11. $y = -2(x - 4)^2 + 8$

12. $y = (x + 3)(x + 1)$

A.

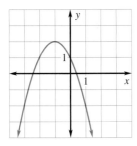

B.

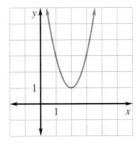

C.

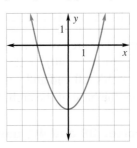

D.

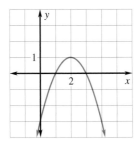

E.

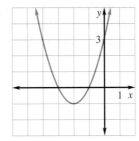

F.

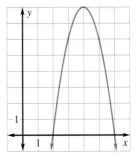

Graph the function. Label the vertex and axis of symmetry.

13. $y = (x + 1)^2 + 3$

14. $y = (x - 2)^2 - 1$

15. $y = (x + 2)^2 - 3$

16. $y = -2(x + 1)^2 - 4$

17. $y = 2(x + 2)^2 - 4$

18. $y = -(x - 4)^2 + 8$

Graph the function. Label the vertex, axis of symmetry, and *x*-intercepts.

19. $y = (x + 2)(x - 4)$

20. $y = (x + 2)(x + 3)$

21. $y = (x + 4)(x + 2)$

22. $y = -(x - 3)(x + 1)$

23. $y = 3(x - 1)(x - 4)$

24. $y = -3x(x + 7)$

UNIT 3

Exercise Set B *(continued)*

Graph the function. Label the vertex, axis of symmetry, and *x*-intercepts.

19. $y = -2(x + 2)(x + 6)$

20. $y = -(x - 2)(x + 1)$

21. $y = 3(x - 2)(x - 5)$

22. $y = -\frac{1}{2}(x - 3)(x + 2)$

23. $y = 5\left(x - \frac{2}{5}\right)\left(x - \frac{11}{5}\right)$

24. $y = 1.5(x - 3.3)(x + 2.7)$

25. $y = (2x - 4)(2x + 2)$

26. $y = (3x - 1)(x - 3)$

Write the quadratic function in standard form.

27. $y = 3(x - 1)^2 + 5$

28. $y = -\frac{5}{4}(x + 4)^2 + 15$

29. $y = \frac{4}{3}(x - 2)^2 - 5$

30. $y = \frac{5}{2}(x - 6)(x - 2)$

31. $y = 4\left(x + \frac{3}{2}\right)\left(\frac{3}{4}x + \frac{1}{4}\right)$

32. $y = -2.5(x - 1.3)(x + 5.2)$

Find the minimum value or the maximum value of the function.

33. $y = (x + 2)^2 - 3$

34. $y = -2(x + 1)^2 + 6$

35. $y = 2(x + 2)^2 - \frac{4}{5}$

36. $y = -2x(x + 8)$

37. $y = (x + 2)(x - 4)$

38. $y = -\frac{1}{2}(x + 2)(x + 3)$

39. **Number Theory** Every odd integer can be represented as $2n + 1$ where n is an integer. Write the product p of two consecutive odd integers as a quadratic function in intercept form.

In Exercises 40 and 41, use the following information.

Golf The flight of a particular golf shot reached a maximum height of 22.5 yards and the golf ball landed 300 yards from the point of impact. Assume the point of impact is $(0, 0)$.

40. Write a quadratic function $y = a(x - p)(x - q)$ that represents the flight of the ball.

41. If the golf ball reached the same maximum height and landed 250 yards from the point of impact, would you expect the new value of a to be greater than or less than the value of a from Exercise 40?

42. **Reasoning** Use the graph of the parabola to find the vertex form of the quadratic function. Write the function in standard form. Use the graph of the parabola to find the intercept form of the quadratic function. Write this function in standard form. Are the two functions the same? Graph the function $y = 2(x + 1)^2 + 3$. *Explain* why this function cannot be written in intercept form.

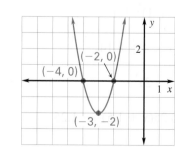

Interpret Rates of Change of Quadratic Functions

Goal Use intervals of increase and decrease to understand average rates of change of quadratic functions.

Example 1 Identify intervals of increase and decrease

Graph the function. Identify the intervals over which the graph increases and decreases.

a. $y = x^2 + 3x - 4$

b. $y = -\frac{1}{2}(x - 2)^2 + 1$

Solution

a. You can see from the graph that as you move from left to right the value of the function increases on the right side of the vertex and decreases on the left side of the vertex. The x-coordinate of the vertex is $x = -\dfrac{b}{2a} = -\dfrac{3}{2(1)} = -\dfrac{3}{2}$. So the graph increases over the interval $x > -\dfrac{3}{2}$ and decreases over the interval $x < -\dfrac{3}{2}$.

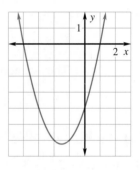

b. You can see from the graph that as you move from left to right the value of the function increases on the left side of the vertex and decreases on the right side of the vertex. Because the function is in vertex form, you know that the x-coordinate of the vertex is $x = 2$. So the graph increases over the interval $x < 2$ and decreases over the interval $x > 2$.

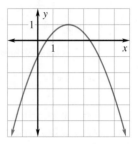

Guided Practice for Example 1

Graph the function. Identify the intervals over which the graph increases and decreases.

1. $y = x^2 - 3$

2. $y = -\frac{1}{2}x^2 + 3x + 2$

3. $y = \frac{1}{2}x^2 + x - 12$

4. $y = x^2 - \frac{3}{2}x - 1$

5. $y = -x^2 - x + 6$

6. $y = -\frac{1}{2}x^2 + \frac{5}{2}$

UNIT 3

Georgia Performance Standards

MM2A3c Investigate and explain characteristics of quadratic functions, including domain, range, vertex, axis of symmetry, zeros, intercepts, extrema, intervals of increase and decrease, and rates of change.

Example 2 **Calculate an average rate of change**

Calculate the average rate of change of the function $y = -0.5x^2 + 4$ on the given interval.

a. $-2 \leq x \leq 0$ **b.** $0 \leq x \leq 1$ **c.** $1 \leq x \leq 3$

Solution

Find the two points on the graph of the function that correspond to the endpoints of the interval. The average rate of change is the slope of the line that passes through these two points.

a. $\quad y = -0.5(-2)^2 + 4 \qquad y = -0.5(0)^2 + 4$

$\qquad\quad = -2 + 4 \qquad\qquad\qquad = 0 + 4$

$\qquad\quad = 2 \qquad\qquad\qquad\qquad = 4$

$\qquad (-2, 2) \qquad\qquad\qquad\quad (0, 4)$

The average rate of change is:

$r = \dfrac{4 - 2}{0 - (-2)} = \dfrac{2}{2} = 1$

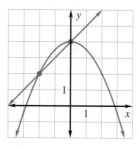

b. $\quad y = -0.5(0)^2 + 4 \qquad y = -0.5(1)^2 + 4$

$\qquad\quad = 0 + 4 \qquad\qquad\qquad = -0.5 + 4$

$\qquad\quad = 4 \qquad\qquad\qquad\qquad = 3.5$

$\qquad (0, 4) \qquad\qquad\qquad\quad (1, 3.5)$

The average rate of change is:

$r = \dfrac{3.5 - 4}{1 - 0} = \dfrac{-0.5}{1} = -0.5$

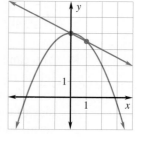

c. $\quad y = -0.5(1)^2 + 4 \qquad y = -0.5(3)^2 + 4$

$\qquad\quad = -0.5 + 4 \qquad\qquad = -4.5 + 4$

$\qquad\quad = 3.5 \qquad\qquad\qquad\quad = -0.5$

$\qquad (1, 3.5) \qquad\qquad\qquad (3, -0.5)$

The average rate of change is:

$r = \dfrac{-0.5 - 3.5}{3 - 1} = \dfrac{-4}{2} = -2$

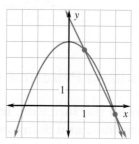

Guided Practice for Example 2

Calculate the average rate of change of the function $y = 2x^2 + 5x - 3$ on the given interval.

7. $-2 \leq x \leq 0$ **8.** $0 \leq x \leq 3$ **9.** $1 \leq x \leq 2$

Example 3 **Compare average rates of change**

Compare the average rates of change of $y = x^2$ and $y = x$ on $0 \le x \le 2$.

Solution

The average rate of change of $y = x$ is the slope of the line, which is 1. The points $(0, 0)$ and $(2, 4)$ correspond to the endpoints of the interval for $y = x^2$. The average rate of change of $y = x^2$ on $0 \le x \le 2$ is $r = \dfrac{4 - 0}{2 - 0} = \dfrac{4}{2} = 2$. The average rate of change for the quadratic function is 2 times as great as the average rate of change of the linear function on the interval $0 \le x \le 2$.

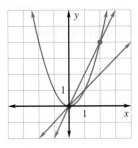

Example 4 **Solve a real world problem**

Shot Put The path of a shot put released at an angle of 35° can be modeled by $y = -0.01x^2 + 0.7x + 6$ where x is the horizontal distance (in feet) and y is the corresponding height (in feet). Find the interval on which the height is increasing. What is the average rate of change on this interval?

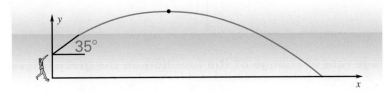

35°

Solution

The height of the shot put will be increasing from the release point until it reaches its maximum height at the vertex. The x-coordinate of the vertex is

$$x = \frac{-0.7}{2(-0.01)} = 35.$$

So the height will be increasing on the interval $0 \le x \le 35$.

When $x = 0$, $y = -0.01(0)^2 + 0.7(0) + 6 = 6$. When $x = 35$, $y = -0.01(35)^2 + 0.7(35) + 6 = 18.25$. The points $(0, 6)$ and $(35, 18.25)$ correspond to the endpoints of the interval of increase.

The average rate of change of $y = -0.01x^2 + 0.7x + 6$ is

$$r = \frac{18.25 - 6}{35 - 0} = \frac{12.25}{35} = 0.35$$

on the interval $0 \le x \le 35$. So, the height of the shot put will increase by an average of 0.35 foot per horizontal foot for the first 35 feet of horizontal distance.

Guided Practice for Examples 3 and 4

10. *Compare* the average rates of change of $y = 2x^2$ and $y = 2x$ on the interval $1 \le x \le 3$.

11. **What If?** In Example 4, suppose the path of the shot put is modeled by $y = -0.02x^2 + x + 6$. Find the interval on which the height is increasing. What is the average rate of change on this interval?

MM2A3c   Investigate and explain characteristics of quadratic functions, including domain, range, vertex, axis of symmetry, zeros, intercepts, extrema, intervals of increase and decrease, and rates of change.

Graph the function. Identify the intervals over which the graph increases and decreases.

1. $y = 2x^2 - 5x + 2$

2. $y = -(x + 3)^2 - 4$

3. $y = -2(x - 1)^2 + 3$

4. $y = (x + 5)(x - 3)$

Classify the given interval as an interval of *increase* or *decrease*.

5. $-4 \leq x \leq -2$

6. $-1 \leq x \leq 1$

7. $1 \leq x \leq 3$

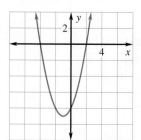

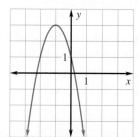

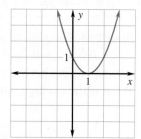

Calculate the average rate of change of the function on the given interval.

8. $y = x^2 + 1, 0 \leq x \leq 2$

9. $y = -2x^2 + 3, 0 \leq x \leq 2$

10. $y = -x^2 - 4x, -1 \leq x \leq 3$

11. $y = 4x^2 - 12x + 9, 0 \leq x \leq 1$

12. $y = -\frac{1}{2}x^2 + 3x - 1, 0 \leq x \leq 4$

13. $y = \frac{1}{3}x^2 + 2x - 1, -3 \leq x \leq 3$

***Compare* the average rates of change of the functions on the given interval.**

14. $y = x - 2$ and $y = -\frac{1}{5}x^2 + 2x - 1$ on the interval $0 \leq x \leq 5$

15. $y = -x^2 - 5x - 2$ and $y = -\frac{1}{4}x^2 + 2$ on the interval $0 \leq x \leq 2$

16. **Error Analysis** *Describe* and correct the error in calculating the average rate of change of $y = x^2 + 3x - 4$ on $1 \leq x \leq 3$.

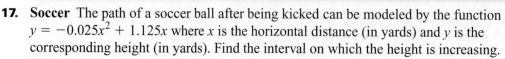

$$y = (1)^2 + 3(1) - 4$$
$$= 1 + 3 - 4$$
$$= 0$$
$$(1, 0)$$

$$y = (3)^2 + 3(3) - 4$$
$$= 9 + 9 - 4$$
$$= 14$$
$$(3, 14)$$

Average rate of change:
$$r = \frac{14 - 0}{1 - 3} = -7$$

17. **Soccer** The path of a soccer ball after being kicked can be modeled by the function $y = -0.025x^2 + 1.125x$ where x is the horizontal distance (in yards) and y is the corresponding height (in yards). Find the interval on which the height is increasing. What is the average rate of change on this interval?

Exercise Set B

MM2A3c   Investigate and explain characteristics of quadratic functions, including domain, range, vertex, axis of symmetry, zeros, intercepts, extrema, intervals of increase and decrease, and rates of change.

Graph the function. Identify the intervals over which the graph increases and decreases.

1. $y = -3(x + 4)(x - 6)$

2. $y = -2(x - 3)^2 + 1$

Classify the given interval as an interval of *increase* or *decrease*.

3. $-2 \leq x \leq 4$

4. $-2 \leq x \leq -1$

5. $-1 \leq x \leq 100$

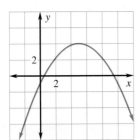

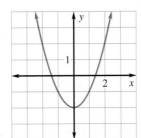

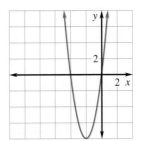

Calculate the average rate of change of the function on the given interval.

6. $y = -6x^2 - 3, 0 \leq x \leq 2$

7. $y = 2x^2 + x - 2, 0 \leq x \leq 2$

8. $y = 2(x + 1)^2 - 1, -2 \leq x \leq 2$

9. $y = 2x^2 - 5x + 3, 0 \leq x \leq 1$

10. $y = -\frac{1}{4}x^2 + x, 2 \leq x \leq 4$

11. $y = \frac{1}{2}x^2 + x - 2, -1 \leq x \leq 5$

Compare the average rates of change of the functions on the given interval.

12. $y = -x^2 - 1$ and $y = -x^2 - 2x - 1$ on the interval $-1 \leq x \leq 2$

13. $y = \frac{1}{2}x^2 - 2$ and $y = \frac{1}{10}x^2 + x - 2$ on the interval $-5 \leq x \leq 0$

14. **Reasoning** Suppose a quadratic function $f(x)$ has an interval of increase on $a \leq x \leq b$. Will the average rate of change be positive on the interval? Write the average rate of change on the interval in terms of a and b.

15. **Multiple Representations** A cable joining two towers on a suspension bridge can be modeled by the function $y = 0.0002x^2 - 0.35x + 250$ where x and y are measured in feet.

 a. **Making a Table** Make a table of values for the quadratic function for x values 0 to 2000 in multiples of 400.

 b. **Drawing a Graph** Use the table to graph the quadratic function.

 c. **Interpreting a Graph** Suppose you calculate the average rate of change on the interval $900 \leq x \leq 1100$. Now you move the interval to the right by 200 units and calculate the average rate of change again on the interval $1100 \leq x \leq 1300$. Repeat this two more times. What do you notice about the average rate of change as the 200 unit interval moves to the right?

UNIT 3

Solve $x^2 + bx + c = 0$ by Factoring

Goal Use factoring to solve quadratic equations.

Vocabulary

A **monomial** is an expression that is a number, a variable, or the product of a number and one or more variables.

A **binomial** is the sum of two monomials.

A **trinomial** is the sum of three monomials.

A **quadratic equation** in one variable can be written as $ax^2 + bx + c = 0$ where $a \neq 0$.

A solution of a quadratic equation is called the **root of the equation**.

The *difference of two squares pattern* is $a^2 - b^2 = (a + b)(a - b)$.

The *perfect square trinomial pattern* is $a^2 + 2ab + b^2 = (a + b)^2$ or $a^2 - 2ab + b^2 = (a - b)^2$.

Example 1   **Factor trinomials of the form $x^2 + bx + c$**

Factor the expression $w^2 - 2w - 15$.

You want $w^2 - 2w - 15 = (w + m)(w + n)$ where $mn = -15$ and $m + n = -2$.

Factors of −15: *m, n*	−1, 15	1, −15	−3, 5	3, −5
Sum of factors: *m + n*	14	−14	2	−2

Notice that $m = 3$ and $n = -5$. So, $w^2 - 2w - 15 = (w + 3)(w - 5)$.

Example 2   **Factor with special patterns**

Factor the expression.

a. $g^2 - 20g + 100 = g^2 - 2(g)(10) + 10^2$ Perfect square trinomial
$$= (g - 10)^2$$

b. $z^2 - 64 = z^2 - 8^2$ Difference of two squares
$$= (z + 8)(z - 8)$$

Guided Practice for Examples 1 and 2

Factor the expression. If the expression cannot be factored, say so.

1. $y^2 + 3y - 4$

2. $j^2 - 11j + 30$

3. $s^2 + s - 5$

4. $s^2 + 4$

5. $d^2 + 14d + 49$

6. $25a^2 - k^2$

Georgia Performance Standards

MM2A3c Investigate and explain characteristics of quadratic functions, including domain, range, vertex, axis of symmetry, zeros, intercepts, extrema, intervals of increase and decrease, and rates of change. ☑

MM2A4b Find real and complex solutions of equations by factoring, taking square roots, and applying the quadratic formula. ☑

Example 3 Find the roots of an equation

$$x^2 - 13x + 42 = 0$$ Original equation

$$(x - 6)(x - 7) = 0$$ Factor.

$$x - 6 = 0 \text{ or } x - 7 = 0$$ Zero product property

$$x = 6 \text{ or } \quad x = 7$$ Solve for x.

The roots are 6 and 7.

Example 4 Use a quadratic equation as a model

Gardening A rectangular garden measures 10 feet by 15 feet. By adding x feet to the width and x feet to the length, the area is doubled. Find the new dimensions.

New area	=	New width	·	New length

$$2(10)(15) = \quad (10 + x) \quad \cdot \quad (15 + x)$$

$$300 = 150 + 25x + x^2$$ Multiply using FOIL.

$$0 = x^2 + 25x - 150$$ Write in standard form.

$$0 = (x + 30)(x - 5)$$ Factor.

$$x + 30 = 0 \quad \text{or} \quad x - 5 = 0$$ Zero product property

$$x = -30 \quad \text{or} \quad x = 5$$ Solve for x.

Reject the negative value. The garden's width and length should each be increased by 5 feet. The new dimensions are 15 feet by 20 feet.

Example 5 Find the zeros of quadratic functions

Find the zeros of $y = x^2 + 3x - 28$ by rewriting the function in intercept form.

$$y = x^2 + 3x - 28$$ Write original function.

$$= (x + 7)(x - 4)$$ Factor.

The zeros of the function are -7 and 4.

Guided Practice for Examples 3, 4, and 5

Find the roots of the equation.

7. $x^2 - 81 = 0$ **8.** $d^2 + d - 2 = 0$ **9.** $p^2 + 6p + 9 = 0$

10. Rework Example 4 where a rectangular garden measures 4 feet by 6 feet.

11. Find the zeros of $y = x^2 - 100$ by rewriting the function in intercept form.

UNIT 3

MM2A3c Investigate and explain characteristics of quadratic functions, including domain, range, vertex, axis of symmetry, zeros, intercepts, extrema, intervals of increase and decrease, and rates of change.

MM2A4b Find real and complex solutions of equations by factoring, taking square roots, and applying the quadratic formula.

Factor the expression. If the expression cannot be factored, say so.

1. $x^2 + 4x - 21$ **2.** $x^2 - 6x + 5$ **3.** $x^2 + 6x + 8$

4. $x^2 - x - 6$ **5.** $x^2 - x - 12$ **6.** $x^2 - 2x - 8$

7. $x^2 - 9x + 20$ **8.** $x^2 + 3x - 18$ **9.** $x^2 - 9$

10. $x^2 + 8x + 16$ **11.** $x^2 - 11x + 28$ **12.** $x^2 - 2x + 2$

13. $x^2 + 4x - 32$ **14.** $x^2 - 3x - 10$ **15.** $x^2 - 25$

16. $x^2 - 9x + 14$ **17.** $x^2 - 100$ **18.** $x^2 - 8x - 15$

Solve the equation.

19. $x^2 + x - 6 = 0$ **20.** $x^2 + 3x - 10 = 0$ **21.** $x^2 - 5x + 6 = 0$

22. $x^2 - 4x + 4 = 0$ **23.** $x^2 + 7x + 12 = 0$ **24.** $x^2 - 3x - 28 = 0$

25. $x^2 - 36 = 0$ **26.** $x^2 - 2x - 15 = 0$ **27.** $x^2 - 11x + 18 = 0$

28. $3x^2 = 48$ **29.** $x^2 - 7x - 4 = -10$ **30.** $9x - 8 = x^2$

Find the zeros of the function by rewriting the function in intercept form.

31. $y = x^2 + 8x + 15$ **32.** $y = x^2 - 12x + 32$ **33.** $f(x) = x^2 - 2x - 35$

34. $y = x^2 - x - 30$ **35.** $g(x) = x^2 + 10x + 9$ **36.** $y = x^2 - 6x$

37. $h(x) = x^2 - 12x + 27$ **38.** $y = x^2 - 9$ **39.** $y = x^2 + 16x + 64$

40. Picture Frame You are making a square frame of uniform width for a square picture that has side lengths of 2 feet. The total area of the frame is 5 square feet. What is the length of the sides of the frame?

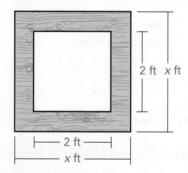

41. Concert Stage The dimensions of the old stage at the concert hall were 30 feet wide and 15 feet deep. The new stage has a total area of 1000 square feet. The dimensions of the new stage were created by adding the same distance x to the width and the depth of the old stage dimensions. What is the value of x?

LESSON
3.4

Exercise Set B

MM2A3c   Investigate and explain characteristics of quadratic functions, including domain, range, vertex, axis of symmetry, zeros, intercepts, extrema, intervals of increase and decrease, and rates of change.

MM2A4b   Find real and complex solutions of equations by factoring, taking square roots, and applying the quadratic formula.

Factor the expression. If the expression cannot be factored, say so.

1. $x^2 + x - 12$

2. $x^2 + 3x + 2$

3. $x^2 - 12x + 35$

4. $x^2 - x - 3$

5. $x^2 + 6x + 9$

6. $x^2 - 3x - 18$

7. $x^2 + 2x - 24$

8. $x^2 - x - 132$

9. $x^2 - 169$

10. $x^2 - 24x + 135$

11. $x^2 + 21x + 98$

12. $x^2 - 21x - 110$

Solve the equation.

13. $x^2 - 10x + 16 = 0$

14. $x^2 + 22x + 121 = 0$

15. $x^2 + x - 72 = 0$

16. $x^2 + 3x - 180 = 0$

17. $x^2 - 20x + 99 = 0$

18. $x^2 + 28x + 196 = 0$

19. $x^2 + 4x = 21$

20. $x^2 = 13x - 42$

21. $2x^2 + x = x^2 + 20$

22. $3x^2 - 8x - 19 = (x - 1)^2$

23. $(x - 3)^2 = 3(x - 3)$

24. $(2x + 1)^2 = (x + 2)^2$

Find the zeros of the function by rewriting the function in intercept form.

25. $y = x^2 + 4x + 3$

26. $y = x^2 - 10x + 24$

27. $f(x) = x^2 + 16x + 64$

28. $y = 2x^2 - 26x + 24$

29. $g(x) = 3x^2 + 24x + 21$

30. $y = x^2 - 11x$

31. $h(x) = x^2 - 4x - 77$

32. $y = 4x^2 + 60x$

33. $y = 2x^2 - 578$

Factor the expression.

34. $x^4 - 81$

35. $4x^3 - 100x$

36. $2x^2 + 5x - 12$

37. Fitness A gym charges $180 for a yearly membership. There are currently 1000 members. For every $5 increase in price, the gym will lose 10 members. How much should the gym charge to maximize its revenue?

38. Road Trip On a recent road trip, you drove a distance of 90 miles at a constant rate. If you had driven 15 miles per hour faster, your travel time would have been reduced by 0.5 hour. What was your original rate?

39. Multiple Representations Use the diagram shown.

a. Writing an Expression Write a quadratic trinomial that represents the area of the diagram.

b. Describing a Model Factor the expression from part (a). *Explain* how the diagram models the factorization.

c. Drawing a Diagram Draw a diagram that models the factorization $x^2 + 8x + 12 = (x + 6)(x + 2)$.

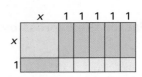

Solve $ax^2 + bx + c = 0$ by Factoring

Georgia Performance Standards: MM2A4b

Goal Use factoring to solve equations of the form $ax^2 + bx + c = 0$.

Example 1   Factor $ax^2 + bx + c$ where $c < 0$

Factor $2x^2 - x - 3$.

You want $2x^2 - x - 3 = (kx + m)(lx + n)$ where k and l are factors of 2 and m and n are factors of -3. Because $mn < 0$, m and n have opposite signs.

k, l	2, 1	2, 1	2, 1	2, 1
m, n	3, -1	-1, 3	-3, 1	1, -3
$(kx + m)(lx + n)$	$(2x + 3)(x - 1)$	$(2x - 1)(x + 3)$	$(2x - 3)(x + 1)$	$(2x + 1)(x - 3)$
$ax^2 + bx + c$	$2x^2 + x - 3$	$2x^2 + 5x - 3$	$2x^2 - x - 3$	$2x^2 - 5x - 3$

The correct factorization is $(2x - 3)(x + 1)$.

Example 2   Factor with special patterns and monomials

$$
\begin{aligned}
\textbf{a.}\quad 6t^2 - 24 &= 6(t^2 - 4) && \text{Factor out monomial.}\\
&= 6(t + 2)(t - 2) && \text{Difference of two squares}\\[6pt]
\textbf{b.}\quad 3m^2 - 18m + 27 &= 3(m^2 - 6m + 9) && \text{Factor out monomial.}\\
&= 3(m - 3)^2 && \text{Perfect square trinomial}
\end{aligned}
$$

Example 3   Solve a quadratic equation

$$
\begin{aligned}
4s^2 + 11s + 8 &= 3s + 4 && \text{Original equation}\\
4s^2 + 8s + 4 &= 0 && \text{Write in standard form.}\\
4(s + 1)^2 &= 0 && \text{Factor.}\\
s + 1 &= 0 && \text{Zero product property}\\
s &= -1 && \text{Solve for } s.
\end{aligned}
$$

Guided Practice for Examples 1, 2, and 3

Factor the expression. If the expression cannot be factored, say so.

1. $2x^2 - 14x + 12$ **2.** $3x^2 + 24x + 21$ **3.** $6x^2 - 42x + 72$

4. $4x^2 + 4x - 24$ **5.** $5x^2 - 20x - 25$ **6.** $3x^2 - 12x - 36$

Solve the equation.

7. $25x^2 - 9 = 0$ **8.** $3x^2 - 12x + 12 = 0$ **9.** $5x^2 - 15x - 20 = 0$

Georgia Performance Standards

MM2A4b Find real and complex solutions of equations by factoring, taking square roots, and applying the quadratic formula.

Example 4 Use a quadratic equation as a model

Paintings The area of a painting is 25 square inches and the length is 5 inches more than twice the width. Find the length of the painting.

Solution

Write a verbal model. Let x represent the width and write an equation.

Area of painting (square inches)	=	Width of painting (inches)	$\cdot$	Length of painting (inches)
25	=	x	$\cdot$	$(2x + 5)$

$$0 = 2x^2 + 5x - 25 \qquad \text{Write in standard form.}$$
$$0 = (2x - 5)(x + 5) \qquad \text{Factor.}$$
$$2x - 5 = 0 \quad \text{or} \quad x + 5 = 0 \qquad \text{Zero product property}$$
$$x = \frac{5}{2} \quad \text{or} \quad x = -5 \qquad \text{Solve for } x.$$

Reject the negative value, $x = -5$. The length is $2\left(\frac{5}{2}\right) + 5$ inches or 10 inches.

Example 5 Solve a multi-step problem

Bicycles A bicycle shop sells about 18 bikes per week when it charges $100 per bike. For each increase of $10, the shop sells 3 fewer bikes per week. How much should the shop charge to maximize revenue? What is the maximum weekly revenue?

STEP 1 **Define** the variables. Let x represent the number of $10 price increases and $R(x)$ represent the weekly revenue.

STEP 2 **Write** a verbal model. Then write and simplify a quadratic equation.

Weekly sales (dollars)	=	Number of bikes sold (bikes)	$\cdot$	Price of bike (dollars/bike)
$R(x)$	=	$(18 - 3x)$	$\cdot$	$(100 + 10x)$

$$R(x) = -30(x - 6)(x + 10)$$

STEP 3 **Identify** the zeros and find their average. The zeros are 6 and -10. The average of the zeros is -2. To maximize revenue, the shop should charge $100 + 10(-2) = \$80$.

STEP 4 **Find** the maximum weekly revenue.
$$R(-2) = -30(-2 - 6)(-2 + 10) = \$1920.$$
The maximum weekly revenue is $1920.

Guided Practice for Examples 4 and 5

10. Rework Example 4 with an area of 24 inches and a length 2 inches more than the width.

11. Rework Example 5 where for each increase of $10, the shop sells 9 fewer bikes per week.

UNIT 3

MM2A4b Find real and complex solutions of equations by factoring, taking square roots, and applying the quadratic formula.

Factor the expression. If the expression cannot be factored, say so.

1. $3x^2 + 10x - 8$

2. $2x^2 + 5x - 3$

3. $4x^2 + 4x + 1$

4. $2x^2 - 5x + 1$

5. $4x^2 + 5x - 6$

6. $2x^2 + 11x + 15$

7. $9x^2 + 12x + 4$

8. $12x^2 - 24x - 9$

9. $18x^2 - 2$

10. $12x^2 + 17x + 6$

11. $15x^2 + 8x - 16$

12. $4x^2 - 5$

13. $12x^2 - 39x + 9$

14. $18x^2 - 9x - 14$

15. $20x^2 - 54x + 36$

16. $42x^2 + 35x + 7$

17. $-12x^2 - x + 11$

18. $80x^2 + 68x + 12$

Solve the equation.

19. $2x^2 + 3x - 2 = 0$

20. $2x^2 - 3x - 9 = 0$

21. $4x^2 - 8x + 3 = 0$

22. $9x^2 - 4 = 0$

23. $8x^2 - 6x + 1 = 0$

24. $18x^2 + 48x = -32$

25. $9x^2 + 11x + 18 = -10x + 8$

26. $5x^2 - 2x - 6 = -3x^2 + 6x$

27. $5x^2 - 3x + 3 = -2x^2 + 3$

28. $25x^2 - 24x - 9 = -7x^2 + 12x - 18$

Find the zeros of the function by rewriting the function in intercept form.

29. $y = 3x^2 + 2x$

30. $y = 12x^2 + 8x - 15$

31. $f(x) = 5x^2 - 25x + 30$

32. $y = 25x^2 + 10x - 24$

33. $g(x) = 33x^2 - 9x - 24$

34. $y = 4x^2 + 1$

Find the value of x.

35. Area of the triangle = 27

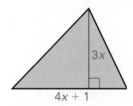

36. Area of the rectangle = 22

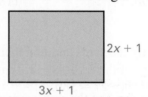

37. Picture Frame You are making a frame of uniform width for a picture that is to be displayed at the local museum. The picture is 3.25 feet tall and 3 feet wide. The museum has allocated 15 square feet of wall space to display the picture. What should the width of the frame be in order to use all of the allocated space?

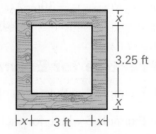

LESSON
3.5

Exercise Set B

MM2A4b   Find real and complex solutions of equations by factoring, taking square roots, and applying the quadratic formula.

Factor the expression. If the expression cannot be factored, say so.

1. $4x^2 - 15x + 9$

2. $6x^2 - 13x - 28$

3. $10x^2 + 29x + 10$

4. $9x^2 + 24x + 16$

5. $-12x^2 + 27$

6. $12x^2 - 40x - 32$

7. $-15x^2 + 3x + 12$

8. $6x^3 - 5x^2 + x$

9. $3x^3 - 7x^2 + x$

10. $4x^4 + 12x^3 + 9x^2$

11. $24x^4 + 18x^3 - 27x^2$

12. $72x^3 - 228x^2 + 140x$

13. $x^4 - 81$

14. $2x^4 + 5x^2 + 3$

15. $6x^4 - 9x^2 + 3$

Solve the equation.

16. $3x^2 - 10x + 3 = 0$

17. $6x^2 - 21x + 15 = 0$

18. $32x^2 - 18 = 0$

19. $6x^2 + 5x = 1$

20. $30x^2 - 5x = 60$

21. $18x^2 + 10x = -3x + 21$

22. $10x^2 - 6 = -14x^2 + 10x + 50$

23. $32x^2 - 3x - 14 = (2x - 1)^2$

24. $(3x - 1)^2 = (2x + 3)^2$

25. $x + \dfrac{2}{x} = 3$

26. $\dfrac{x}{2} - \dfrac{2}{3x} = \dfrac{2}{3}$

27. $3x + \dfrac{14}{5x} = \dfrac{31}{5}$

Find the value of x.

28. Area of the circle $= \dfrac{9}{4}\pi$

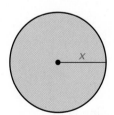

29. Area of the trapezoid $= 266$

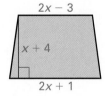

30. **New Parking Lot** A new department store needs a new rectangular parking lot to surround the store. The front of the department store is 200 feet wide and the store is 100 feet deep. The front of the store faces north. The contractor wants the width of the parking lot on the south and east sides of the store to be the same. Also, the width of the parking lot on the north side is to be 8 times as wide as the south and the width of the parking lot on the west side is to be 10 times as wide as the east. When completed, the parking lot will be 38,900 square feet of blacktop. Write a quadratic equation in standard form that represents the square footage of the parking lot. Using a graphing calculator, how wide is the parking lot on the west side of the store?

Solve Quadratic Equations by Finding Square Roots

Georgia Performance Standards: MM2A4b

Goal Solve quadratic equations by finding square roots.

Vocabulary

To **rationalize a denominator** $\sqrt{b}$ of a fraction, multiply the numerator and denominator by $\sqrt{b}$. To **rationalize a denominator** $a + \sqrt{b}$ of a fraction, multiply the numerator and denominator by $a - \sqrt{b}$, and to **rationalize a denominator** $a - \sqrt{b}$ of a fraction, multiply the numerator and denominator by $a + \sqrt{b}$.

The expressions $a + \sqrt{b}$ and $a - \sqrt{b}$ are called **conjugates.**

Example 1   Rationalize denominators of fractions

Simplify the expression.

a. $\sqrt{\dfrac{7}{3}}$ **b.** $\dfrac{12}{\sqrt{6}}$ **c.** $\dfrac{5}{3 - \sqrt{7}}$

Solution

a. $\sqrt{\dfrac{7}{3}} = \dfrac{\sqrt{7}}{\sqrt{3}} \cdot \dfrac{\sqrt{3}}{\sqrt{3}}$ Multiply numerator and denominator by $\sqrt{3}$.

$\quad = \dfrac{\sqrt{21}}{3}$ Product property

b. $\dfrac{12}{\sqrt{6}} = \dfrac{12}{\sqrt{6}} \cdot \dfrac{\sqrt{6}}{\sqrt{6}}$ Multiply numerator and denominator by $\sqrt{6}$.

$\quad = \dfrac{12\sqrt{6}}{6}$ Product property

$\quad = 2\sqrt{6}$ Simplify.

c. $\dfrac{5}{3 - \sqrt{7}} = \dfrac{5}{3 - \sqrt{7}} \cdot \dfrac{3 + \sqrt{7}}{3 + \sqrt{7}}$ Multiply by $\dfrac{3 + \sqrt{7}}{3 + \sqrt{7}}$.

$\quad = \dfrac{15 + 5\sqrt{7}}{9 + 3\sqrt{7} - 3\sqrt{7} - 7}$ Multiply denominator using FOIL.

$\quad = \dfrac{15 + 5\sqrt{7}}{2}$ Simplify.

Guided Practice for Example 1

Simplify the expression.

1. $\sqrt{\dfrac{7}{5}}$ **2.** $\sqrt{\dfrac{2}{5}}$ **3.** $\dfrac{21}{\sqrt{7}}$

4. $\dfrac{3}{\sqrt{15}}$ **5.** $\dfrac{8}{\sqrt{5} - 4}$ **6.** $\dfrac{2}{\sqrt{3} + 5}$

Georgia Performance Standards

MM2A4b Find real and complex solutions of equations by factoring, taking square roots, and applying the quadratic formula. ☑

Example 2 Solve a quadratic equation

$2x^2 - 3 = -93$	Original equation
$2x^2 = -90$	Add 3 to each side.
$x^2 = -45$	Divide each side by 2.
$x = \pm\sqrt{-45}$	Take square roots of each side.
$x = \pm\sqrt{-9} \cdot \sqrt{5}$	Product property
$x = \pm3i\sqrt{5}$	Simplify.

Example 3 Finding solutions of a quadratic equation

Find the solutions of $\frac{1}{2}(w - 2)^2 + 1 = 4$.

$\frac{1}{2}(w - 2)^2 + 1 = 4$	Write original equation.
$(w - 2)^2 + 2 = 8$	Multiply each side by 2.
$(w - 2)^2 = 6$	Subtract 2 from each side.
$w - 2 = \pm\sqrt{6}$	Take square roots of each side.
$w = 2 \pm \sqrt{6}$	Add 2 to each side.

The solutions are $2 + \sqrt{6}$ and $2 - \sqrt{6}$.

Example 4 Model a dropped object with a quadratic equation

Dropped Object When an object is dropped, its height h (in feet) above the ground after t seconds can be modeled by $h = -16t^2 + h_0$ where h_0 is the object's initial height (in feet). How long does it take for an object to hit the ground when dropped from a height of 72 feet?

$h = -16t^2 + h_0$	Write height function.
$0 = -16t^2 + 72$	Substitute 0 for h and 72 for h_0.
$4.5 = t^2$	Subtract 72 from each side. Divide each side by -16.
$\pm\sqrt{4.5} = t$	Take square roots of each side.
$\pm2.1 \approx t$	Use a calculator.

Reject the negative solution because time must be positive. The object will fall for about 2.1 seconds before it hits the ground.

Guided Practice for Examples 2, 3, and 4

Solve the equation.

7. $-9d^2 = 243$ **8.** $11y^2 + 3 = 36$ **9.** $\frac{1}{5}j^2 + 4 = 12$

10. Rework Example 5 where the object is dropped from a height of 120 feet.

UNIT 3

**Exercise
Set A**

MM2A4b Find real and complex solutions of equations by
factoring, taking square roots, and applying the
quadratic formula.

Simplify the expression.

1. $\sqrt{\dfrac{6}{11}}$

2. $\sqrt{\dfrac{15}{7}}$

3. $\sqrt{\dfrac{12}{13}}$

4. $\dfrac{5}{\sqrt{5}}$

5. $\dfrac{24}{\sqrt{3}}$

6. $\dfrac{36}{\sqrt{15}}$

7. $\sqrt{\dfrac{2}{3}} \cdot \sqrt{\dfrac{3}{7}}$

8. $\sqrt{\dfrac{7}{9}} \cdot \sqrt{\dfrac{4}{7}}$

9. $\sqrt{24} \cdot \sqrt{\dfrac{80}{192}}$

10. $\dfrac{3}{4 + \sqrt{5}}$

11. $\dfrac{-6}{5 - \sqrt{11}}$

12. $\dfrac{7 - \sqrt{7}}{10 + \sqrt{3}}$

Solve the equation.

13. $x^2 = 289$

14. $x^2 + 169 = 0$

15. $2x^2 - 512 = 0$

16. $3x^2 - 150 = -282$

17. $\dfrac{1}{2}x^2 - 8 = 16$

18. $\dfrac{2}{3}x^2 - 4 = 12$

19. $2x^2 + 5 = 5x^2 - 37$

20. $-4(x^2 - 8) = 84$

21. $3(x^2 + 2) = 18$

22. $2(x + 2)^2 = 72$

23. $3(x - 3)^2 + 2 = 26$

24. $(3x + 2)^2 - 49 = 0$

25. $(4x - 5)^2 = 64$

26. $\dfrac{1}{2}(x - 4)^2 = 8$

27. $\dfrac{2}{3}(x + 8)^2 - 66 = 0$

**When an object is dropped, its height *h* (in feet) after *t* seconds can
be determined by using the falling object model $h = -16t^2 + h_0$ where
h_0 is the initial height (in feet). Find the time it takes an object to hit
the ground when it is dropped from a height of h_0 feet.**

28. $h_0 = 160$

29. $h_0 = 300$

30. $h_0 = 550$

31. $h_0 = 690$

32. $h_0 = 900$

33. $h_0 = 1600$

Use the Pythagorean theorem to find *x*. Round to the nearest hundredth.

34.

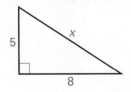

35.

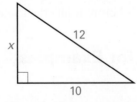

36. Operating Costs For a period of 48 months, the average monthly operating cost for
a small business C (in dollars) can be approximated by the model $C = 0.55t^2 + 550$
where t is the number of months. During which month was the average operating
cost $1430?

**Exercise
Set B**

MM2A4b   Find real and complex solutions of equations by
factoring, taking square roots, and applying the
quadratic formula.

Simplify the expression.

1. $\sqrt{\dfrac{10}{21}}$

2. $\sqrt{\dfrac{30}{77}}$

3. $\dfrac{25}{\sqrt{125}}$

4. $\dfrac{33}{\sqrt{99}}$

5. $\sqrt{\dfrac{343}{280}}$

6. $\sqrt{\dfrac{250}{252}}$

7. $\sqrt{\dfrac{12}{27}} \cdot \sqrt{\dfrac{1}{4}}$

8. $\sqrt{\dfrac{16}{27}} \cdot \sqrt{\dfrac{5}{3}}$

9. $\sqrt{\dfrac{44}{9}} \cdot \sqrt{\dfrac{18}{7}} \cdot \sqrt{\dfrac{35}{72}}$

10. $\dfrac{6}{2 + \sqrt{12}}$

11. $\dfrac{3 - \sqrt{7}}{5 + 2\sqrt{7}}$

12. $\dfrac{4 + \sqrt{2}}{3 + 2\sqrt{3}}$

Solve the equation.

13. $x^2 - 324 = 0$

14. $x^2 - 19 = 0$

15. $2x^2 + 338 = 0$

16. $\dfrac{1}{7}x^2 - 3 = 4$

17. $\dfrac{1}{2}x^2 + 3 = 12$

18. $-\dfrac{3}{5}x^2 - 2 = -5$

19. $2x^2 + 16 = x^2 + 7$

20. $2(x^2 - 5) = -x^2 - 1$

21. $4(x + 5)^2 = -64$

22. $5(x - 4)^2 = 125$

23. $3(x - 1)^2 = \dfrac{5}{27}$

24. $\dfrac{1}{3}(x + 4)^2 - 1 = 5$

25. $\left(3x - \dfrac{2}{3}\right)^2 - 2 = \dfrac{5}{2}$

26. $\dfrac{(x - 2)^2}{4} + \dfrac{3}{2} = \dfrac{5}{3}$

27. $\dfrac{2(x + 3)^2}{3} - \dfrac{4}{9} = \dfrac{1}{3}$

Find the values of *a* for which the equation has two real number solutions.

28. $x^2 = a$

29. $x^2 - 3 = a$

30. $4x^2 + 1 = a$

31. $x^2 + a = 4$

32. $a - 2x^2 = -5$

33. $ax^2 + 5 = 3$

Error Analysis *Describe* **and correct the error in simplifying the expression or
solving the equation.**

34.

$$\sqrt{\dfrac{4}{5}} = \dfrac{\sqrt{4}}{\sqrt{5}} \cdot \dfrac{\sqrt{5}}{\sqrt{5}} = \dfrac{\sqrt{20}}{5}$$

35.

$$3x^2 = 192$$
$$x^2 = 64$$
$$x = 8$$

36. Compound Interest The formula $A = P\left(1 + \dfrac{r}{n}\right)^{nt}$ gives the amount of money A in an
account after t years if the annual interest rate is r (in decimal form), n is the number
of times interest is compounded per year, and P is the original principal. What interest
rate is required to earn \$7 in two months if the principal is \$500 and the interest rate is
compounded monthly? Round the answer to the nearest tenth of a percentage.

Complete the Square

Georgia Performance Standards: MM2A3a, MM2A4b

Goal Solve quadratic equations by completing the square.

Vocabulary

To **complete the square** for the expression $x^2 + bx$, add $\left(\dfrac{b}{2}\right)^2$.

When you complete the square, $x^2 + bx + \left(\dfrac{b}{2}\right)^2 = \left(x + \dfrac{b}{2}\right)^2$.

Example 1   Make a perfect square trinomial

Find the value of c that makes $x^2 - 10x + c$ a perfect square trinomial. Then write the expression as the square of a binomial.

STEP 1 Find half the coefficient of x. $\dfrac{-10}{2} = -5$

STEP 2 Square the result of Step 1. $(-5)^2 = 25$

STEP 3 Replace c with the result of Step 2. $x^2 - 10x + 25$

The trinomial $x^2 - 10x + c$ is a perfect square when $c = 25$.
So, $x^2 - 10x + 25 = (x - 5)(x - 5) = (x - 5)^2$.

Guided Practice for Example 1

Find the value of c that makes the expression a perfect square trinomial. Then write the expression as the square of a binomial.

1. $x^2 + 12x + c$ **2.** $x^2 - 18x + c$ **3.** $x^2 - 40x + c$

Example 2   Solve $ax^2 + bx + c = 0$ when $a = 1$

Solve $x^2 - 16x + 8 = 0$ by completing the square.

$x^2 - 16x + 8 = 0$ Write original equation.

$x^2 - 16x = -8$ Write left side in the form $x^2 + bx$.

$x^2 - 16x + 64 = -8 + 64$ Add $\left(\dfrac{-16}{2}\right)^2 = 64$ to each side.

$(x - 8)^2 = 56$ Write left side as a binomial squared.

$x - 8 = \pm\sqrt{56}$ Take square roots of each side.

$x = 8 \pm \sqrt{56}$ Solve for x.

$x = 8 \pm 2\sqrt{14}$ Simplify: $\sqrt{56} = \sqrt{4} \cdot \sqrt{14} = 2\sqrt{14}$

The solutions are $8 + 2\sqrt{14}$ and $8 - 2\sqrt{14}$.

Example 3   Solve $ax^2 + bx + c = 0$ when $a \neq 1$

$3x^2 + 6x + 15 = 0$	Original equation
$x^2 + 2x + 5 = 0$	Divide each side by the coefficient of x^2, 3.
$x^2 + 2x = -5$	Write left side in the form $x^2 + bx$.
$x^2 + 2x + 1 = -5 + 1$	Add $\left(\frac{2}{2}\right)^2 = 1^2 = 1$ to each side.
$(x + 1)^2 = -4$	Write left side as a binomial squared.
$x + 1 = \pm \sqrt{-4}$	Take square roots of each side.
$x + 1 = \pm 2i$	Write in terms of the imaginary unit i.
$x = -1 \pm 2i$	Solve for x.

The solutions are $-1 + 2i$ and $-1 - 2i$.

Example 4   Find the maximum value of a quadratic equation

Revenue   A retailer's revenue is modeled by $R = (300 + 10x)(50 - x)$. Rewrite in vertex form to find the number of units x that maximizes the revenue R.

Solution

$R = (300 + 10x)(50 - x)$	Write original function.
$R = 15{,}000 - 300x + 500x - 10x^2$	Use FOIL.
$R = -10x^2 + 200x + 15{,}000$	Combine like terms.
$R = -10(x^2 - 20x) + 15{,}000$	Prepare to complete the square.
$R = -10\left[x^2 - 20x + \left(\frac{-20}{2}\right)^2\right] + 10\left(\frac{-20}{2}\right)^2 + 15{,}000$	Add and subtract $10\left(\frac{-20}{2}\right)$.
$R = -10(x - 10)^2 + 16{,}000$	Write a perfect square trinomial as the square of a binomial.

The vertex is $(10, 16{,}000)$, so the number of units that maximizes R is 10.

Guided Practice for Examples 2, 3, and 4

Solve the equation by completing the square.

4. $x^2 - 10x + 6 = 0$ **5.** $2x^2 + 16x + 8 = 0$ **6.** $5x^2 - 10x + 30 = 0$

Write the equation in vertex form and identify the vertex.

7. $y = x^2 - 12x + 38$ **8.** $y = x^2 - 14x + 50$ **9.** $y = 2x^2 + 12x + 13$

10. Rework Example 4 where $R = (200 + 10x)(40 - x)$.

UNIT 3

MM2A3a   Convert between standard and vertex form.

MM2A4b   Find real and complex solutions of equations by factoring, taking square roots, and applying the quadratic formula.

Solve the equation by finding square roots.

1. $x^2 + 8x + 16 = 9$

2. $x^2 - 6x + 9 = 25$

3. $x^2 - 12x + 36 = 49$

4. $2x^2 - 12x + 18 = 32$

5. $4x^2 - 4x + 1 = 36$

6. $5x^2 - 20x + 20 = 35$

7. $x^2 - \frac{2}{3}x + \frac{1}{9} = 1$

8. $x^2 + \frac{3}{2}x + \frac{9}{16} = 3$

9. $9x^2 + 12x + 4 = 5$

Find the value of c that makes the expression a perfect square trinomial. Then write the expression as a square of a binomial.

10. $x^2 + 8x + c$

11. $x^2 - 22x + c$

12. $x^2 + 16x + c$

13. $x^2 + 3x + c$

14. $x^2 - 9x + c$

15. $9x^2 - 12x + c$

Solve the equation by completing the square.

16. $x^2 + 4x = 1$

17. $x^2 - 10x = -10$

18. $x^2 - 2x - 9 = 0$

19. $x^2 + 6x + 10 = 0$

20. $x^2 + 8x + 4 = 0$

21. $3x^2 + 36x = -42$

22. $x^2 - 24x + 81 = 0$

23. $4x^2 + 20x + 25 = 0$

24. $3x^2 - 3x + 9 = 0$

25. $6x^2 - 12x - 18 = 0$

Write the quadratic function in vertex form. Then identify the vertex.

26. $y = x^2 + 14x + 11$

27. $y = x^2 - 8x + 10$

28. $y = 2x^2 + 4x - 5$

29. $y = 3x^2 - 9x + 18$

Find the value of x.

30. Area of rectangle $= 84$

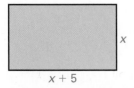

x

$x + 5$

31. Area of triangle $= 20$

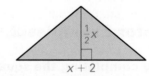

$\frac{1}{2}x$

$x + 2$

32. **Shot Put** In a track and field event, a contestant made a throw in the shot put that can be modeled by $y = -0.02x^2 + x + 6$ where x is the shot put's horizontal distance (in feet) and y is the corresponding height (in feet). How long was the throw? Round the answer to the nearest tenth.

LESSON
3.7

Exercise Set B

MM2A3a   Convert between standard and vertex form.

MM2A4b   Find real and complex solutions of equations by factoring, taking square roots, and applying the quadratic formula.

Solve the equation by finding square roots.

1. $x^2 - \frac{4}{3}x + \frac{4}{9} = \frac{16}{9}$

2. $4x^2 - 20x + 25 = 64$

3. $9x^2 + \frac{6}{5}x + \frac{1}{25} = 4$

4. $100x^2 + 60x + 9 = 28$

5. $x^2 + 1.4x + 0.49 = 3$

6. $0.04x^2 - 0.2x + 0.25 = 1.21$

Solve the equation by completing the square.

7. $x^2 + 8x - 1 = 0$

8. $x^2 - 16x = -20$

9. $x^2 - 3x - 7 = 0$

10. $x^2 + 7x + 15 = 0$

11. $2x^2 + 8x + 4 = x^2 + 4x$

12. $3x^2 + 6x = 2x^2 + 3x - 4$

13. $3x^2 - 24x + 27 = 0$

14. $2x^2 + 10x + 1 = 13$

15. $2x^2 + 10x = -17$

16. $3x^2 - 5x - 8 = 2x - 3$

17. $3x^2 - x + 5 = x^2 + 3x - 14$

18. $6x^2 - 5x - 13 = x^2 - 11$

Write the quadratic function in vertex form. Then identify the vertex.

19. $y = x^2 + 12x + 6$

20. $y = x^2 - 4x + 15$

21. $y = -2x^2 + 6x - 3$

22. $y = -4x^2 - 2x - 3$

23. **Multiple Representations** The path of a football thrown by a quarterback can be modeled by the function $y = -0.025x^2 + 0.45x + 2$ where x is the football's horizontal position (in yards) and y is the corresponding height (in yards).

    a. Rewriting a Function Write the given function in vertex form.

    b. Making a Table Make a table of values for the function. Include values of x from 0 to 20 in increments of 2.

    c. Drawing a Graph Use your table to graph the function. What is the maximum height of the football? How far does it travel?

24. **Softball** A recreational softball team paid a league entry fee of $825. The cost was covered by equal contributions from each member on the team. If there were 4 more team members, each person could contribute $20 less. How many members does the team have?

25. **Falling Object** An object is propelled upward from the top of a 300 foot building. The path that the object takes as it falls to the ground can be modeled by $y = -16t^2 + 80t + 300$ where t is the time (in seconds) and y is the corresponding height (in feet) of the object. The velocity of the object can be modeled by $v = -32t + 80$ where t is time (in seconds) and v is the corresponding velocity of the object. What is the velocity of the object when it hits the ground?

Investigating Math Activity
Find the Number of Real Solutions

Use before Lesson 3.8

Materials   graphing calculator

Question

How does the discriminant help you determine the number of real solutions of a quadratic equation?

The quadratic formula is used to find solutions to quadratic equations.

$$x = \frac{-b \pm \sqrt{b^2 - 4ac}}{2a}$$ Quadratic formula

The discriminant is the part of the quadratic formula that is under the radical sign, and can help you determine the number of real solutions of the quadratic equation. You can use this as a way to verify your solutions.

$b^2 - 4ac$ Discriminant

Explore

Determine the number of real solutions.

Graph the function on a graphing calculator to find the number of real solutions.

Function	Number of real solutions	Value of discriminant
$y = 3x^2 + 5x + 2$	?	$b^2 - 4ac = 1$
$y = x^2 + 4x + 4$	?	$b^2 - 4ac = 0$
$y = 4x^2 - 2x + 5$	?	$b^2 - 4ac = -76$

Draw Conclusions

1. What do you notice about the number of real solutions and the value of the discriminant for the function $y = 3x^2 + 5x + 2$?

2. What do you notice about the number of real solutions and the value of the discriminant for the function $y = x^2 + 4x + 4$?

3. What do you notice about the number of real solutions and the value of the discriminant for the function $y = 4x^2 - 2x + 5$?

4. **Reasoning** Why do you think the value of the discriminant helps you determine the number of real solutions? (*Hint:* Notice that the discriminant is under a radical sign in the quadratic formula.)

Use the Quadratic Formula and the Discriminant

Georgia Performance Standards: MM2A4b, MM2A4c

Goal Solve quadratic equations using the quadratic formula.

Vocabulary

The **quadratic formula:** Let a, b, and c be real numbers where $a \neq 0$. The solutions of the quadratic equation $ax^2 + bx + c = 0$ are

$$x = \frac{-b \pm \sqrt{b^2 - 4ac}}{2a}.$$

In the quadratic formula, the expression $b^2 - 4ac$ is called the **discriminant** of the associated equation $ax^2 + bx + c = 0$.

Example 1   **Solve a quadratic equation with two real solutions**

Solve $x^2 - 5x = 4$.

$x^2 - 5x = 4$	Write original equation.
$x^2 - 5x - 4 = 0$	Write in standard form.
$x = \dfrac{-b \pm \sqrt{b^2 - 4ac}}{2a}$	Quadratic formula
$x = \dfrac{-(-5) \pm \sqrt{(-5)^2 - 4(1)(-4)}}{2(1)}$	$a = 1$, $b = -5$, $c = -4$
$x = \dfrac{5 \pm \sqrt{41}}{2}$	Simplify.

The solutions are $x = \dfrac{5 + \sqrt{41}}{2} \approx 5.70$ and $x = \dfrac{5 - \sqrt{41}}{2} \approx -0.70$.

Example 2   **Solve a quadratic equation with one real solution**

Solve $4x^2 + 10x = -10x - 25$.

$4x^2 + 10x = -10x - 25$	Write original equation.
$4x^2 + 20x + 25 = 0$	Write in standard form.
$x = \dfrac{-b \pm \sqrt{b^2 - 4ac}}{2a}$	Quadratic formula
$x = \dfrac{-20 \pm \sqrt{20^2 - 4(4)25}}{2(4)}$	$a = 4$, $b = 20$, $c = 25$
$x = \dfrac{-20 \pm 0}{8}$	Simplify.
$x = -\dfrac{5}{2}$	Simplify.

The solution is $-\dfrac{5}{2}$.

UNIT 3

Georgia Performance Standards

MM2A4b Find real and complex solutions of equations by factoring, taking square roots, and applying the quadratic formula. ☑

MM2A4c Analyze the nature of roots using technology and using the discriminant. ☑

Example 3 Solve a quadratic equation with imaginary solutions

Solve $x^2 - 6x = -10$.

$x^2 - 6x + 10 = 0$	Write in standard form.
$x = \dfrac{6 \pm \sqrt{(-6)^2 - 4(1)10}}{2(1)}$	$a = 1, b = -6, c = 10$
$x = \dfrac{6 \pm \sqrt{-4}}{2}$	Simplify.
$x = \dfrac{6 \pm 2i}{2}$	Rewrite using the imaginary unit i.
$x = 3 \pm i$	Simplify.

The solutions are $3 + i$ and $3 - i$.

Guided Practice for Examples 1, 2, and 3

Use the quadratic formula to solve the equation.

1. $x^2 + 4x = 2$ **2.** $2x^2 - 8x = 1$ **3.** $4x^2 + 2x = -2x - 1$

4. $16x^2 - 20x = 4x - 9$ **5.** $x^2 - 4x + 5 = 0$ **6.** $x^2 - x = -7$

Example 4 Use a discriminant

Find the discriminant of the quadratic equation and give the number and type of roots of the equation.

a. $x^2 + 6x + 11 = 0$ **b.** $x^2 + 6x + 9 = 0$ **c.** $x^2 + 6x + 5 = 0$

Solution

Equation	Discriminant	Root(s)
$ax^2 + bx + c = 0$	$b^2 - 4ac$	$x = \dfrac{-b \pm \sqrt{b^2 - 4ac}}{2a}$
a. $x^2 + 6x + 11 = 0$	$6^2 - 4(1)(11) = -8$	Two imaginary: $-3 \pm i\sqrt{2}$
b. $x^2 + 6x + 9 = 0$	$6^2 - 4(1)(9) = 0$	One real: -3
c. $x^2 + 6x + 5 = 0$	$6^2 - 4(1)(5) = 16$	Two real: $-5, -1$

Guided Practice for Example 4

Find the discriminant of the quadratic equation and give the number and type of roots of the equation.

7. $x^2 - 2x - 1 = 0$ **8.** $x^2 - 12x + 36 = 0$ **9.** $x^2 + 7x + 14 = 0$

UNIT 3

LESSON 3.8 **Exercise Set A**

MM2A4b   Find real and complex solutions of equations by factoring, taking square roots, and applying the quadratic formula.

MM2A4c   Analyze the nature of roots using technology and using the discriminant.

Find the discriminant and use it to determine if the equation has *one real*, *two real*, or *two imaginary* root(s).

1. $x^2 + 4x + 3 = 0$

2. $x^2 - 2x + 4 = 0$

3. $x^2 - 2x + 1 = 0$

4. $3x^2 + 2x - 1 = 0$

5. $-x^2 - x = 4$

6. $5x^2 - 4x + 1 = 3x + 4$

Use the quadratic formula to solve the equation.

7. $x^2 + 4x - 2 = 0$

8. $2x^2 - 5x - 2 = 0$

9. $x^2 + 2x = 4x$

10. $-6x^2 + 3x + 2 = 3$

11. $-x^2 + 1 = -5x^2 + 4x$

12. $2(x - 3)^2 = -2x + 9$

13. $2.5x^2 - 2.8x = 0.4$

14. $4.8x^2 = 5.2x + 2.7$

Solve the equation using the quadratic formula. Then solve the equation by factoring to check your solution(s).

15. $x^2 - 2x - 24 = 0$

16. $x^2 - 2x + 1 = 0$

17. $2x^2 - 9x + 9 = 0$

18. $6x^2 + 17x + 5 = 0$

19. $10x^2 + x = 2$

20. $6x^2 = 5x + 6$

21. New Carpet You have new carpeting installed in a rectangular room. You are charged for 28 square yards of carpet and 60 feet (20 yards) of tack strip. Tack strip is used along the perimeter to secure the carpet in place. Do you think these figures are correct? *Explain* your answer.

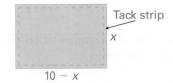

In Exercises 22–25, use the following information.

Launched Object The height h (in feet) of a dropped object after t seconds is modeled by the function $h = -16t^2 + h_0$ where h_0 is the object's initial height (in feet). An object that is launched or thrown has an extra term v_0t that is added to account for the object's initial velocity v_0 (in feet per second). The function then becomes $h = -16t^2 + v_0t + h_0$. The value of v_0 depends on whether the object is launched upward (positive), downward (negative), or parallel (zero) to the ground.

An object is launched upward with an initial velocity of 64 feet per second from a platform 80 feet high.

22. Write a height model for the object.

23. How many seconds until the maximum height is reached?

24. What will be the maximum height?

25. How many seconds until the object hits the ground?

UNIT 3

Exercise Set B

MM2A4b Find real and complex solutions of equations by factoring, taking square roots, and applying the quadratic formula.

MM2A4c Analyze the nature of roots using technology and using the discriminant.

Find the discriminant and use it to determine if the equation has *one real*, *two real*, or *two imaginary* root(s).

1. $x^2 + 4x - 1 = 0$

2. $x^2 - 2x + 1 = 0$

3. $2x^2 - 3x + 1 = 0$

4. $7x^2 + 6x + 2 = 0$

5. $-3x^2 + 9x = 4$

6. $10x^2 - 2x + 2 = 3x - 4$

Use the quadratic formula to solve the equation.

7. $x^2 + 5x - 2 = 0$

8. $2x^2 - 3x + 2 = 0$

9. $\frac{1}{4}x^2 + 5x - 4 = 0$

10. $2x^2 + 2x = 4x - 1$

11. $-2x^2 + 3x + 4 = 1 - 2x$

12. $\frac{1}{2}x^2 - 3x + 2 = 3x - 1$

13. $-x^2 + 1 = -6x^2 - x$

14. $\frac{2}{3}x^2 - 2 = \frac{1}{2}x + 1$

15. $2.5x^2 - 3.3x = 1.2x - 1.5$

16. $\frac{3}{4}(x - 1)^2 = -\frac{4}{3}x + \frac{4}{5}$

17. $-2.8x = -3.8x^2 + 1.4$

18. $3.8x^2 = 4.7x - 2.1$

Use the discriminant to find all values of *b* for which the equation has one real root.

19. $x^2 - bx + 4 = 0$

20. $3x^2 + bx + 5 = 0$

21. $2x^2 - bx - 9 = 0$

Use the discriminant to find all values of *c* for which the equation has two real roots.

22. $3x^2 - 4x + c = 0$

23. $2x^2 + 5x + c = 0$

24. $2x^2 - x - c = 0$

25. **Road Trip** You drove 180 miles at a constant rate of speed. If you had driven 15 miles per hour faster, you would have traveled the same distance in an hour less. How fast did you drive?

In Exercises 26–29, use the information from Exercises 22–25 on page 93 and the following information.

Vertical Motion Three objects are launched from the top of a 220 foot platform. The first object is launched upward at 25 feet per second. The second object is dropped. The third object is launched downward at 15 feet per second.

26. Write a height model for the first object.

27. Write a height model for the second object.

28. Write a height model for the third object.

29. How many seconds until each object hits the ground?

UNIT 3

LESSON 3.8

Problem Solving Workshop

Problem In Example 2 on page 91, you solved a quadratic equation by using the quadratic formula. You can also solve a quadratic equation using a graph.

Solve $4x^2 + 10x = -10x - 25$.

Method You can write the quadratic equation in standard form and then use a graph to solve the equation. You can use a graphing calculator to make the graph.

STEP 1 Rewrite the quadratic equation in standard form.

$$4x^2 + 10x = -10x - 25$$
$$4x^2 + 20x = -25$$
$$4x^2 + 20x + 25 = 0$$

STEP 2 Enter the function $y = 4x^2 + 20x + 25$ into a graphing calculator.

STEP 3 Graph the function. Adjust the viewing window so that you can see the point(s) where the graph crosses the x-axis. Find the x-value(s) for which $y = 0$ using the *zero* feature. The graph shows that $y = 0$ when $x = -2.5$.

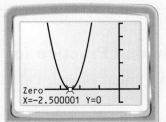

Practice

Solve the quadratic equation using a graph.

1. $2x^2 - 12x + 10 = 0$

2. $x^2 + 7x + 12 = 0$

3. $9x^2 - 30x + 25 = 0$

4. $7x^2 - 3 = 0$

5. $x^2 + 3x - 6 = 0$

6. **Dropped Object** You are dropping a ball from a window 29 feet above the ground to your friend who will catch it 4 feet above the ground. How long is the ball in the air before your friend catches it?

UNIT 3

Graph and Solve Quadratic Inequalities

Georgia Performance Standards: MM2A4d

Goal Graph and solve quadratic inequalities.

Vocabulary

A **quadratic inequality in two variables** can be written in one of the following forms:
$y < ax^2 + bx + c$, $y \le ax^2 + bx + c$, $y > ax^2 + bx + c$, $y \ge ax^2 + bx + c$

A **quadratic inequality in one variable** can be written in one of the following forms:
$ax^2 + bx + c < 0$, $ax^2 + bx + c \le 0$, $ax^2 + bx + c > 0$, $ax^2 + bx + c \ge 0$

Example 1 Use a quadratic inequality in real life

Rock Climbing A rope used for rock climbing can support a weight W (in pounds) if $W \le 6500d^2$ where d is the diameter of the rope (in centimeters). Graph the inequality.

Solution

Graph $W = 6500d^2$ for nonnegative values of d. Because the inequality symbol is $\le$, make the parabola solid. Test the point $(2, 20{,}000)$ which is below the parabola.

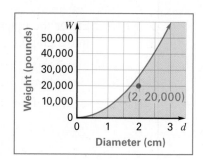

$$W \le 6500d^2$$
$$20{,}000 \overset{?}{\le} 6500(2)^2$$
$$20{,}000 \le 26{,}000$$

Because $(2, 20{,}000)$ is a solution, shade the region below the parabola.

Guided Practice for Example 1

1. Rework Example 1 if $W \le 6000d^2$ where d is the diameter of the rope in centimeters.

Example 2 Graph a system of quadratic inequalities

Graph the system of quadratic inequalities.

$$y < -x^2 - x + 2 \qquad \text{Inequality 1}$$
$$y \ge x^2 - 2x - 2 \qquad \text{Inequality 2}$$

STEP 1 Graph $y < -x^2 - x + 2$. The graph is the region inside but not including the parabola $y = -x^2 - x + 2$.

STEP 2 Graph $y \ge x^2 - 2x - 2$. The graph is the region inside and including the parabola.

STEP 3 Identify the shaded region where the two graphs overlap. It is the graph of the system.

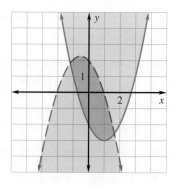

Georgia Performance Standards

MM2A4d Solve quadratic inequalities both graphically and algebraically, and describe the solutions using linear inequalities.

Example 3 Solve a quadratic inequality

Solve $x^2 - 5x \le -4$ (a) using a table, (b) by graphing, and (c) algebraically.

a. Rewrite as $x^2 - 5x + 4 \le 0$ and make a table of values.

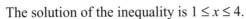

x	0	1	2	3	4	5
$x^2 - 5x + 4$	4	0	-2	-2	0	4

The solution of the inequality is $1 \le x \le 4$.

b. The solution consists of the x-values for which the graph of $y = x^2 - 5x + 4$ lies on or below the x-axis. To find the graph's x-intercepts, let $y = 0$ and solve for x.

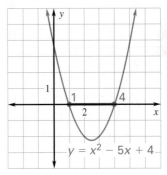

$$0 = x^2 - 5x + 4$$

$$x = \frac{5 \pm \sqrt{(-5)^2 - 4(1)(4)}}{2(1)} = \frac{5 \pm \sqrt{9}}{2}$$

$$x = 4 \text{ or } x = 1$$

Sketch a parabola that opens up and has 1 and 4 as x-intercepts. The graph lies on or below the x-axis to the right of (and including) $x = 1$ and to the left of (and including) $x = 4$.

The solution of the inequality is $1 \le x \le 4$.

c. To solve $x^2 - 5x \le -4$ algebraically, first replace $\le$ with $=$.

$$x^2 - 5x = -4$$ Write equation that corresponds to original inequality.

$$x^2 - 5x + 4 = 0$$ Write in standard form.

$$(x - 4)(x - 1) = 0$$ Factor.

$$x = 4 \quad \text{or} \quad x = 1$$ Zero product property

The numbers 4 and 1 are the critical x-values of the inequality. Plot 4 and 1 on a number line using closed dots. Test an x-value in each interval to see if it satisfies the inequality.

When you test $x = 0$, the inequality is not satisfied. When you test $x = 2$, the inequality is satisfied. When you test $x = 5$, the inequality is not satisfied. The solution is $1 \le x \le 4$.

Guided Practice for Examples 2 and 3

Graph the system of quadratic inequalities.

2. $y < x^2 + 2, y < -x^2 + 4$

3. $y \le -x^2 - 5x - 4, y \ge x^2 + 2x - 3$

4. Solve $x^2 + 3x - 4 < 0$ using a table.

5. Solve $x^2 - x - 2 \le 0$ by graphing.

6. Solve $-x^2 - 4x - 3 > 0$ algebraically.

LESSON 3.9

Exercise Set A

MM2A4d Solve quadratic inequalities both graphically and algebraically, and describe the solutions using linear inequalities.

Determine whether the ordered pair is a solution of the inequality.

1. $y < x^2 + 2x + 2$, $(1, 6)$

2. $y > x^2 - 5x$, $(2, -3)$

3. $y \leq 2x^2 - 7x$, $(4, 4)$

4. $y \geq -2x^2 + 3x - 6$, $(-1, -12)$

Match the inequality with its graph.

5. $y \geq x^2 + 4x - 1$

6. $y < -2x^2 + 3x - 5$

7. $y \leq \frac{1}{2}x^2 - x - 1$

8. $y \geq x^2 - 2$

9. $y < -x^2 - 2x + 1$

10. $y \leq x^2 - 3x + 2$

A.
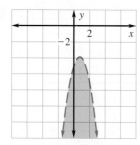

B.
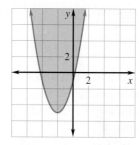

C.
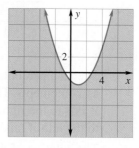

D.
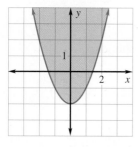

E.
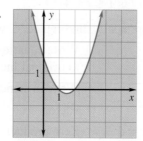

F.
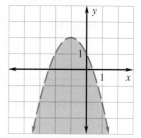

Graph the inequality.

11. $y > 3x^2 - 8x$

12. $y < -6x^2 + 2x + 3$

13. $y \geq 4x^2 - x - 7$

14. $y \geq x^2 + 2x - 8$

15. $y > -2x^2 - 14x + 21$

16. $y \leq 5x^2 + 2x - 6$

Error Analysis *Describe* and correct the error in graphing $y \geq x^2 - 1$.

17.
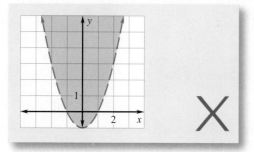

18.
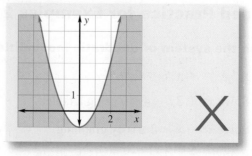

Exercise Set A (continued)

Match the system of inequalities with its graph.

19. $y < x^2 - 2x - 1$

$y > x^2 + 3x + 1$

20. $y \leq -2x^2 - x + 2$

$y > \frac{2}{3}x^2 - 3$

21. $y \leq 3x^2 + x + 2$

$y \geq -x^2 - 3x - 2$

A.
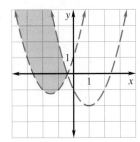

B.
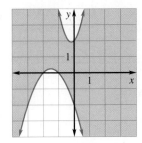

C.
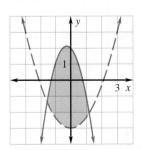

Graph the system of inequalities.

22. $y \geq x^2 + 2x - 3$

$y < -x^2 - x - 2$

23. $y \leq -\frac{1}{2}x^2 + 2x + 1$

$y \leq -\frac{1}{2}x^2 - 2x + 1$

24. $y < x^2 + 2x - 2$

$y < x^2 - 2x - 2$

25. $y \geq x^2 - 4x + 4$

$y \leq x^2 + 4x + 3$

26. $y > x^2 + 4x + 3$

$y > -x^2 - 2x + 3$

27. $y < -\frac{1}{2}x^2 - x + 4$

$y < \frac{1}{4}x^2 - \frac{1}{2}x - 2$

Solve the inequality algebraically.

28. $-x^2 + 5x + 36 < 0$

29. $3x^2 - 13x - 10 > 0$

30. $2x^2 + 13x + 6 < 0$

Solve the inequality graphically.

31. $x^2 - x - 30 \geq 0$

32. $x^2 + x - 12 > 0$

33. $x^2 - 3x - 18 \leq 0$

In Exercises 34–36, use the following information.

Football The path of a football kicked from the ground can be modeled by $h = -0.02x^2 + 1.2x$ where x is the horizontal distance (in yards) from where the ball is kicked and h is the corresponding height (in yards). The crossbar on a field goal post is 10 feet above the ground.

34. Write an inequality to find the values of x where the ball is high enough to go over the crossbar.

35. Solve the inequality.

36. A player attempts to kick a field goal from 52 yards away. Will the ball have enough height to go over the crossbar from this distance?

UNIT 3

LESSON
3.9

Exercise
Set B

MM2A4d Solve quadratic inequalities both graphically and
algebraically, and describe the solutions using
linear inequalities.

Match the inequality with its graph.

1. $y \leq 2x^2 - x - 3$

2. $y > -3x^2 + 14x - 8$

3. $y < -2x^2 + 8x - 6$

A.

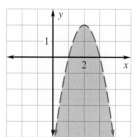

B.

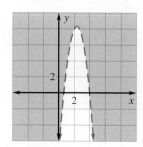

C.

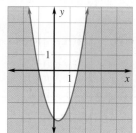

Graph the inequality.

4. $y > 3x^2 - 2x + 3$

5. $y < -2x^2 - x + 1$

6. $y \geq 4x^2 - 6x - 1$

7. $y \geq x^2 - 4x - 5$

8. $y > -2x^2 - 3x + 7$

9. $y \leq \frac{1}{2}x^2 + x - 4$

10. $y < -x^2 - x$

11. $y \leq x^2 - 2x - 10$

12. $y \geq x^2 - 2x + 4$

Match the system of inequalities with its graph.

13. $y \leq -2x^2 - 3x - 1$
$y < 2x^2 + 6x + 1$

14. $y > \frac{1}{2}x^2 + x - 2$
$y > x^2 - 4x + 1$

15. $y > -2x^2 + 4x - 3$
$y \leq -x^2 + 5x + 2$

16. $y > \frac{1}{2}x^2 - 2$
$y < -\frac{1}{2}x^2 + 2$

17. $y \leq -x^2 + 4x + 2$
$y \geq x^2 - 3x - 1$

18. $y < 3x^2 - 3$
$y \geq -\frac{1}{2}x^2 + 6$

A.

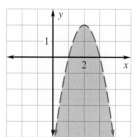

B.

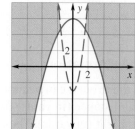

C.

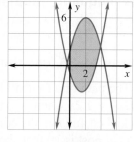

D.

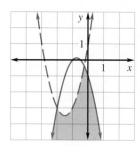

E.

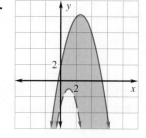

F.

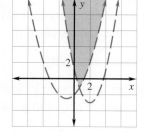

UNIT 3

Exercise Set B *(continued)*

Graph the system of inequalities.

19. $y \geq x^2 + 3x - 1$

$y < -x^2 + 4x + 6$

20. $y \leq -x^2 + 4x - 1$

$y > 2x^2 - 5x + 1$

21. $y < x^2 - 2x - 1$

$y > \frac{1}{2}x^2 - x - 2$

Solve the inequality algebraically.

22. $3x^2 + 23x + 30 \leq 0$

23. $x^2 + 2x + 4 \geq 0$

24. $12x^2 + 5x - 25 < 0$

25. $-2x^2 - 2x - 5 \geq 0$

26. $5x^2 + 47x - 30 < 0$

27. $-3x^2 + 35x - 50 > 0$

28. $6x^2 + 23x + 21 < 0$

29. $15x^2 - 11x - 14 \leq 0$

30. $32 + 44x - 21x^2 \geq 0$

31. $-18 + 39x - 20x^2 > 0$

Solve the inequality graphically.

32. $x^2 - 5x - 14 > 0$

33. $x^2 - 11x + 24 \leq 0$

34. $2x^2 - 18 > 0$

35. $-x^2 + 7x - 12 < 0$

In Exercises 36–39, use the following information.

Geometry The area of a region bounded by two parabolas, is given by

$$\text{Area} = \left(\frac{a-d}{3}\right)(B^3 - A^3) + \left(\frac{b-e}{2}\right)(B^2 - A^2) + (c - f)(B - A)$$

where $y = ax^2 + bx + c$ is the top parabola, $y = dx^2 + ex + f$ is the bottom parabola, and A and B are the x-coordinates of the intersection points of the two parabolas with $A < B$.

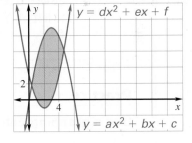

36. To find the x-coordinates of the intersection points of two parabolas, set the two quadratic equations equal to each other and solve for x. Find the x-coordinates of the intersection points of $y = x^2 - x - 5$ and $y = -x^2 - 4x + 4$.

37. Graph the system of inequalities.

$y \geq x^2 - x - 5$

$y \leq -x^2 - 4x + 4$

38. Find the area of the region from Exercise 37.

39. Find the area of the region from the following system of inequalities.

$y \geq x^2 - 3$

$y \geq \frac{1}{2}x^2$

Georgia Performance Standards

MM2A4d Solve quadratic inequalities both graphically and algebraically, and describe the solutions using linear inequalities.

Technology Activity

Quadratic Inequalities

Use after Lesson 3.9

Question

How can you use a graphing calculator to graph quadratic inequalities?

You can use a graphing calculator to graph quadratic inequalities. A quadratic inequality in two variables can be written in one of the following forms:

$$y < ax^2 + bx + c \qquad y \le ax^2 + bx + c \qquad y > ax^2 + bx + c \qquad y \ge ax^2 + bx + c$$

The graph of any such inequality consists of all solutions (x, y) of the inequality.

Example

Graph quadratic inequalities.

Use a graphing calculator to graph $y < 3x^2 + 2x + 1$.

Solution

STEP 1 Enter the equation $y = 3x^2 + 2x + 1$ in the equation editor window.

STEP 2 Change the icon to the left of the equation to indicate that the graph should be shaded below the line (◣). (*Note:* If the inequality is > or ≥, the symbol to the left of Y= should be ◥. If the inequality is < or ≤, the symbol to the left of Y= should be ◣.)

STEP 3 Graph the inequality.

Practice

Use a graphing calculator to graph the inequality.

1. $y \le 2x^2 - 3x + 1$ **2.** $y > 4x^2 + 3$ **3.** $y \ge x^2 - 5x + 8$

4. $y < -3x^2 + x + 2$ **5.** $y \le -x^2 - 4x - 2$ **6.** $y \ge -4x^2 + 3x$

Use your observations to complete the following statements with the word *inside* or *outside*.

7. If the leading coefficient of a quadratic inequality is positive, and the > or ≥ symbol is used, then the graph of the inequality will be shaded on the __?__ of the parabola.

8. If the leading coefficient of a quadratic inequality is positive, and the < or ≤ symbol is used, then the graph of the inequality will be shaded on the __?__ of the parabola.

9. If the leading coefficient of a quadratic inequality is negative, and the > or ≥ symbol is used, then the graph of the inequality will be shaded on the __?__ of the parabola.

TEST | for Unit 3

Graph the function. Label the vertex and axis of symmetry. Identify the domain and range.

1. $y = x^2 + 2x + 1$

2. $y = -2x^2 - 6x + 3$

3. $y = (x + 2)(x - 3)$

4. $y = 2(x + 4)(x + 1)$

5. $y = (x + 4)^2$

6. $y = -(x - 2)^2 + 3$

Find the minimum or maximum value of the function.

7. $y = (x + 3)(x + 4)$

8. $y = 8x(x + 15)$

9. $y = -x^2 + 2x + 100$

10. $y = -4(x + 6)^2 - 12$

11. $y = x^2 + 6x$

12. $y = 4(x - 4)^2 + 14$

Calculate the average rate of change of the function on the given interval.

13. $y = x^2 - x - 12, 0 \le x \le 2$

14. $y = -x^2 + 2x + 6, 1 \le x \le 3$

15. $y = -x^2 - x, -5 \le x \le -1$

16. $y = \frac{1}{3}x^2 - 2x + 1, 3 \le x \le 6$

Solve the equation.

17. $x^2 - 6x - 40 = 0$

18. $r^2 + 14r + 45 = 0$

19. $2w^2 + 5w - 3 = 0$

20. $6y^2 + 5y + 1 = 0$

21. $2(m - 3)^2 = -16$

22. $(x + 6)^2 - 8 = 16$

Using the model $h = -16t^2 + h_0$ where h_0 is the initial height, find the time it takes an object to hit the ground when it is dropped from a height of h_0 feet.

23. $h_0 = 64$

24. $h_0 = 36$

25. $h_0 = 144$

Solve the equation by completing the square.

26. $x^2 + 4x - 23 = 0$

27. $x^2 - 8x - 5 = 0$

28. $4x^2 - 8x + 9 = 0$

Write the quadratic function in vertex form. Then identify the vertex.

29. $y = x^2 - 4x + 6$

30. $y = 2x^2 - 4x - 1$

31. $y = -x^2 - 6x - 13$

Find the discriminant and use it to determine if the equation has _one real_, _two real_, or _two imaginary_ root(s).

32. $x^2 + 12 = 0$

33. $x^2 + 2x + 1 = 0$

34. $x^2 + 3x - 12 = 0$

Use the quadratic formula to solve the equation.

35. $x^2 + 2x - 7 = 0$

36. $2x^2 - 4x + 5 = 0$

37. $3x^2 + 8x + 6 = 0$

Graph the inequality.

38. $y \ge x^2 - 2$

39. $y < x^2 - 2x - 24$

40. $y > -x^2 - 5x + 36$

Solve the inequality algebraically.

41. $2x^2 < 32$

42. $2x^2 - 8x > -6$

43. $x^2 + 3x - 10 \le 0$

44. Aspect Ratio The *aspect ratio* of a widescreen TV is the ratio of the screen's width to its height or $16:9$. What are the width and height of a 54 inch widescreen TV? (*Hint:* Use the Pythagorean theorem and the fact that TV sizes such as 32 inches refer to the length of the screen's diagonal.)

45. Operating Cost A cost accountant at a manufacturing plant calculated that the operating cost of the plant can be modeled by $c(x) = 0.005x^2 - x + 75$ where x is the number of units (in thousands) produced and c is the operating cost (in thousands of dollars). Write and solve an inequality to find the total number of units produced that keeps the operating cost below $100,000.

46. Compound Interest The formula $A = P\left(1 + \dfrac{r}{n}\right)^{nt}$ gives the amount of money A in an account after t years if the annual interest rate is r (in decimal form), n is the number of times interest is compounded per year, and P is the original principal. What interest rate is required to earn $7 in six months if the principal is $1000 and the interest rate is compounded monthly? Round your answer to the nearest tenth of a percentage.

Performance Task

Catapults

In the fourth century, the catapult was used as a weapon during sieges. The catapult was designed to launch either large arrows or large stones at castles.

There were two types of catapults: torsion and non-torsion. A non-torsion catapult was invented first. The non-torsion catapult closely resembled a large bow and arrow. The torsion catapult used tension from a wound rope to launch large stones.

For parts (a) and (b), use the following information.

The path of a large stone fired from a torsion catapult can be modeled by $y = -0.00545x^2 + 1.145x$ where x is the distance (in yards) and y is the corresponding height (in yards).

  a. Find the distance the stone traveled.

  b. Find the maximum height of the stone.

For parts (c) and (d), use the following information.

The path of a large arrow fired from a non-torsion catapult can be modeled by $y = -0.0044x^2 + 1.68x$ where x is the distance (in yards) and y is the corresponding height (in yards). Given the height of a castle wall, find the greatest distance at which you can successfully launch an arrow over the wall.

  c. The height of the wall is 120 yards.

  d. The height of the wall is 100 feet.

UNIT 4
Algebra: Function Operations, Exponential Functions, and Sequences

Georgia Performance Standards

MM2A2a   Extend properties of exponents to include all integer exponents.

Investigating Math Activity
Properties of Exponents

Use before Lesson 4.1

Question

How can you discover the properties of exponents?

You can discover the properties of exponents by writing exponential functions in expanded form without any exponents. For example, 3^4 can be rewritten in expanded form as $3 \cdot 3 \cdot 3 \cdot 3$.

Explore

Write exponential expressions in expanded form.

Rewrite the exponential expression in expanded form, and then simplify the expression by writing it with an exponent. Several examples have been done.

Property	Exponential expression	Expanded form	Simplified form
Product of powers	$3^5 \cdot 3^2$	$(3 \cdot 3 \cdot 3 \cdot 3 \cdot 3) \cdot (3 \cdot 3)$	3^7
Power of a power	$(2^3)^2$	$(2 \cdot 2 \cdot 2) \cdot (2 \cdot 2 \cdot 2)$	2^6
Quotient of powers	$\dfrac{2^4}{2^2}$	$\dfrac{2 \cdot 2 \cdot 2 \cdot 2}{2 \cdot 2} = 2 \cdot 2$	2^2
Power of a quotient	$\left(\dfrac{2}{5}\right)^3$	$\dfrac{2}{5} \cdot \dfrac{2}{5} \cdot \dfrac{2}{5} = \dfrac{2 \cdot 2 \cdot 2}{5 \cdot 5 \cdot 5}$	$\dfrac{2^3}{5^3}$
Product of powers	$6^4 \cdot 6^7$	?	?
Power of a power	$(3^4)^3$	?	?
Quotient of powers	$\dfrac{5^8}{5^4}$	?	?
Power of a quotient	$\left(\dfrac{4}{7}\right)^5$	?	?

Draw Conclusions

1. **Writing** How do the exponents in the *Exponential expression* column compare to the exponents in the *Simplified form* column for each property?

2. **Reasoning** *Explain* what each property means in general.

LESSON 4.1

Use Properties of Exponents

Georgia Performance Standards: MM2A2a

Goal Simplify expressions involving powers.

Vocabulary

A number is expressed in **scientific notation** if it is in the form $c \times 10^n$ where $1 \leq c < 10$ and n is an integer.

Properties of Exponents

Let a and b be real numbers and let m and n be integers.

Property Name	Definition	Example
Product of Powers	$a^m \cdot a^n = a^{m+n}$	$5^3 \cdot 5^{-1} = 5^{3+(-1)} = 5^2 = 25$
Power of a Power	$(a^m)^n = a^{mn}$	$(3^3)^2 = 3^{3 \cdot 2} = 3^6 = 729$
Power of a Product	$(ab)^m = a^m b^m$	$(2 \cdot 3)^4 = 2^4 \cdot 3^4 = 1296$
Negative Exponent	$a^{-m} = \dfrac{1}{a^m}, a \neq 0$	$7^{-2} = \dfrac{1}{7^2} = \dfrac{1}{49}$
Zero Exponent	$a^0 = 1, a \neq 0$	$(-89)^0 = 1$
Quotient of Powers	$\dfrac{a^m}{a^n} = a^{m-n}, a \neq 0$	$\dfrac{6^{-3}}{6^{-6}} = 6^{-3-(-6)} = 6^3 = 216$
Power of a Quotient	$\left(\dfrac{a}{b}\right)^m = \dfrac{a^m}{b^m}, b \neq 0$	$\left(\dfrac{4}{7}\right)^2 = \dfrac{4^2}{7^2} = \dfrac{16}{49}$

Example 1   Evaluate a numerical expression

a. $\left(\dfrac{1}{3^{-2}}\right)^3 (-4)^3 = (3^2)^3 (-4)^3$ Negative exponent property

$\qquad\qquad\quad = 3^6 (-4)^3$ Power of a power property

$\qquad\qquad\quad = 729(-64) = -46{,}656$ Evaluate powers.

b. $(-3 \cdot 2^5)^2 = (-3)^2 \cdot (2^5)^2$ Power of a product property

$\qquad\qquad\quad = 9 \cdot 2^{5 \cdot 2}$ Power of a power property

$\qquad\qquad\quad = 9 \cdot 2^{10} = 9216$ Simplify and evaluate power.

c. $\left(\dfrac{10^5}{10^8}\right)^{-1} = \dfrac{10^8}{10^5}$ Negative exponent property

$\qquad\qquad\quad = 10^{8-5}$ Quotient of powers property

$\qquad\qquad\quad = 10^3 = 1000$ Simplify and evaluate power.

Georgia Performance Standards

MM2A2a   Extend properties of exponents to include all integer exponents.

Example 2 Use scientific notation in real life

Hoover Dam The volume of concrete that was used to construct the Hoover Dam is about 3,325,000 cubic yards. One cubic yard of concrete weighs about 4050 pounds. About how many pounds of concrete were used to construct the Hoover Dam?

Solution

$$\boxed{\text{Pounds of concrete}} = \boxed{\text{Weight per cubic yard}} \times \boxed{\text{Number of cubic yards}}$$

$$= \quad 4050 \quad \times \quad 3{,}325{,}000 \qquad \text{Substitute values.}$$

$$= (4.05 \times 10^3)(3.325 \times 10^6) \qquad \text{Write in scientific notation.}$$

$$= (4.05 \times 3.325)(10^3 \times 10^6) \qquad \text{Use multiplication properties.}$$

$$= 13.46625 \times 10^9 \qquad \text{Product of powers property}$$

$$= 1.346625 \times 10^1 \times 10^9 \qquad \text{Write 13.46625 in scientific notation.}$$

$$= 1.346625 \times 10^{10} \qquad \text{Product of powers property}$$

About 1.346625×10^{10}, or 13,466,250,000, pounds of concrete were used.

Guided Practice for Examples 1 and 2

Evaluate the expression. Tell which properties of exponents you used.

1. $(2^2 \cdot 5)^3$

2. $7^3 \cdot 7^{-1}$

3. $(8^0 \cdot 6^{-2})^{-1}$

4. $\left(\dfrac{9^6}{9^4}\right)^3$

5. Rework Example 2 for the Shasta Dam that was constructed with 6.3 million cubic yards of concrete.

Example 3 Simplify expressions

Simplify the expression. Tell which properties of exponents you used.

a. $\dfrac{y^7 z^4}{(z^{-2})^{-1} z^2} = \dfrac{y^7 z^4}{z^2 z^2}$ Power of a power property

$$= \dfrac{y^7 z^4}{z^4} \qquad \text{Product of powers property}$$

$$= y^7 z^0 \qquad \text{Quotient of powers property}$$

$$= y^7 \cdot 1 \qquad \text{Zero exponent property}$$

$$= y^7 \qquad \text{Identity property of multiplication}$$

UNIT 4

Example 3 **Simplify expressions** *(continued)*

b. $k^{-3}k^5k^8 = k^{-3+5+8} = k^{10}$ Product of powers property

c. $\left(\dfrac{b^{-3}}{c^5}\right)^{-2} = \dfrac{(b^{-3})^{-2}}{(c^5)^{-2}}$ Power of a quotient property

$\qquad = \dfrac{b^6}{c^{-10}}$ Power of a power property

$\qquad = b^6 c^{10}$ Negative exponent property

d. $\dfrac{9s^5t^{-4}}{3t^{-4}} = 3s^5t^{-4-(-4)}$ Quotient of powers property

$\qquad = 3s^5t^0 = 3s^5$ Zero exponent property

Example 4   Compare real-life volumes

Softball The radius of a softball is about $\dfrac{4}{3}$ times the radius of a baseball. How many times as great as the baseball's volume is the softball's volume?

Solution

Let r represent the radius of a baseball. Then $\dfrac{4}{3}r$ represents the radius of a softball.

$\dfrac{\text{softball's volume}}{\text{baseball's volume}} = \dfrac{\frac{4}{3}\pi\left(\frac{4}{3}r\right)^3}{\frac{4}{3}\pi r^3}$ The volume of a sphere is $\dfrac{4}{3}\pi r^3$.

$\qquad = \dfrac{\frac{4}{3}\pi\left(\frac{4}{3}\right)^3 r^3}{\frac{4}{3}\pi r^3}$ Power of a product property

$\qquad = \dfrac{64}{27}r^0$ Power of a quotient and quotient of powers

$\qquad = \dfrac{64}{27} \cdot 1$ Zero exponent property

$\qquad \approx 2.370370$ Use a calculator.

The volume of a softball is about 2.37 times as great as the volume of a baseball.

Guided Practice for Examples 3 and 4

Simplify the expression. Tell which properties of exponents you used.

6. $t^7t^2t^{-8}$ **7.** $(k^{-3}m^4)^{-2}$

8. $\left(\dfrac{f^5}{g^{-2}}\right)^{-3}$ **9.** $\left(\dfrac{3x}{z^2}\right)^0$

10. Rework Example 4 where the radius of a volleyball is about 3 times the radius of a baseball.

Exercise Set A

MM2A2a Extend properties of exponents to include all integer exponents.

Evaluate the expression. Tell which properties of exponents you used.

1. $2^5 \cdot 2^3$

2. $(-7)^2(-7)$

3. $4^{-6} \cdot 4^{-1}$

4. $(5^{-2})^2$

5. $\dfrac{4^{-7}}{4^{-3}}$

6. $\dfrac{8^{-4}}{8^2}$

Error Analysis *Describe* **and correct the error in simplifying the expression.**

7.
$$\dfrac{x^{10}}{x^2} = x^5$$

8.
$$x^5 \cdot x^3 = x^{15}$$

Write the answer in scientific notation.

9. $(6.1 \times 10^5)(2.2 \times 10^6)$

10. $(2.6 \times 10^{-7})(1.3 \times 10^2)$

11. $(3.4 \times 10^{-1})(3.1 \times 10^{-2})$

12. $(5.8 \times 10^{-7})(8.1 \times 10^{12})$

13. $(4.5 \times 10^4)^2$

14. $(3.7 \times 10^{-5})^2$

15. $(7.2 \times 10^{-3})^3$

16. $\dfrac{9.9 \times 10^9}{1.5 \times 10^8}$

17. $\dfrac{8.4 \times 10^{-6}}{2.4 \times 10^9}$

Simplify the expression. Tell which properties of exponents you used.

18. $\dfrac{x^8}{x^4}$

19. $\dfrac{y^4}{y^{-7}}$

20. $(3^2 s^3)^6$

21. $(4^0 w^2)^{-5}$

22. $(y^4 z^2)(y^{-3} z^{-5})$

23. $(2m^3 n^{-1})(8m^4 n^{-2})$

24. $(7c^7 d^2)^{-2}$

25. $(5g^4 h^{-3})^{-3}$

26. $\dfrac{x^5 y^{-8}}{x^5 y^{-6}}$

27. $\dfrac{16q^0 r^{-6}}{4q^{-3} r^{-7}}$

28. $\dfrac{12a^{-3} b^9}{21a^2 b^{-5}}$

29. $\dfrac{8e^{-4} f^{-2}}{18ef^{-5}}$

Write an expression for the surface area or volume in terms of x.

30. $S = 4\pi r^2$

31. $V = \dfrac{1}{3}\pi r^2 h$

32. $V = \dfrac{4}{3}\pi r^3$

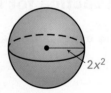

33. Birds Some scientists estimate that there are about 8600 species of birds in the world. The mean number of birds per species is approximately 12,000,000. About how many birds are there in the world? Write your answer in scientific notation.

LESSON
4.1

**Exercise
Set B**

MM2A2a   Extend properties of exponents to include all
integer exponents.

Evaluate the expression. Tell which properties of exponents you used.

1. $5^0 \cdot 5^5 \cdot 5^{-3}$

2. $\dfrac{3^{-2} \cdot 3^4}{3^{-5}}$

3. $\dfrac{(2^3)^2}{2^{-4}}$

4. $\dfrac{(-4)^2(-4)^{-3}}{(-4)^{-5}}$

5. $\left(\dfrac{3}{4}\right)^{-3}$

6. $\left[\left(\dfrac{1}{3}\right)^{-2}\right]^3$

7. $\dfrac{\left(\frac{2}{3}\right)^4}{\left(\frac{2}{3}\right)^{-5}\left(\frac{2}{3}\right)^0}$

8. $\dfrac{\left(\frac{1}{5}\right)^{-4}}{\left(\frac{1}{5}\right)^{-2}\left(\frac{1}{5}\right)^{-5}}$

Write the answer in scientific notation.

9. $(2.3 \times 10^{-4})(9.3 \times 10^8)$

10. $(5.4 \times 10^{-5})(1.8 \times 10^{-1})$

11. $(2.5 \times 10^{-3})^{-2}$

12. $\dfrac{(3.3 \times 10^9)(2.8 \times 10^{-7})}{4.62 \times 10^5}$

13. $\dfrac{(1.2 \times 10^{-4})^2}{(9.0 \times 10^5)(1.6 \times 10^{-8})}$

14. $\dfrac{2.1 \times 10^{-4}}{8.4 \times 10^{-6}}$

Simplify the expression. Tell which properties of exponents you used.

15. $\dfrac{x^2 y^3}{2} \cdot \dfrac{2x^4}{y^3}$

16. $\dfrac{4m^4}{-6m^{-1}n^5} \cdot \dfrac{3n^{-1}}{m^{-2}}$

17. $\dfrac{(c^4)^3}{4} \cdot \dfrac{12d^{-6}}{(15cd)^{-1}}$

18. $\dfrac{w^{-3}}{v^{-5}} \cdot \dfrac{v^{-5}}{w^{-3}}$

19. $\left(\dfrac{x^7 y^{-2}}{3y^{-3}}\right)^{-2}$

20. $\left(\dfrac{qr^2 s}{3r^4}\right)^{-3}$

21. $[(z^{-2})^2]^3$

22. $[(b^9)^{-1}]^{-2}$

Write an expression that makes the statement true.

23. $a^4 b^{-3} c^5 \cdot \underline{\ \ ?\ \ } = a^8 bc^{10}$

24. $\dfrac{?}{9x^2 y^6 z} = \dfrac{2x}{3y^2}$

25. $(2m^3 n^2)^6 = \underline{\ \ ?\ \ } \cdot 4m^{12} n^{-5}$

26. **Chemistry** One milliliter of water contains about 3.33×10^{22} molecules. About how many molecules are in a 0.5 liter bottle of water? Write your answer in scientific notation.

27. **Manufacturing** A package designer for a company that makes holiday ornaments needs to decide how to package a special edition glass ornament shaped like a sphere. It must be packaged as tightly as possible in a cylinder or a cube.

   a. Write an expression for the ratio of the volume of the ornament to the volume of the cylinder.

   b. Write an expression for the ratio of the volume of the ornament to the volume of the cube.

   c. Which package do you think the designer should choose? *Explain.*

Perform Function Operations and Composition

Georgia Performance Standards: MM2A5d

Goal Perform operations with functions.

Vocabulary

A **power function** has the form $y = ax^b$ where a is a real number and b is a rational number.

The **composition** of a function g with a function f is: $h(x) = g(f(x))$ where the domain of h is the set of all x-values such that x is in the domain of f and $f(x)$ is in the domain of g.

Example 1 Add and subtract functions

Let $f(x) = -3x^3$ and $g(x) = -x^3$. Find the following.

a. $f(x) + g(x)$ **b.** $f(x) - g(x)$ **c.** the domains of $f + g$ and $f - g$

Solution

a. $f(x) + g(x) = -3x^3 + (-x^3) = [(-3) + (-1)]x^3 = -4x^3$

b. $f(x) - g(x) = -3x^3 - (-x^3) = [(-3) - (-1)]x^3 = -2x^3$

c. The functions f and g each have the same domain: all real numbers. So, the domains of $f + g$ and $f - g$ also consist of all real numbers.

Example 2 Multiply and divide functions

Let $f(x) = 2x^4$ and $g(x) = x^2$. Find the following.

a. $f(x) \cdot g(x)$ **b.** $\dfrac{f(x)}{g(x)}$ **c.** the domains of $f \cdot g$ and $\dfrac{f}{g}$

Solution

a. $f(x) \cdot g(x) = (2x^4)(x^2) = 2x^{(4+2)} = 2x^6$

b. $\dfrac{f(x)}{g(x)} = \dfrac{2x^4}{x^2} = 2x^{(4-2)} = 2x^2$ for x not equal to zero.

c. The domain of f consists of all real numbers, and the domain of g consists of all real numbers. So the domain of $f \cdot g$ consists of all real numbers. Because $g(0) = 0$, the domain of $\dfrac{f}{g}$ is restricted to all nonzero real numbers.

Guided Practice for Examples 1 and 2

Let $f(x) = 2x^2$ and $g(x) = -3x^2$. Perform the indicated operation. State the domain.

1. $f(x) + g(x)$ **2.** $f(x) - g(x)$ **3.** $f(x) \cdot g(x)$ **4.** $\dfrac{f(x)}{g(x)}$

Example 3   Find compositions of functions

Let $f(x) = 2x^3$ and $g(x) = x^{-1}$. Find the following.

a. $f(g(x))$ **b.** $g(f(x))$ **c.** the domain of each composition

Solution

a. $f(g(x)) = f(x^{-1}) = 2(x^{-1})^3 = 2x^{-3} = \dfrac{2}{x^3}$

b. $g(f(x)) = g(2x^3) = (2x^3)^{-1} = \dfrac{1}{2x^3}$

c. The domain of $f(g(x))$ consists of all real numbers except 0 because $x = 0$ is not in the domain of g. The domain of $g(f(x))$ consists of all real numbers except 0 because $f(0) = 0$ is not in the domain of g.

Example 4   Solve a multi-step problem

Sports Store You purchase water skis with a price tag of $180. The sports store applies a newspaper coupon of $50 and a 10% store discount. Use composition to find the final price of the purchase when the coupon is applied before the discount. Use composition to find the final price of the purchase when the discount is applied before the coupon.

STEP 1 **Write** functions for the discounts. Let x be the tag price, $f(x)$ be the price after the $50 coupon, and $g(x)$ be the price after the 10% store discount.

Function for $50 coupon: $f(x) = x - 50$

Function for 10% discount: $g(x) = x - 0.10x = 0.90x$

STEP 2 **Compose** the functions.

$50 coupon is applied first: $g(f(x)) = g(x - 50) = 0.90(x - 50)$

10% discount is applied first: $f(g(x)) = f(0.90x) = 0.90x - 50$

STEP 3 **Evaluate** the functions $g(f(x))$ and $f(g(x))$ when $x = 180$.

$g(f(180)) = 0.90(180 - 50) = 0.90(130) = \$117$

$f(g(180)) = 0.90(180) - 50 = 162 - 50 = \$112$

The final price is $117 when the $50 coupon is applied before the 10% discount. The final price is $112 when the 10% discount is applied before the $50 coupon.

Guided Practice for Examples 3 and 4

5. Let $f(x) = 3x^2$ and $g(x) = x^2 + 5$. Find (a) $f(g(x))$ and (b) $g(f(x))$.

6. Let $f(x) = x + 2$ and $g(x) = x^3$. Find (a) $f(g(x))$ and (b) $g(f(x))$.

7. Rework Example 4 for a price tag of $200, a $30 coupon, and a 20% discount.

UNIT 4

Exercise Set A

MM2A5d Use composition to verify that functions are inverses of each other.

Let $f(x) = 7x^5 - 2$, $g(x) = -x^5 + 4$, and $h(x) = -4x^5 + 1$. Perform the indicated operation.

1. $f(x) + g(x)$ **2.** $f(x) + h(x)$ **3.** $h(x) + g(x)$

4. $f(x) - g(x)$ **5.** $h(x) - f(x)$ **6.** $g(x) - h(x)$

Let $f(x) = 4x^2$, $g(x) = -3x^4$, and $h(x) = x^3$. Perform the indicated operation.

7. $f(x) \cdot g(x)$ **8.** $f(x) \cdot h(x)$ **9.** $h(x) \cdot g(x)$

10. $\dfrac{f(x)}{g(x)}$ **11.** $\dfrac{h(x)}{f(x)}$ **12.** $\dfrac{h(x)}{g(x)}$

Let $f(x) = 2x + 3$, $g(x) = \dfrac{3}{x+1}$, and $h(x) = \dfrac{x+5}{2}$. Perform the indicated operation.

13. $f(g(x))$ **14.** $g(h(x))$ **15.** $f(h(x))$

16. $g(f(x))$ **17.** $h(f(x))$ **18.** $g(g(x))$

Let $f(x) = 3x + 2$, $g(x) = 2x^2$, and $h(x) = \dfrac{-4}{x+3}$. State the domain of the operation.

19. $f(x) + g(x)$ **20.** $h(x) - f(x)$ **21.** $h(x) \cdot g(x)$

22. $\dfrac{g(x)}{f(x)}$ **23.** $h(g(x))$ **24.** $f(g(x))$

In Exercises 25–29, use the following information.

Computer Sale You have a coupon for $200 off the price of a personal computer. When you arrive at the store, you find that the computers are on sale for 20% off. Let x represent the original price of the computer.

25. Use a function notation to describe your cost, $f(x)$, using only the coupon.

26. Use a function notation to describe your cost, $g(x)$, with only the 20% discount.

27. Form the composition of the functions f and g that represents your cost if you use the coupon first, then take the 20% discount.

28. Form the composition of the functions f and g that represents your cost if you use the discount first, then use the coupon.

29. Would you pay less for the computer if you used the coupon first or took the 20% discount first?

Exercise Set B

MM2A5d Use composition to verify that functions are inverses of each other.

Let $f(x) = 2x^3 + 3x^2 - 5$, $g(x) = -4x^2 + x + 1$, and $h(x) = 4x^3 - x^2$. Perform the indicated operation.

1. $f(x) + g(x)$

2. $f(x) + h(x)$

3. $h(x) + g(x)$

4. $f(x) - g(x)$

Let $f(x) = x^2 + 1$, $g(x) = -3x^{-3}$, and $h(x) = x^3$. Perform the indicated operation.

5. $f(x) \cdot g(x)$

6. $f(x) \cdot h(x)$

7. $h(x) \cdot g(x)$

8. $\dfrac{f(x)}{g(x)}$

Let $f(x) = 2x^2 - x$, $g(x) = x^{-2}$, and $h(x) = \dfrac{x - 1}{3}$. Perform the indicated operation and state the domain.

9. $f(g(x))$

10. $g(h(x))$

11. $f(h(x))$

12. $g(f(x))$

State whether or not the following statements are always true. If they are false, give an example.

13. $f(x) + g(x) = g(x) + f(x)$

14. $f(x) - g(x) = g(x) - f(x)$

15. $f(x) \cdot g(x) = g(x) \cdot f(x)$

16. $\dfrac{g(x)}{f(x)} = \dfrac{f(x)}{g(x)}$

Find functions f and g such that $h(x) = f(g(x))$.

17. $h(x) = \sqrt{x + 1}$

18. $h(x) = x^2 + 2$

19. $h(x) = \dfrac{x}{x^2 - 2x + 1}$

20. Multiple Representations A woman at a lake throws a tennis ball from point A along the water's edge to point B in the water, as shown. Her dog, Daisy, first runs along the beach from point A to point D and then swims to fetch the ball at point B.

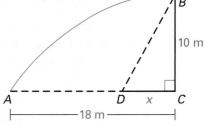

  a. Using a Diagram Daisy's running speed is about 6.2 meters per second. Write a function $r(x)$ for the time she spends running from point A to point D. Daisy's swimming speed is about 0.8 meter per second. Write a function $s(x)$ for the time she spends swimming from point D to point B.

  b. Writing a Function Write a function $t(x)$ that represents the total time Daisy spends traveling from point A to point D to point B.

  c. Using a Graph Use a graphing calculator to graph $t(x)$. Find the value of x that minimizes $t(x)$. *Explain* the meaning of this value.

UNIT 4

Use Inverse Functions

Georgia Performance Standards: MM2A5a, MM2A5b, MM2A5c, MM2A5d

Goal Find inverse functions.

Vocabulary

An **inverse relation** interchanges the input and output values of the original relation.

Functions f and g are **inverse functions** of each other provided $f(g(x)) = x$ and $g(f(x)) = x$. The function g is denoted by f^{-1}, read as "f inverse."

The inverse of a function f is also a function if and only if no horizontal line intersects the graph of f more than once. Equivalently, if a function is one-to-one, then the inverse of the function is also a function.

For an integer n greater than 1, if $b^n = a$, then b is an **nth root of a,** written $\sqrt[n]{a}$ or $a^{1/n}$.

Example 1 **Verify that functions are inverses**

Verify that $f(x) = 4x + 3$ and $f^{-1}(x) = \frac{1}{4}x - \frac{3}{4}$ are inverse functions.

STEP 1 Show that $f(f^{-1}(x)) = x$.

$$f(f^{-1}(x)) = f\left(\frac{1}{4}x - \frac{3}{4}\right)$$

$$= 4\left(\frac{1}{4}x - \frac{3}{4}\right) + 3$$

$$= x - 3 + 3$$

$$= x \ \checkmark$$

STEP 2 Show that $f^{-1}(f(x)) = x$.

$$f^{-1}(f(x)) = f^{-1}(4x + 3)$$

$$= \frac{1}{4}(4x + 3) - \frac{3}{4}$$

$$= x + \frac{3}{4} - \frac{3}{4}$$

$$= x \ \checkmark$$

Example 2 **Find the inverse of a function of the form $y = \frac{a}{x}$**

Consider the function $f(x) = \frac{2}{x}$. Determine whether the inverse of f is a function. Then find the inverse.

Graph the function. Notice that no horizontal line intersects the graph more than once. The inverse of f is a function. To find an equation for f^{-1}, complete the following steps.

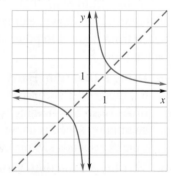

$y = \dfrac{2}{x}$ Write original function. Replace $f(x)$ with y.

$x = \dfrac{2}{y}$ Switch x and y.

$xy = 2$ Multiply each side by y.

$y = \dfrac{2}{x}$ Divide each side by x.

The inverse of f is $f^{-1}(x) = \dfrac{2}{x}$.

Georgia Performance Standards

MM2A5a Discuss the characteristics of functions and their inverses, including one-to-oneness, domain, and range.

MM2A5b Determine inverses of linear, quadratic, and power functions and functions of the form $f(x) = \dfrac{a}{x}$, including the use of restricted domains.

MM2A5c Explore the graphs of functions and their inverses.

MM2A5d Use composition to verify that functions are inverses of each other.

Example 3 Find the inverse of a quadratic function

Find the inverse of $f(x) = x^2$, $x \ge 0$. Then graph f and f^{-1}.

Solution

$f(x) = x^2$ Write original function.

$y = x^2$ Replace $f(x)$ with y.

$x = y^2$ Switch x and y.

$\pm\sqrt{x} = y$ Take square roots of each side.

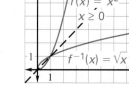

The domain of f is restricted to nonnegative values of x. So, the range of f^{-1} must also be restricted to nonnegative values, and therefore the inverse of $f^{-1}(x) = \sqrt{x}$.

Example 4 Find the inverse of a power function

$f(x) = 17x^5$ Original function

$y = 17x^5$ Replace $f(x)$ with y.

$x = 17y^5$ Switch x and y.

$\dfrac{x}{17} = y^5$ Divide each side by 17.

$\sqrt[5]{\dfrac{x}{17}} = \sqrt[5]{y^5}$ Take the fifth root of each side.

$\sqrt[5]{\dfrac{x}{17}} = y$ Simplify. This is the inverse model.

Guided Practice for Examples 1, 2, 3, and 4

Find $g(x)$, the inverse of the function. Verify that $f(x)$ and $g(x)$ are inverse functions.

1. $f(x) = -5x + 2$

2. $f(x) = 2x^4 - 3, x \le 0$

3. $f(x) = 4x^3 - 5$

4. $f(x) = 3x^4, x \ge 0$

5. $f(x) = \dfrac{4}{x}$

6. $f(x) = (x + 1)^2, x \ge -1$

MM2A5a Discuss the characteristics of functions and their inverses, including one-to-oneness, domain, and range.

MM2A5b Determine inverses of linear, quadratic, and power functions and functions of the form $f(x) = \frac{a}{x}$, including the use of restricted domains.

MM2A5c Explore the graphs of functions and their inverses.

MM2A5d Use composition to verify that functions are inverses of each other.

Find an equation for the inverse relation.

1. $y = 2x + 1$

2. $y = \frac{1}{3}x$

3. $y = 6x - 3$

4. $y = -4x + 6$

5. $y = \frac{1}{2} - \frac{2}{3}x$

6. $y = x^2 + 2, x \geq 0$

Error Analysis *Describe* **and correct the error in finding the inverse of the relation.**

7.
$$y = 4x - 12$$
$$x = 4y - 12$$
$$x + 12 = 4y$$
$$\frac{x}{4} + 12 = y$$

✗

8.
$$y = -x + 6$$
$$-x = y + 6$$
$$-x - 6 = y$$

✗

Verify that *f* and *g* are inverse functions.

9. $f(x) = x + 4; g(x) = x - 4$

10. $f(x) = 7x; g(x) = \frac{1}{7}x$

11. $f(x) = x^5; g(x) = \sqrt[5]{x}$

12. $f(x) = 2x - 4; g(x) = \frac{1}{2}x + 2$

13. $f(x) = 3 - x; g(x) = 3 - x$

14. $f(x) = x^2 + 5, x \geq 0; g(x) = \sqrt{x - 5}$

Graph the function *f*. Then use the horizontal line test to determine whether the inverse of *f* is a function.

15. $f(x) = 2x + 1$

16. $f(x) = -x - 2$

17. $f(x) = \frac{1}{2}x^2 - 1$

18. $f(x) = -x^2 + 3, x \geq 0$

19. $f(x) = \frac{1}{4}x^3$

20. $f(x) = \frac{3}{x}$

21. **Temperature Conversion** The formula to convert temperatures from degrees Celsius to Fahrenheit is $F = \frac{9}{5}C + 32$. Write the inverse function, which converts temperatures from Fahrenheit to Celsius. What is the Celsius temperature that is equal to 94 degrees Fahrenheit?

22. **Sale Price** A department store is having a storewide 20% discount sale. The sale price *s* of an item that has a regular price of *r* is $s = r - 0.2r$. Write the inverse function. What is the regular price for an item that is on sale for $38.40?

Exercise Set B

MM2A5a Discuss the characteristics of functions and their inverses, including one-to-oneness, domain, and range.

MM2A5b Determine inverses of linear, quadratic, and power functions and functions of the form $f(x) = \dfrac{a}{x}$, including the use of restricted domains.

MM2A5c Explore the graphs of functions and their inverses.

MM2A5d Use composition to verify that functions are inverses of each other.

Verify that *f* and *g* are inverse functions.

1. $f(x) = 3x + 5;\ g(x) = \dfrac{1}{3}x - \dfrac{5}{3}$

2. $f(x) = -2x - 3;\ g(x) = -\dfrac{1}{2}x - \dfrac{3}{2}$

3. $f(x) = x^2 + 2,\ x \ge 0;\ g(x) = \sqrt{x - 2}$

4. $f(x) = \dfrac{1}{3}x^3 - 2;\ g(x) = \sqrt[3]{3x + 6}$

5. $f(x) = 3x^4 + 1,\ x \ge 0;\ g(x) = \sqrt[4]{\dfrac{1}{3}x - \dfrac{1}{3}}$

6. $f(x) = \dfrac{3 - x}{x};\ g(x) = \dfrac{3}{x + 1}$

Find the inverse of the function.

7. $f(x) = 3 - 2x$

8. $f(x) = \dfrac{1}{5}x + 3$

9. $f(x) = \sqrt{x - 3}$

10. $f(x) = \sqrt{2x + 5}$

11. $f(x) = 4x^7$

12. $f(x) = 4x^2 + 1,\ x \ge 0$

13. $f(x) = \dfrac{4 - x}{3x}$

14. $f(x) = \sqrt[5]{5x + 4}$

15. $f(x) = \dfrac{1}{2x}$

Graph the function *f*. Then use the horizontal line test to determine whether the inverse of *f* is a function.

16. $f(x) = -x^3 + 1$

17. $f(x) = (x + 3)(x - 1)$

18. $f(x) = \dfrac{5}{x}$

19. **Exchange Rates** On a certain day, the number of British pounds *P* that could be obtained for *E* euros is modeled by $P = 1.48598E$. Also, the number of euros *E* that could be obtained for *D* U.S. dollars is modeled by $E = 1.22660D$. How many U.S. dollars could be obtained for 1000 British pounds?

In Exercises 20–22, use the following information.

Visual Thinking The function $f(x) = \dfrac{1}{x}$ is its own inverse.

20. Graph $f(x)$ and $f^{-1}(x)$ to verify that $f(x)$ is its own inverse.

21. Verify that $f(x)$ is its own inverse by showing that $f(f(x)) = x$.

22. If $g(x) = \dfrac{a}{x}$ where *a* is a nonzero constant, is it true that $g(x)$ is its own inverse? *Explain.*

UNIT 4

Graph Exponential Growth Functions

Georgia Performance Standards: MM2A2b, MM2A2c, MM2A2e

Goal Graph and use exponential growth functions.

Vocabulary

An **exponential function** has the form $y = ab^x$, where $a \neq 0$ and the base b is a positive number other than 1.

If $a > 0$ and $b > 1$, then the function $y = ab^x$ is an **exponential growth function,** and b is called the **growth factor.**

An **asymptote** is a line that a graph approaches more and more closely.

The **end behavior** of a function's graph is the behavior of the graph as x approaches positive or negative infinity.

Example 1   **Graph $y = b^x$ for $b > 1$**

Graph $y = 4^x$. Analyze the graph. Find the average rate of change over the interval $-2 \leq x \leq 2$.

STEP 1 **Make** a table of values.

x	-2	-1	0	1	2
y	$\dfrac{1}{16}$	$\dfrac{1}{4}$	1	4	16

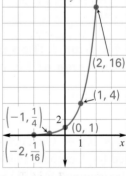

STEP 2 **Plot** the points from the table.

STEP 3 **Draw** from *left* to *right*, a smooth curve that begins just above the x-axis, passes through the plotted points, and moves up to the right.

STEP 4 **Examine** the graph. The graph intersects the y-axis at point $(0, 1)$. So the y-intercept of $y = 4^x$ is $(0, 1)$.

You can see from the graph that as the value of x approaches negative infinity $(-\infty)$ the value of the function approaches but never reaches 0. So the function has no zeros or x-intercepts. As the value of x approaches positive infinity $(+\infty)$ the value of the function approaches $+\infty$.

Also, the function is increasing on the interval $(-\infty, +\infty)$. There are no intervals of decrease because the graph is always increasing.

Using the points $\left(-2, \dfrac{1}{16}\right)$ and $(2, 16)$, the average rate of change over the interval $-2 \leq x \leq 2$ is $\dfrac{255}{64}$, or about 4.

Example 2 Graph $y = ab^x$ for $b > 1$

Graph the function.

a. $y = \left(\frac{4}{3}\right)^x$

b. $y = -\left(\frac{1}{3}\right) \cdot 3^x$

Solution

a. Plot $(0, 1)$ and $\left(1, \frac{4}{3}\right)$. From *left* to *right*, draw a curve that begins above the x-axis, passes through the two points, and moves up to the right.

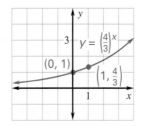

b. Plot $\left(0, -\frac{1}{3}\right)$ and $(1, -1)$. From *left* to *right*, draw a curve that begins just below below the x-axis, passes through the two points, and moves down to the right.

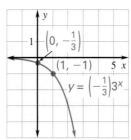

Example 3 Graph $y = ab^{x-h} + k$ for $b > 1$

Graph $y = 2 \cdot 3^{x+2} - 1$. State the domain and range.

Begin by sketching the graph of $y = 2 \cdot 3^x$, which passes through $(0, 2)$ and $(1, 6)$. Then translate the graph left 2 units and down 1 unit.

The asymptote of the graph is the line $y = -1$. The domain is all real numbers, and the range is $y > -1$.

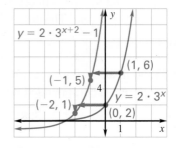

Guided Practice for Examples 1, 2, and 3

Graph the function. State the domain and range.

1. $y = 5^x$

2. $f(x) = \frac{1}{3} \cdot 4^x$

3. $y = 2^{x+1} - 1$

UNIT 4

MM2A2b Investigate and explain characteristics of exponential functions, including domain and range, asymptotes, zeros, intercepts, intervals of increase and decrease, rates of change, and end behavior.

MM2A2c Graph functions as transformations of $f(x) = a^x$.

MM2A2e Understand and use basic exponential functions as models of real phenomena.

Match the function with its graph.

1. $f(x) = \left(\dfrac{4}{3}\right)^x - 3$

2. $f(x) = 3^x + 2$

3. $f(x) = -4^{x+1} + 1$

A.

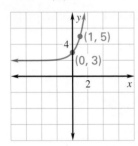

B.

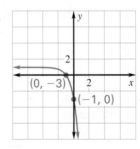

C.

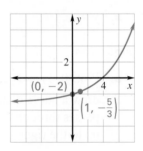

Graph the function. State the domain and range.

4. $f(x) = 4^{x-2}$

5. $f(x) = 2^x + 1$

6. $f(x) = -3^{x+1}$

7. $f(x) = 2^{x-2} - 3$

8. $f(x) = -2(3^{x+1}) + 2$

9. $f(x) = \left(\dfrac{3}{2}\right)^x - 2$

Describe **the end behavior of the graph of the function. If possible, find any intercepts. Find the average rate of change over the interval** $-2 \le x \le 2$.

10. $y = 6^x$

11. $y = \left(\dfrac{3}{2}\right)^x$

12. $y = -\dfrac{1}{2} \cdot 2^x$

In Exercises 13–15, use the following information.

Account Balance Compound interest is interest paid on the initial investment, called the principal, and on previously earned interest. Consider an initial principal P deposited in an account that pays interest at an annual rate, r (expressed as a decimal), compounded n times per year. The amount A in the account after t years is given by the equation $A = P\left(1 + \dfrac{r}{n}\right)^{nt}$.

You deposit $3500 in an account that earns 2.5% annual interest. Find the balance after one year if the interest is compounded with the given frequency.

13. annually

14. quarterly

15. monthly

In Exercises 16 and 17, use the following information.

Population From 1990 to 2000, the population of California can be modeled by $P = 29{,}816{,}591(1.0128)^t$ where t is the number of years since 1990.

16. What was the population in 1990?

17. What is the growth factor and annual percent increase?

LESSON
4.4

Exercise
Set B

MM2A2b Investigate and explain characteristics of exponential functions, including domain and range, asymptotes, zeros, intercepts, intervals of increase and decrease, rates of change, and end behavior.

MM2A2c Graph functions as transformations of $f(x) = a^x$.

MM2A2e Understand and use basic exponential functions as models of real phenomena.

Graph the function. State the domain and range.

1. $f(x) = 2^{x-1} - 3$

2. $f(x) = 4(2^x) + 1$

3. $f(x) = -2(3^{x+3}) + 3$

4. $f(x) = 7^{x-2} - 5$

5. $f(x) = -2\left(\frac{5}{2}\right)^{x+1} + 2$

6. $f(x) = 4\left(\frac{3}{2}\right)^{x-2} - \frac{3}{2}$

7. Find the average rate of change of the function $f(x) = 2(4)^x + 3$ over the interval $-2 \le x \le 2$.

Error Analysis **Describe** and correct the error in graphing the function.

8.

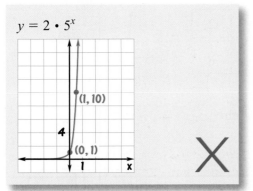

$y = 2 \cdot 5^x$

9.

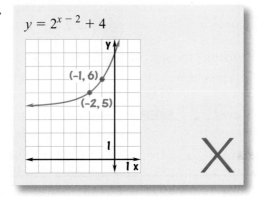

$y = 2^{x-2} + 4$

10. **Generate Equation** Write an exponential function of the form $y = ab^{x-h} + k$ whose graph has a y-intercept of 0 and an asymptote of $y = 3$.

In Exercises 11 and 12, refer to Exercises 13–15 on page 122 and use the following information.

Initial Deposit You want to have $10,000 in your account after five years. Find the amount your initial deposit should be for each of the following described situations.

11. The account pays 3.5% annual interest compounded monthly.

12. The account pays 2.75% annual interest compounded quarterly.

In Exercises 13–15, use the following information.

Population From 1990 to 2000, the population of Florida increased by 23.5%. The population in 2000 was 15,982,378.

13. What was the average annual percent increase from 1990 to 2000?

14. Write a model giving the population P of Florida t years after 1990.

15. Estimate the population in 2010.

Graph Exponential Decay Functions

Georgia Performance Standards: MM2A2b, MM2A2c, MM2A2e

Goal Graph and use exponential decay functions.

....

Vocabulary

An **exponential decay function** has the form $y = ab^x$, where $a > 0$ and $0 < b < 1$.

The base b of an exponential decay function is called the **decay factor.**

Example 1 **Graph $y = b^x$ for $0 < b < 1$**

Graph $y = \left(\dfrac{1}{3}\right)^x$. **Analyze the graph. Find the average rate of change over the interval $-2 \le x \le 2$.**

STEP 1 **Make** a table of values.

x	−2	−1	0	1	2
y	9	3	1	$\dfrac{1}{3}$	$\dfrac{1}{9}$

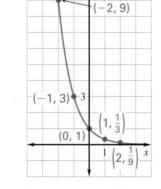

STEP 2 **Plot** the points from the table.

STEP 3 **Draw** from *right* to *left*, a smooth curve that begins just above the x-axis, passes through the plotted points, and moves up to the left.

STEP 4 **Examine** the graph. The y-intercept of the function is $(0, 1)$. As the value of x approaches $-\infty$ the value of the function approaches $+\infty$. As the value of x approaches $+\infty$ the value of the function approaches 0. So the function has no zeros or x-intercepts.

Also, the function is decreasing on the interval $(-\infty, +\infty)$. There are no intervals of increase because the graph is always decreasing.

Using the points $(-2, 9)$ and $\left(2, \dfrac{1}{9}\right)$, the average rate of change over the interval $-2 \le x \le 2$ is $-\dfrac{20}{9}$, or about -2.2.

Example 2 **Graph $y = ab^x$ for $0 < b < 1$**

Graph $y = 3\left(\dfrac{1}{4}\right)^x$.

Plot $(0, 3)$ and $\left(1, \dfrac{3}{4}\right)$. From *right* to *left*, draw a curve that begins just above the x-axis, passes through the two points, and moves up to the left.

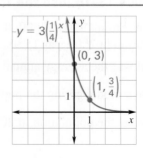

Georgia Performance Standards

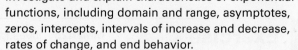

MM2A2b Investigate and explain characteristics of exponential functions, including domain and range, asymptotes, zeros, intercepts, intervals of increase and decrease, rates of change, and end behavior. ☑

MM2A2c Graph functions as transformations of $f(x) = a^x$. ☑

MM2A2e Understand and use basic exponential functions as models of real phenomena. ☑

Example 3 Graph $y = ab^{x-h} + k$ for $0 < b < 1$

Graph $y = 2\left(\dfrac{2}{3}\right)^{x-1} + 1$. State the domain and range.

Begin by sketching the graph of $y = 2\left(\dfrac{2}{3}\right)^{x}$ which passes through $(0, 2)$ and $\left(1, \dfrac{4}{3}\right)$. Then translate the graph right 1 unit and up 1 unit. The graph passes through $(1, 3)$ and $\left(2, \dfrac{7}{3}\right)$.

The asymptote of the graph is the line $y = 1$. The domain is all real numbers, and the range is $y > 1$.

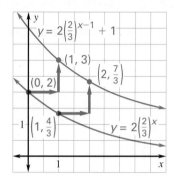

Guided Practice for Examples 1, 2, and 3

Graph the function. State the domain and range.

1. $y = \left(\dfrac{3}{5}\right)^{x}$

2. $f(x) = \left(\dfrac{3}{4}\right)^{x}$

3. $f(x) = -3\left(\dfrac{2}{3}\right)^{x}$

4. $y = 4\left(\dfrac{1}{4}\right)^{x}$

5. $f(x) = 2\left(\dfrac{1}{3}\right)^{x-2} + 3$

6. $y = 4\left(\dfrac{1}{2}\right)^{x+1} - 1$

Example 4 Find a value after depreciation

All-Terrain Vehicles A new all-terrain vehicle (ATV) costs $800. The value of the ATV decreases by 10% each year. Write an exponential decay model for the value of the ATV y (in dollars) after t years. Estimate the value after 5 years.

Solution

The initial amount is $800 and the percent decrease is $r = 0.10$. So, the exponential decay model is $y = a(1 - r)^t = 800(1 - 0.10)^t = 800(0.90)^t$. The value after 5 years is $y = 800(0.90)^5 = 472.39$ dollars.

Guided Practice for Example 4

7. Determine the value of a new ATV after 4 years if its original price is $550 and its value decreases by 7% each year.

Exercise Set A

MM2A2b Investigate and explain characteristics of exponential functions, including domain and range, asymptotes, zeros, intercepts, intervals of increase and decrease, rates of change, and end behavior.

MM2A2c Graph functions as transformations of $f(x) = a^x$.

MM2A2e Understand and use basic exponential functions as models of real phenomena.

Tell whether the function represents *exponential growth* or *exponential decay*.

1. $f(x) = \frac{5}{3}\left(\frac{4}{5}\right)^x$

2. $f(x) = \frac{3}{5}\left(\frac{5}{4}\right)^x$

3. $f(x) = 5(2)^{-x}$

Match the function with its graph.

4. $f(x) = \left(\frac{2}{3}\right)^{x+2}$

5. $f(x) = -\left(\frac{1}{2}\right)^x + 3$

6. $f(x) = 2\left(\frac{2}{3}\right)^{x-1} - 2$

A.

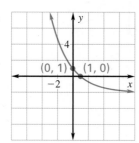

B.

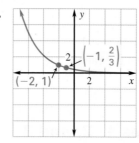

C.

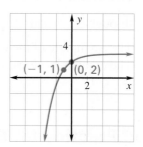

Graph the function. State the domain and range.

7. $f(x) = \left(\frac{1}{3}\right)^{x+1} + 2$

8. $f(x) = \left(\frac{1}{2}\right)^x - 3$

9. $f(x) = 3\left(\frac{1}{4}\right)^{x-2} + 1$

10. $f(x) = -\left(\frac{2}{3}\right)^x + 3$

11. $f(x) = 4\left(\frac{3}{4}\right)^{x+1} - 5$

12. $f(x) = -2\left(\frac{1}{6}\right)^{x-4} + 6$

Describe **the end behavior of the graph of the function. If possible, find any intercepts. Find the average rate of change over the interval −2 ≤ x ≤ 2.**

13. $y = \left(\frac{2}{3}\right)^x$

14. $y = \left(\frac{1}{2}\right)^x$

15. $y = -2\left(\frac{1}{3}\right)^x$

In Exercises 16–19, use the following information.

Depreciation You buy a new car for $22,500. The value of the car decreases by 25% each year.

16. Write an exponential decay model giving the car's value V (in dollars) after t years.

17. What is the value of the car after three years?

18. Graph the model.

19. In approximately how many years is the car worth $5300?

MM2A2b Investigate and explain characteristics of exponential functions, including domain and range, asymptotes, zeros, intercepts, intervals of increase and decrease, rates of change, and end behavior.

MM2A2c Graph functions as transformations of $f(x) = a^x$.

MM2A2e Understand and use basic exponential functions as models of real phenomena.

Tell whether the function represents *exponential growth* or *exponential decay*.

1. $f(x) = \left(\frac{5}{6}\right)^x$

2. $f(x) = \left(\frac{6}{5}\right)^x$

3. $f(x) = \left(\frac{5}{6}\right)^{-x}$

4. $f(x) = \left(\frac{6}{5}\right)^{-x}$

5. $f(x) = -\left(\frac{5}{6}\right)^{-x}$

6. $f(x) = -\left(\frac{6}{5}\right)^{-x}$

Graph the function. State the domain and range.

7. $f(x) = \left(\frac{1}{4}\right)^{x+3} - 2$

8. $f(x) = 4\left(\frac{1}{2}\right)^{x-1} - 3$

9. $f(x) = 3\left(\frac{3}{4}\right)^{x+2} + 1$

10. $f(x) = -3\left(\frac{2}{5}\right)^{x-2} + \frac{5}{2}$

11. $f(x) = \left(\frac{1}{4}\right)^{x+4} - 3$

12. $f(x) = -\left(\frac{3}{4}\right)^{x+2} + 5$

13. Open-Ended Write an exponential function whose graph lies between the graphs of $y = (0.4)^x$ and $y = (0.2)^x + 5$.

***Describe* the end behavior of the graph of the function. If possible, find any intercepts. Find the average rate of change over the interval $-2 \le x \le 2$.**

14. $y = \left(\frac{1}{4}\right)^x$

15. $y = \left(\frac{2}{7}\right)^x$

16. $y = -3\left(\frac{4}{5}\right)^x$

17. Error Analysis You invest $100 in the stock of a company. The value of the stock decreases 4% each year. *Describe* and correct the error in writing a model for the value of the stock after t years.

$$y = \left(\boxed{\begin{array}{c}\text{Initial}\\\text{amount}\end{array}}\right)\left(\boxed{\begin{array}{c}\text{Decay}\\\text{factor}\end{array}}\right)^t$$

$$y = 100(0.04)^t$$

X

In Exercises 18–20, use the following information.

Depreciation A manufacturing company purchases a piece of equipment for its assembly line for $175,000. The value of the equipment depreciates at a rate of 18% each year.

18. Write an exponential decay model for the value of the equipment.

19. What is the value of the equipment after ten years?

20. Graph the model. Estimate when the equipment will have a value of $65,000.

21. Lawn Mower Five years ago, you purchased a riding lawn mower for $1600. Recently, you resold the mower for $525. Assume that the value of the mower decays exponentially with time. Write an exponential decay model that gives the value V (in dollars) as a function of time t (in years) of the mower since you bought it.

UNIT 4

Solve Exponential Equations and Inequalities

Georgia Performance Standards: MM2A2d

Goal Solve exponential equations and inequalities.

Vocabulary

Exponential equations are equations in which variable expressions occur as exponents.

Exponential inequalities in one variable are inequalities that can be written in the form $ab^x + k < 0$, $ab^x + k > 0$, $ab^x + k \leq 0$, or $ab^x + k \geq 0$, where $a \neq 0$, $b > 0$, and $b \neq 1$.

Example 1 | **Solve by equating exponents**

Solve $125^x = 25^{x+1}$.

Solution

$125^x = 25^{x+1}$	Write original equation.
$(5^3)^x = (5^2)^{x+1}$	Rewrite 125 and 25 as powers with base 5.
$5^{3x} = 5^{2x+2}$	Power of a power property
$3x = 2x + 2$	Property of equality for exponential equations
$x = 2$	Solve for x.

The solution is 2.

Example 2 | **Solve an exponential equation by graphing**

Solve $4^x = \left(\dfrac{1}{2}\right)^{x-3}$.

Graph $y = 4^x$ and $y = \left(\dfrac{1}{2}\right)^{x-3}$ in the same coordinate plane. The graphs intersect only once, when $x = 1$. So, 1 is the only solution.

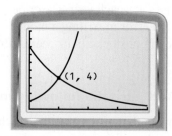

Guided Practice for Examples 1 and 2

Solve the equation.

1. $3^x = \left(\dfrac{1}{9}\right)^{x-3}$

2. $5^{3x+1} = 25^{x+1}$

3. $\left(\dfrac{1}{4}\right)^{x-1} = 2^{2x}$

Solve the equation using a graph.

4. $9^x = 3^{x+2}$

5. $4^{3x} = 2^{x+1}$

6. $2^{x+7} = 16^{x-2}$

Georgia Performance Standards

MM2A2d   Solve simple exponential equations and inequalities analytically, graphically, and by using appropriate technology.

Example 3   Solve an exponential inequality

Solve $4^{3z} \leq 8^{z+1}$.

$4^{3z} \leq 8^{z+1}$	Write original inequality.
$(2^2)^{3z} \leq (2^3)^{z+1}$	Rewrite each power with base 2.
$2^{6z} \leq 2^{3z+3}$	Power of a power property
$6z \leq 3z + 3$	Because $f(x) = 2^x$ is an increasing function, $f(x_1) \leq f(x_2)$ implies that $x_1 \leq x_2$.
$z \leq 1$	Solve for z.

The solution is $z \leq 1$.

Check Check that the solution is reasonable by substituting several values into the original inequality.

Substitute $z = -1$.   Substitute $z = 2$.

$4^{3(-1)} \overset{?}{\leq} 8^{-1+1}$ $4^{3(2)} \overset{?}{\leq} 8^{2+1}$

$\dfrac{1}{64} \leq 1$ ✓ $4096 \leq 512$ ✗

Because $z = -1$ is a solution of the inequality and $z = 2$ is not, the solution $z \leq 1$ is reasonable.

Example 4   Solve an exponential inequality by graphing

Solve $2^{2x+1} - 1 > -0.75$.

Graph $y = 2^{2x+1} - 1$ and $y = -0.75$ in the same coordinate plane. The graphs intersect only once, when $x = -1.5$.

The graph of $y = 2^{2x+1} - 1$ is above the graph of $y = -0.75$ when $x > -1.5$.

The solution is $x > -1.5$.

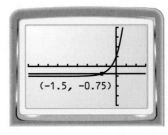

(−1.5, −0.75)

Guided Practice for Examples 3 and 4

Solve the inequality.

7. $8^x \geq 2^{2x+1}$

8. $4^{2x-5} \leq 64^{3x}$

9. $36^{5x+2} \geq \left(\dfrac{1}{6}\right)^{11-x}$

Solve the inequality using a graph.

10. $2^{4x-3} + 0.75 \geq 1$

11. $3^{3x-7} \geq 81^{12-3x}$

12. $25^{10x+8} \geq \left(\dfrac{1}{125}\right)^{4-2x}$

UNIT 4

LESSON
4.6
Exercise Set A

MM2A2d Solve simple exponential equations and inequalities analytically, graphically, and by using appropriate technology.

Solve the exponential equation.

1. $7^x = 7^{2x - 3}$

2. $3^{x + 1} = 3^{x + 1}$

3. $4^{2x} = 4^{x + 2}$

4. $2^{x + 1} = 16^{x + 2}$

5. $9^x = 3^{x + 4}$

6. $16^{x + 1} = 4^{4x + 1}$

7. $8^{x - 1} = 2^{x + 2}$

8. $9^{2x + 1} = 3^{5x - 1}$

9. $8^{5x} = 16^{3x + 4}$

Solve the exponential inequality.

10. $4^x \leq 4^{3x - 1}$

11. $9^{2x - 3} \leq 9^{x + 2}$

12. $2^{x + 3} \leq 16^{4x - 2}$

13. $9^x \geq 3^{x + 4}$

14. $2^{4x} \geq 8^{x + 5}$

15. $5^{2x + 2} \geq 25^{2x - 3}$

Solve the exponential equation or inequality using a graph.

16. $2^{x + 2} = 16^x$

17. $9^x = 3^{x + 27}$

18. $3^{x - 2} \leq 3^{2x + 4}$

19. **Error Analysis** *Describe* and correct the error in solving $2^x = \left(\dfrac{1}{2}\right)^{x - 4}$.

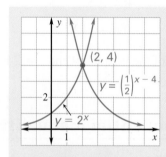

(2, 4)

$y = \left(\dfrac{1}{2}\right)^{x - 4}$

$y = 2^x$

The graphs intersect only once. So, 4 is the only solution.

20. **Multiple Choice** What is the solution of the equation $2^{x + 14} = 16^{2x}$?

A. 2   **B.** 4   **C.** 6   **D.** 8

21. **Open-Ended** Give an example of an exponential equation whose only solution is 4.

22. Fill in the missing steps and properties.

$3^{3x} = 9^{x + 1}$	Write original equation.
_____?_____	Rewrite the power with base 3.
$3^{3x} = 3^{2x + 2}$	_____?_____
$3x = 2x + 2$	_____?_____
_____?_____	Solve for x.

23. **Economics** From 1998 to 2003, the United States gross national product y (in billions of dollars) can be modeled by $y = 8882(1.04)^x$ where x is the number of years since 1998. For what years in this period was the gross national product greater than $9 trillion?

LESSON
4.6

**Exercise
Set B**

MM2A2d   Solve simple exponential equations and inequalities analytically, graphically, and by using appropriate technology.

Solve the exponential equation.

1. $9^{2x} = 27^{x-1}$

2. $5^{3x} = 25^{x-4}$

3. $100^{7x+1} = 1000^{3x-2}$

4. $2^{3x} = 4^{x-1}$

5. $9^{2x} = 3^{x-6}$

6. $81^{3-x} = \left(\dfrac{1}{3}\right)^{5x-6}$

7. $10^{x-3} = 100^{4x-5}$

8. $25^{x-1} = 125^{4x}$

9. $3^{x-7} = 27^{2x}$

Solve the exponential inequality.

10. $3^{3x+1} \le 3^{x-9}$

11. $8^{2x} \ge 8^{x+7}$

12. $5^{x-4} \le 25^{x-6}$

13. $7^{3x+4} \ge 49^{2x+1}$

14. $8^{x-1} \le 32^{3x-2}$

15. $27^{4x-1} \ge 9^{3x+8}$

Solve the exponential equation or inequality using a graph.

16. $9^{2x} = 3^{2x+4}$

17. $25^{x-4} = 5^{3x+1}$

18. $8^{x-1} \le \left(\dfrac{1}{2}\right)^{2x-1}$

19. $2^{3x} = 64$

20. $4^x + 5 \ge 21$

21. $\left(\dfrac{1}{3}\right)^x - 9 < 18$

22. **Error Analysis** *Describe* and correct the error in solving the equation.

$$3^{x+4} = 9^{2x-5}$$
$$3^{x+4} = (3^3)^{2x-5}$$
$$3^{x+4} = 3^{6x-15}$$
$$x + 4 = 6x - 15$$
$$\frac{19}{5} = x$$

23. **Multiple Representations** The number of items purchased from an auction website by two individuals can be modeled by $y = 8^x$ and $y = 2^{2x+1}$ where y is the number of items purchased and x is the number of months.

   a. **Drawing a Graph** Graph the functions using a graphing calculator.

   b. **Interpreting a Graph** After how many months will each individual purchase the same number of items?

   c. **Solving an Equation** Check your result by solving $8^x = 2^{2x+1}$.

24. **Baseball Cards** You are collecting baseball cards of players. The number of cards you have can be modeled by $y = 25^x$ where y is the number of cards collected and x is the number of years. For how many years after you started your collection will you have 125 or fewer cards?

Georgia Performance Standards

MM2A2d Solve simple exponential equations and inequalities analytically, graphically, and by using appropriate technology.

Technology Activity

Using Technology to Solve Exponential Equations and Inequalities

Use after Lesson 4.6

Question

How can you use technology to solve exponential equations and inequalities?

One way to solve an exponential equation or inequality is to make a table of values.

Example 1

Solve $2^{x+2} = 4^x$.

STEP 1 **Enter** the functions $y = 2^{x+2}$ and $y = 4x$ into a graphing calculator.

STEP 2 **Create** a table of values for the functions.

STEP 3 **Scroll** through the table to find a value of x where $Y_1 = Y_2$. The table in Step 2 shows that $Y_1 = 16$ and $Y_2 = 16$ when $x = 2$. The solution is $x = 2$.

Example 2

Solve $2^x \le 4^{x+1}$.

STEP 1 **Enter** the functions $y = 2^x$ and $y = 4^{x+1}$ into a graphing calculator.

STEP 2 **Create** a table of values for the functions.

STEP 3 **Scroll** through the table to find that $Y_1 \le Y_2$ when $x \ge -2$. The solution of $2^x \le 4^{x+1}$ is $x \ge -2$.

Practice

Solve the equation or inequality using a table.

1. $3^{x+2} = 9^{x-1}$

2. $6^{x-16} = 36^{2x+4}$

3. $3^{2x+2} \le 27^{x-3}$

4. $5^{6x-12} \ge 25^{2x-4}$

Define and Use Sequences and Series

Georgia Performance Standards: MM2A3d

Goal Recognize and write rules for number patterns.

Vocabulary

A **sequence** is a function whose domain is a set of consecutive integers. If a domain is not specified, it is understood that the domain starts with 1. The values in the range are called the **terms** of the sequence. A *finite sequence* has a limited number of terms. An *infinite sequence* continues without stopping. A sequence can be specified by an equation, or *rule*.

When the terms of a sequence are added together, the resulting expression is a **series.** **Summation notation,** or **sigma notation,** is used to write a series. For example, in the series $\sum_{i=1}^{4} 2i$, i is the *index of summation*, 1 is the *lower limit of summation*, and 4 is the *upper limit of summation*.

Example 1 **Write terms of sequences**

Write the first six terms of (a) $a_n = 4n + 3$ and (b) $a_n = (-1)^{n+1}$.

Solution

Because no domain is specified, begin with $n = 1$.

a. $a_1 = 4(1) + 3 = 7$
$a_2 = 4(2) + 3 = 11$
$a_3 = 4(3) + 3 = 15$
$a_4 = 4(4) + 3 = 19$
$a_5 = 4(5) + 3 = 23$
$a_6 = 4(6) + 3 = 27$

b. $a_1 = (-1)^{1+1} = 1$
$a_2 = (-1)^{2+1} = -1$
$a_3 = (-1)^{3+1} = 1$
$a_4 = (-1)^{4+1} = -1$
$a_5 = (-1)^{5+1} = 1$
$a_6 = (-1)^{6+1} = -1$

Guided Practice for Example 1

Write the first six terms of the sequence.

1. $a_n = n - 2$ **2.** $a_n = 5n - 3$ **3.** $a_n = 2^n$ **4.** $a_n = \dfrac{(-1)^n}{n}$

Example 2 **Write rules for sequences**

Describe the pattern, write the next term, and write a rule for the *n*th term of the sequence 2, 6, 12, 20, ...

Solution

You can write the terms as 1(2), 2(3), 3(4), 4(5), ... The next term is $a_5 = 5(6) = 30$. A rule for the *n*th term is $a_n = n(n + 1)$.

Georgia Performance Standards

MM2A3d   Explore arithmetic series and various ways of
computing their sums.

Guided Practice for Example 2

For the sequence, describe the pattern, write the next term, and write a rule for the nth term.

5. $3, 6, 9, 12, \ldots$

6. $\dfrac{1}{1}, \dfrac{1}{3}, \dfrac{1}{5}, \dfrac{1}{7}, \ldots$

7. $-4, -3, -2, -1, \ldots$

8. $\dfrac{2}{3}, \dfrac{3}{4}, \dfrac{4}{5}, \dfrac{5}{6}, \ldots$

Example 3 Write series using summation notation

Write the series using summation notation.

a. $1 + 4 + 9 + 16 + \cdots$

b. $\dfrac{1}{3} + \dfrac{2}{4} + \dfrac{3}{5} + \cdots + \dfrac{9}{11}$

Solution

a. Notice that the first term is 1^2, the second is 2^2, the third is 3^2, and the fourth is 4^2. So, the terms of the series can be written as:

$a_i = i^2$ where $i = 1, 2, 3, 4, \ldots$

The lower limit of summation is 1 and the upper limit of summation is infinity.

The summation notation for the series is $\displaystyle\sum_{i=1}^{\infty} i^2$.

b. Notice that for each term the denominator of the fraction is 2 more than the numerator. So, the terms of the series can be written as:

$a_i = \dfrac{i}{i+2}$ where $i = 1, 2, 3, 4, \ldots, 9$

The lower limit of summation is 1 and the upper limit of summation is 9.

The summation notation for the series is $\displaystyle\sum_{i=1}^{9} \dfrac{i}{i+2}$.

Guided Practice for Example 3

Write the series using summation notation.

9. $5 + 6 + 7 + \cdots + 12$

10. $4 + 8 + 12 + \cdots$

11. $\dfrac{1}{3} + \dfrac{2}{4} + \dfrac{3}{5} + \cdots + \dfrac{12}{14}$

12. $3 + 5 + 7 + \cdots$

UNIT 4

LESSON
4.7

Exercise
Set A

MM2A3d   Explore arithmetic series and various ways of
computing their sums.

Write the first six terms of the sequence.

1. $a_n = n^2 + 6$

2. $a_n = n^2 - 3$

3. $a_n = 3^{n+1}$

4. $f(n) = 2^{n-1}$

5. $f(n) = -\dfrac{4}{3n}$

6. $f(n) = \dfrac{n}{3n+2}$

For the sequence, describe the pattern, write the next term, and write a rule for the nth term.

7. $2, 4, 8, 16, \ldots$

8. $1, 8, 27, 64, \ldots$

9. $\dfrac{1}{1}, \dfrac{1}{4}, \dfrac{1}{9}, \dfrac{1}{16}, \ldots$

10. $\dfrac{4}{3}, \dfrac{5}{3}, \dfrac{6}{3}, \dfrac{7}{3}, \ldots$

11. $3, 5, 7, 9, \ldots$

12. $\dfrac{4}{2}, \dfrac{8}{3}, \dfrac{12}{4}, \dfrac{16}{5}, \ldots$

13. $0.7, 1.3, 1.9, 2.5, \ldots$

14. $1.0, 0.5, 0.0, -0.5, \ldots$

Graph the sequence.

15. $1, 2, 3, 4, 5$

16. $2, 4, 6, 8, 10$

17. $\dfrac{1}{2}, 1, \dfrac{3}{2}, 2, \dfrac{5}{2}$

Write the series using summation notation.

18. $-2 + 1 + 6 + 13 + 22 + \cdots$

19. $\dfrac{2}{4} + \dfrac{4}{5} + \dfrac{6}{6} + \dfrac{8}{7}$

20. $\dfrac{1}{5} + \dfrac{2}{6} + \dfrac{3}{7} + \dfrac{4}{8} + \dfrac{5}{9} + \dfrac{6}{10}$

21. $3 + 8 + 13 + 18 + 23 + \cdots$

Find the sum of the series.

22. $\displaystyle\sum_{k=4}^{8} 3k - 2$

23. $\displaystyle\sum_{i=2}^{4} i^2 + i + 4$

24. $\displaystyle\sum_{i=1}^{8} i$

25. **Error Analysis** *Describe* and correct the error in finding the sum of the series.

$$\sum_{i=0}^{4} (3i + 4) = 7 + 10 + 13 + 16 = 46$$

26. **Jacket** You want to save $30 to buy a jacket. You begin by saving a dollar in the first week. You plan to save an additional dollar each week after that. For example, you will save $2 in the second week, $3 in the third week, and so on. How many weeks must you save to have saved $30?

UNIT 4

MM2A3d Explore arithmetic series and various ways of computing their sums.

Write the first six terms of the sequence.

1. $a_n = (n + 1)^2$

2. $f(n) = \dfrac{3n}{3n - 2}$

3. $a_n = \dfrac{2n}{3n + 5}$

For the sequence, describe the pattern, write the next term, and write a rule for the nth term.

4. $2, 6, 12, 20, 30, \ldots$

5. $6.6, 5.5, 4.4, 3.3, \ldots$

6. $0.3, -1.7, 3.1, -4.5, \ldots$

Graph the first five terms of the sequence.

7. $a_n = \dfrac{1}{n^2}$

8. $f(n) = (-1)^n(6 - n)$

9. $a_n = 9 - 0.4n(n - 1)$

Write the series using summation notation.

10. $36 + 30 + 24 + 18 + 12$

11. $-3 + 9 - 27 + 81 - \cdots$

12. $2.8 + 3.4 + 4.0 + 4.6 + \cdots$

13. $3 + 5 + 9 + 17 + 33$

14. $\dfrac{5}{6} + \dfrac{6}{7} + \dfrac{7}{8} + \dfrac{8}{9} + \cdots$

15. $\dfrac{2}{3} + \dfrac{4}{9} + \dfrac{8}{27} + \dfrac{16}{81}$

Find the sum of the series.

16. $\displaystyle\sum_{n=1}^{5} n^3 - 1$

17. $\displaystyle\sum_{i=2}^{6} \dfrac{i}{i + 4}$

18. $\displaystyle\sum_{k=1}^{4} \dfrac{k^2}{k + 1}$

Tell whether the statement about summation notation is *true* or *false*. If the statement is true, prove it. If it is false, give a counterexample.

19. $\displaystyle\sum_{i=1}^{n} (a_i + k) = nk + \sum_{i=1}^{n} a_i$

20. $\displaystyle\sum_{i=1}^{n} (ka_i + r) = nr + nk \sum_{i=1}^{n} a_i$

21. Bouncing Ball You drop a hard rubber ball from a height of five feet. The height reached by the ball after each bounce is 90 percent of the previous height.

    a. Write a rule for the nth term of the sequence of heights (in inches) reached by the ball.

    b. After how many bounces is the height of the ball under 3 feet?

    c. Assume that the ball makes an infinite number of bounces. Use summation notation to represent the total vertical distance traveled by the ball.

22. Retail Displays You work in a grocery store and are stacking oranges in a pyramid whose base is an equilateral triangle. The number a_n of oranges per layer is given by $a_n = \dfrac{n(n + 1)}{2}$ where $n = 1$ represents the top layer.

    a. How many oranges are in the fourth layer?

    b. How many oranges are in a stack with seven layers?

Investigating Math Activity
Calculate the Sum of an Arithmetic Sequence

Use before Lesson 4.8

Question

What is the relationship between the first and last term of an arithmetic sequence and the sum of all of the terms?

An *arithmetic sequence* is a sequence in which the difference of consecutive terms is constant. This constant difference is known as the *common difference.* An example of an arithmetic sequence would be 2, 4, 6, 8, . . . because it has a common difference of 2. The sequence 1, 3, 7, 13, . . . is not an arithmetic sequence, because it does not have a common difference.

Explore Calculate the sum of the terms of an arithmetic sequence.

Find the sum of the terms of the given arithmetic sequence.

   a. 2, 5, 8, 11, 14   **b.** 1, 8, 15, 22   **c.** −1, 1, 3

STEP 1 **Add** the given terms of the sequence to find the sum for those terms.

STEP 2 **Calculate** the average of the first and last terms of the sequence.

STEP 3 **Multiply** the average found in Step 2 by the number of terms in the sequence.

STEP 4 **Record** your answers in a table.

Sequence	Sum	Average of first and last term	Average × number of terms
2, 5, 8, 11, 14	40	8	40
?	?	?	?
?	?	?	?

Draw Conclusions

1. Copy and complete the table above.

2. **Reasoning** *Compare* your answers from Steps 1 and 3. What do you notice?

3. **Writing** Write a rule that explains how to calculate the sum of the first *n* terms of a sequence without adding all of the terms.

4. Write a formula for the rule you gave in Exercise 3. Use a_1 to represent the first term, a_n to represent the last term, and *n* to represent the number of terms.

5. Use your formula to find the sum of the terms in the sequence 3, 9, 15, 21.

Analyze Arithmetic Sequences and Series

Georgia Performance Standards: MM2A3d, MM2A3e

Goal Study arithmetic sequences and series.

Vocabulary

In an **arithmetic sequence,** the difference of consecutive terms is constant. This constant difference is called the **common difference** and is denoted by d. The nth term of an arithmetic sequence with first term a_1 and common difference d is given by:

$$a_n = a_1 + (n-1)d$$

The expression formed by adding the terms of an arithmetic sequence is called an **arithmetic series.** The sum of the first n terms of an arithmetic series is:

$$S_n = n\left(\frac{a_1 + a_n}{2}\right)$$

In words, S_n is the mean of the first and nth terms, multiplied by the number of terms.

The sum of the first n terms of an infinite sequence is the *nth partial sum.*

Example 1   Identify arithmetic sequences

Tell whether the sequence 2, 11, 20, 29, 38, . . . is arithmetic.

Find the differences of consecutive terms. If the differences are constant, then the sequence is arithmetic.

$a_2 - a_1 = 11 - 2 = 9$ $a_3 - a_2 = 20 - 11 = 9$

$a_4 - a_3 = 29 - 20 = 9$ $a_5 - a_4 = 38 - 29 = 9$

Each difference is 9, so the sequence is arithmetic.

Example 2   Write a rule for the nth term

**Write a rule for the nth term of the sequence 2, 11, 20, 29, 38, ...
Then find a_{15}.**

The sequence is arithmetic with first term $a_1 = 2$ and common difference $d = 11 - 2 = 9$. So, a rule for the nth term is:

$$a_n = a_1 + (n-1)d = 2 + (n-1)9 = -7 + 9n$$

The 15th term is $a_{15} = -7 + 9(15) = -7 + 135 = 128$.

Guided Practice for Examples 1 and 2

1. Tell whether the sequence 4, 8, 16, 22, 32, . . . is arithmetic.

Write a rule for the nth term of the sequence. Then find a_{15}.

2. 19, 23, 27, 31, 35, . . .   **3.** 5, 7, 9, 11, 13, . . .   **4.** 4, 3, 2, 1, 0, . . .

Georgia Performance Standards

MM2A3d Explore arithmetic series and various ways of computing their sums.

MM2A3e Explore sequences of partial sums of arithmetic series as examples of quadratic functions.

Example 3 **Find the sum of an arithmetic series**

Find the sum of the first 50 terms of the arithmetic series
$3 + 6 + 9 + 12 + 15 + \cdots$.

The sequence is arithmetic with first term $a_1 = 3$ and common difference $d = 6 - 3 = 3$. So, a rule for the nth term is:

$a_n = a_1 + (n - 1)d$	Write general rule.
$\quad = 3 + (n - 1)3$	Substitute 3 for a_1 and 3 for d.
$\quad = 3n$	Simplify.

The 50th term is $a_{50} = 3(50) = 150$. The sum of the first 50 terms is:

$S_{50} = 50\left(\dfrac{a_1 + a_{50}}{2}\right)$	Write rule for S_{50}.
$\quad = 50\left(\dfrac{3 + 150}{2}\right)$	Substitute 3 for a_1 and 150 for a_{50}.
$\quad = 3825$	Simplify.

The sum of the first 50 terms is 3825.

Example 4 **Find a formula for the sum of a series**

Find a formula for the sum of the series
$1 + 2 + 3 + \cdots + (n - 2) + (n - 1) + n$.

The sequence is arithmetic with first term $a_1 = 1$ and common difference $d = 2 - 1 = 1$. So, a rule for the nth term is:

$$a_n = a_1 + (n - 1)d = 1 + (n - 1)1 = n$$

The sum of the first n terms is:

$S_n = n\left(\dfrac{a_1 + a_n}{2}\right)$	Write rule for S_n.
$\quad = n\left(\dfrac{1 + n}{2}\right)$	Substitute 1 for a_1 and n for a_n.

S_n represents the partial sum of the first n terms of this series. Note that S_n is a quadratic function that can be written as $S_n = n\left(\dfrac{1 + n}{2}\right) = \dfrac{1}{2}n^2 + \dfrac{1}{2}n$.

Guided Practice for Examples 3 and 4

Find the sum of the first n terms of the arithmetic series.

5. $2 + 3 + 4 + 5 + \cdots$; $n = 19$ **6.** $25 + 35 + 45 + 55 + \cdots$; $n = 50$

7. Find a formula for the partial sum of this series:
$1 + 3 + 5 + \cdots + (2n - 5) + (2n - 3) + (2n - 1)$

UNIT 4

Exercise Set A

MM2A3d Explore arithmetic series and various ways of computing their sums.

MM2A3e Explore sequences of partial sums of arithmetic series as examples of quadratic functions.

Tell whether the sequence is arithmetic. *Explain* why or why not.

1. $2, -5, -12, -19, -26$

2. $3, 5.5, 8, 10.5, 13$

3. $0, -5, -10, -12, -20$

4. $2, 4, 8, 16, 32$

5. $1, 2, 4, 7, 11$

6. $\dfrac{3}{4}, \dfrac{7}{8}, 1, \dfrac{9}{8}, \dfrac{5}{4}$

Write a rule for the *n*th term of the arithmetic sequence. Then find a_{10}.

7. $-4, 2, 8, 14, 20$

8. $-25, -29, -33, -37, -41$

9. $\dfrac{1}{4}, 0, -\dfrac{1}{4}, -\dfrac{1}{2}, -\dfrac{3}{4}$

10. $d = 5, a_5 = 33$

Write a rule for the *n*th term of the arithmetic sequence that has the two given terms.

11. $a_{20} = 240, a_{15} = 170$

12. $a_6 = 13, a_{14} = 25$

13. $a_9 = -14, a_{15} = -20$

14. $a_8 = -44, a_5 = -32$

15. $a_{16} = 6, a_{20} = 7$

16. $a_7 = \dfrac{6}{7}, a_9 = \dfrac{2}{3}$

Find the sum of the arithmetic series.

17. $\displaystyle\sum_{i=1}^{8} (3i - 1)$

18. $\displaystyle\sum_{i=1}^{20} (-2i + 14)$

19. $\displaystyle\sum_{i=1}^{15} (-i - 6)$

20. Multiple Choice Which formula represents the partial sum of the first n terms of the series: $1 + 4 + 7 + \cdots + (3n - 2)$?

A. $S_n = \dfrac{3}{2}n^2 - \dfrac{1}{2}n$ **B.** $S_n = n^2 - n$ **C.** $S_n = \dfrac{1}{2}n^2 - n$ **D.** $S_n = n^2$

Write a rule for the sequence whose graph is shown.

21.

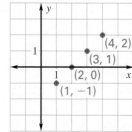

22.

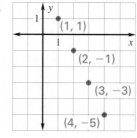

23.

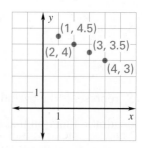

24. Auditorium An auditorium has 25 rows. The first row has 10 seats, and each row after the first has 1 more seat than the row before it.

  a. Write a rule for the number of seats in the *n*th row.

  b. Find the total number of seats in the auditorium.

UNIT 4

MM2A3d Explore arithmetic series and various ways of computing their sums.

MM2A3e Explore sequences of partial sums of arithmetic series as examples of quadratic functions.

Tell whether the sequence is arithmetic. *Explain* why or why not.

1. $17, 35, 57, 75, 97, \ldots$

2. $9, 6, 3, 0, 3, 6, 9, \ldots$

3. $23, -12, -47, -82, \ldots$

Write a rule for the *n*th term of the arithmetic sequence. Then find a_{22}.

4. $-12, -5, 2, 9, \ldots$

5. $45, 31, 17, 3, \ldots$

6. $\dfrac{5}{8}, \dfrac{5}{4}, \dfrac{15}{8}, \dfrac{5}{2}, \ldots$

7. $d = -11 \ a_{13} = 99$

8. $d = 14, a_6 = -10$

9. $d = 3.8, a_8 = 76.4$

Write a rule for the *n*th term of the arithmetic sequence that has the two given terms.

10. $a_{11} = 29, a_{20} = 101$

11. $a_6 = -31, a_{14} = -135$

12. $a_7 = 21, a_{13} = 42$

13. $a_6 = 43, a_{15} = 107.8$

14. $a_{10} = 2, a_{22} = -8.8$

15. $a_8 = \dfrac{19}{5}, a_{12} = \dfrac{27}{5}$

Tell whether it is possible that the sequence with the three given terms is arithmetic. *Explain* why or why not.

16. $a_2 = 8, a_4 = 16, a_6 = 26$

17. $a_3 = 21, a_5 = 27, a_{12} = 48$

18. $a_2 = 0, a_3 = -5, a_9 = -35$

Find the sum of the arithmetic series.

19. $\displaystyle\sum_{i=1}^{8} (2i + 5)$

20. $\displaystyle\sum_{i=1}^{10} (i - 3)$

21. $\displaystyle\sum_{i=1}^{7} (3i - 8)$

22. $\displaystyle\sum_{i=1}^{9} (5 - 6i)$

23. $\displaystyle\sum_{i=1}^{9} (25 - 6i)$

24. $\displaystyle\sum_{i=1}^{15} \dfrac{3}{4} i$

Find the value of *n*.

25. $\displaystyle\sum_{i=1}^{n} (-3 + i) = 18$

26. $\displaystyle\sum_{i=1}^{n} (5i + 3) = 161$

27. $\displaystyle\sum_{i=1}^{n} 3i = 198$

28. Multiple Representations The distance D (in feet) that an object falls in t seconds can be modeled by $D(t) = 16t^2$.

   a. Making a Table Let $d(n)$ represent the distance the object falls in the *n*th second. Make a table of values showing $d(1)$, $d(2)$, $d(3)$, and $d(4)$. (*Hint:* The distance $d(1)$ that the object falls in the first second is $D(1) - D(0)$.)

   b. Writing a Rule Write a rule for the sequence of distances given by $d(n)$.

   c. Drawing a Graph Graph the sequence from part (b).

LESSON 4.8

Problem Solving Workshop

Problem The first row of a concert hall has 25 seats and each row after the first has one more seat than the row before it. Write a rule for the number of seats in the *n*th row. What is the total number of seats if the concert hall has 32 rows of seats?

STEP 1 Read and Understand

What do you know? The number of seats in each row and the number of rows

What do you want to find out? The total number of seats in the concert hall

STEP 2 Make a Plan Use the rule for the sum of an arithmetic series to solve the problem.

STEP 3 Solve the Problem Starting with the first row, the number of seats in the rows are 25, 26, 27, 28, ... These numbers form an arithmetic sequence with a first term of 25 and a common difference of 1. So, a rule for the sequence is:

$$a_n = a_1 + (n - 1)d \qquad \text{Write general rule.}$$

$$= 25 + (n - 1)1 \qquad \text{Substitute 25 for } a_1 \text{ and 1 for } d.$$

$$= 24 + n \qquad \text{Simplify.}$$

Find the sum of an arithmetic series with first term $a_1 = 25$ and last term $a_{32} = 24 + 32 = 56$.

$$\text{Total number of seats} = S_{32} = 32\left(\frac{a_1 + a_{32}}{2}\right) = 32\left(\frac{25 + 56}{2}\right) = 1296$$

STEP 4 Look Back You can check this by using the *summation* feature of a graphing calculator to find the sum of the first 32 terms of the sequence $a_n = 24 + n$. The screen shows that the sum is 1296.

```
sum(seq(24+n,n,1,32)
                  1296
```

Practice

1. **What If?** In the Example, suppose nine more rows of seats are added (where each row has one more seat than the row before it). How many additional seats will the concert hall have?

2. **Stacking Logs** Logs are stacked on top of each other in a pile. The bottom row has 21 logs and the top row has 15 logs. Each row has one less log than the row below it. How many logs are in the pile?

3. **Taxi** You enter a taxi that charges an initial fee of $2 and you watch the meter for the total cost of the ride. After 1 mile, the total cost is $3.50. After 2 miles, the total cost is $5. After 3 miles, the total cost is $6.50. Write a rule for the total cost a_n of a taxi ride for *n* miles. What is the total cost of a taxi ride for 13 miles?

Analyze Geometric Sequences and Series

Georgia Performance Standards: MM2A2f, MM2A2g

Goal Study geometric sequences and series.

Vocabulary

In a **geometric sequence,** the ratio of any term to the previous term is constant. This constant ratio is called the **common ratio** and is denoted by r. The nth term of a geometric sequence with first term a_1 and common ratio r is given by:

$$a_n = a_1 r^{n-1}$$

The expression formed by adding the terms of a geometric sequence is called a **geometric series.** The sum of the first n terms of a geometric series with common ratio $r \neq 1$ is:

$$S_n = a_1 \left(\frac{1 - r^n}{1 - r} \right)$$

Example 1 **Identify geometric sequences**

Tell whether the sequence 4, 8, 16, 32, 64, . . . is geometric.

Find the ratios of consecutive terms. If the ratios are constant, then the sequence is geometric.

$$\frac{a_2}{a_1} = \frac{8}{4} = 2 \qquad \frac{a_3}{a_2} = \frac{16}{8} = 2 \qquad \frac{a_4}{a_3} = \frac{32}{16} = 2 \qquad \frac{a_5}{a_4} = \frac{64}{32} = 2$$

Each ratio is 2, so the sequence is geometric.

Example 2 **Write a rule for the nth term**

Write a rule for the nth term of the sequence 6, 24, 96, 384, ... Then find a_7.

The sequence is geometric with first term $a_1 = 6$ and common ratio $r = \frac{24}{6} = 4$.

So, a rule for the nth term is:

$$a_n = a_1 r^{n-1} \qquad \text{Write general rule.}$$
$$= 6(4)^{n-1} \qquad \text{Substitute 6 for } a_1 \text{ and 4 for } r.$$

The 7th term is $a_7 = 6(4)^{7-1} = 6(4)^6 = 24{,}576$.

Guided Practice for Examples 1 and 2

1. Tell whether the sequence 3, 7, 11, 15, 19, . . . is geometric.

Write a rule for the nth term of the geometric sequence. Then find a_7.

2. 1, 6, 36, 216, 1296, . . .   **3.** 7, 14, 28, 56, 128, . . .

UNIT 4

Example 3   Write a rule given a term and common ratio

One term of a geometric sequence is $a_3 = 18$. The common ratio is $r = 3$.

a. Write a rule for the nth term.   **b.** Graph the sequence.

Solution

a. Use the general rule to find the first term.

$a_n = a_1 r^{n-1}$ Write general rule.

$a_3 = a_1 r^{3-1}$ Substitute 3 for n.

$18 = a_1 (3)^2$ Substitute 18 for a_3 and 3 for r.

$2 = a_1$ Solve for a_1.

So a rule for the nth term is $a_n = 2(3)^{n-1}$.

b. Create a table of values for the sequence. The graph of the first 5 terms of the sequence is shown. Notice that the points lie on an exponential curve. Recall that an exponential function has the form $y = ab^x$. An exponential function for this geometric sequence is given by $y = 2(3)^{x-1}$ where x is all whole numbers. Notice that the common ratio of the sequence is the same as the base of the exponential function.

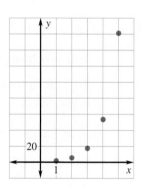

n	1	2	3	4	5
a_n	2	6	18	54	162

Example 4   Find the sum of a geometric series

Find the sum of the geometric series $\sum_{i=1}^{10} 3(2)^{i-1}$.

$a_1 = 3(2)^{1-1} = 3, r = 2$

$S_{10} = a_1 \left(\dfrac{1 - r^{10}}{1 - r} \right) = 3 \left(\dfrac{1 - 2^{10}}{1 - 2} \right) = 3069$

The sum of the series is 3069.

Guided Practice for Examples 3 and 4

4. One term of a geometric sequence is $a_3 = 16$. The common ratio is $r = 4$. Write a rule for the nth term.

5. Find the sum of the geometric series $\sum_{i=1}^{12} 2(4)^{i-1}$.

Exercise Set A

MM2A2f Understand and recognize geometric sequences as exponential functions with domains that are whole numbers.

MM2A2g Interpret the constant ratio in a geometric sequence as the base of the associated exponential function.

Tell whether the sequence is geometric. *Explain* **why or why not.**

1. $3, 5, 7, 9, 11, \ldots$

2. $5, 10, 20, 40, 80, \ldots$

3. $100, 50, 25, \dfrac{25}{2}, \dfrac{25}{4}, \ldots$

4. $1, 3, 7, 15, 31, \ldots$

5. $3, 9, 27, 81, 243, \ldots$

6. $-6, -2, -\dfrac{2}{3}, -\dfrac{2}{9}, -\dfrac{2}{27}, \ldots$

Write a rule for the *n*th term of the geometric sequence. Find a_6. Then graph the first five terms of the sequence.

7. $r = 3, a_1 = 2$

8. $r = \dfrac{1}{10}, a_2 = 4$

9. $r = -\dfrac{1}{2}, a_3 = 8$

Error Analysis *Describe* **and correct the error in writing the rule for the *n*th term of the geometric sequence for which $a_1 = 4$ and $r = 3$.**

10.

$$a_n = a_1 r^n$$
$$a_n = 4(3)^n$$

✗

11.

$$a_n = r a_1^{\,n-1}$$
$$a_n = 3(4)^{n-1}$$

✗

Write a rule for the *n*th term of the geometric sequence that has the two given terms.

12. $a_1 = 1, a_3 = 9$

13. $a_3 = 24, a_5 = 96$

14. $a_2 = 2, a_6 = 512$

15. $a_2 = 2, a_5 = \dfrac{1}{4}$

16. $a_3 = 25, a_6 = -\dfrac{25}{64}$

17. $a_4 = -\dfrac{8}{9}, a_7 = -\dfrac{64}{243}$

Find the sum of the geometric series.

18. $\displaystyle\sum_{i=1}^{5} 3(2)^{i-1}$

19. $\displaystyle\sum_{i=1}^{8} 90\left(\dfrac{1}{3}\right)^{i-1}$

20. $\displaystyle\sum_{i=1}^{10} 32\left(\dfrac{1}{2}\right)^{i-1}$

21. $\displaystyle\sum_{i=1}^{10} 8(3)^{i-1}$

22. $\displaystyle\sum_{i=0}^{7} 2\left(\dfrac{3}{2}\right)^{i-1}$

23. $\displaystyle\sum_{i=0}^{10} 1000\left(\dfrac{1}{2}\right)^{i-1}$

24. Retirement You invest $20,000 in a retirement plan. The plan is expected to have an annual return of 12%. Write a rule for the amount of money a_n available in the plan at the beginning of the *n*th year. What is the balance of the account at the beginning of the 20th year?

LESSON
4.9

Exercise Set B

MM2A2f Understand and recognize geometric sequences as exponential functions with domains that are whole numbers.

MM2A2g Interpret the constant ratio in a geometric sequence as the base of the associated exponential function.

Tell whether the sequence is geometric. *Explain* why or why not.

1. $0.8, 1, 8, 64, \ldots$

2. $\dfrac{3}{28}, \dfrac{3}{7}, \dfrac{12}{7}, \dfrac{48}{7}, \ldots$

3. $31, 213, 4459, 637, 91, \ldots$

Write a rule for the *n*th term of the geometric sequence. Then find a_6.

4. $13, 104, 832, 6656, \ldots$

5. $3.125, 10, 32, 102.4, \ldots$

6. $-43.2, -36, -30, -25, \ldots$

7. $35, -7, \dfrac{7}{5}, -\dfrac{7}{25}, \ldots$

8. $2808, 468, 78, 13, \ldots$

9. $-\dfrac{34}{3}, \dfrac{68}{9}, -\dfrac{136}{27}, \dfrac{272}{81}, \ldots$

Write a rule for the *n*th term of the geometric sequence. Then find a_5.

10. $a_1 = 17, r = -2$

11. $a_4 = -3, r = -2$

12. $a_3 = -144, r = 0.5$

13. $a_4 = \dfrac{1}{27}, r = \dfrac{4}{3}$

14. $a_4 = \dfrac{189}{1000}, r = \dfrac{3}{5}$

15. $a_3 = -28, r = \dfrac{7}{3}$

Write a rule for the *n*th term of the geometric sequence that has the two given terms.

16. $a_2 = 36, a_4 = 576$

17. $a_2 = -153, a_4 = -17$

18. $a_4 = 351, a_7 = 13$

19. $a_3 = 5, a_6 = 5000$

20. $a_2 = 4, a_5 = \dfrac{256}{27}$

21. $a_2 = \dfrac{32}{9}, a_7 = -27$

Find the sum of the geometric series.

22. $\displaystyle\sum_{i=1}^{5} 17(2)^{i-1}$

23. $\displaystyle\sum_{i=1}^{7} 3(-4)^{i-1}$

24. $\displaystyle\sum_{i=0}^{4} 3(-2)^{i}$

25. $\displaystyle\sum_{i=1}^{7} 81\left(\dfrac{1}{3}\right)^{i-1}$

26. $\displaystyle\sum_{i=0}^{5} 256\left(\dfrac{5}{4}\right)^{i}$

27. $\displaystyle\sum_{i=1}^{6} 25\left(-\dfrac{9}{5}\right)^{i-1}$

28. Savings Account You open a savings account with $500. The account pays 2.2% interest per year, compounded annually. You do not make any withdrawals from or deposits into the account. Write a rule for the amount in the account after *n* years. Then find the amount in the account after 10 years.

29. Bouncing Ball You drop a ball from a height of 66 inches and the ball starts bouncing. After each bounce, the ball reaches a height that is 80% of the previous height. Write a rule for the height of the ball after the *n*th bounce. Then find the height of the ball after the sixth bounce.

30. Pendulum A pendulum is released. It swings forward, traveling a distance of 120 centimeters. On each successive swing, the pendulum travels 97% of the distance of the previous swing. Find the total distance traveled by the pendulum in the first 12 swings.

UNIT 4

TEST | for Unit 4

Simplify the expression. Tell which properties of exponents you used.

1. $2^2 \cdot 2^5$

2. $(3^2)^{-3}(3^3)$

3. $(x^{-2}y^5)^2$

4. $(3x^4y^{-2})^{-3}$

5. $\left(\dfrac{3}{4}\right)^{-2}$

6. $\dfrac{8 \times 10^7}{2 \times 10^3}$

7. $\left(\dfrac{x^2}{y^{-2}}\right)^{-4}$

8. $\dfrac{2x^{-6}y^5}{16x^3y^{-2}}$

Let $f(x) = 2x + 9$ and $g(x) = 3x - 1$. Perform the indicated operation and state the domain.

9. $f(x) + g(x)$

10. $f(x) - g(x)$

11. $f(x) \cdot g(x)$

12. $\dfrac{f(x)}{g(x)}$

13. $f(g(x))$

14. $g(f(x))$

15. $f(f(x))$

16. $g(g(x))$

Find the inverse of the function.

17. $y = -2x + 5$

18. $y = \dfrac{1}{3}x + 4$

19. $f(x) = 5x - 12$

20. $y = \dfrac{1}{2}x^4, x \geq 0$

21. $f(x) = x^2 + 5, x \geq 0$

22. $f(x) = -2x^3 + 1$

Graph the function. State the domain and range.

23. $y = 5^x$

24. $y = \left(\dfrac{1}{3}\right)^x - 4$

25. $f(x) = -3 \cdot 4^{x+1} - 2$

26. $y = \left(\dfrac{1}{8}\right)^x$

27. $y = 3(2.5)^x$

28. $f(x) = 2(0.8)^{x-1} + 3$

Solve the exponential equation or inequality.

29. $6^{x+3} = 6^{3x-1}$

30. $2^{x-1} = 8^{2x+1}$

31. $9^{x+5} \leq 3^{4x}$

Write a rule for the nth term of the arithmetic sequence.

32. $8, 5, 2, -1, -4, \ldots$

33. $d = 7, a_8 = 54$

34. $a_4 = 27, a_{11} = 69$

Write a rule for the nth term of the geometric sequence.

35. $256, 64, 16, 4, 1, \ldots$

36. $r = 5, a_2 = 200$

37. $a_1 = 144, a_3 = 16$

Find the sum of the series.

38. $\displaystyle\sum_{i=1}^{15}(3 + 2i)$

39. $\displaystyle\sum_{i=1}^{26}(25 - 3i)$

40. $\displaystyle\sum_{i=1}^{22}(6i - 5)$

41. $\displaystyle\sum_{i=1}^{30}(-84 + 8i)$

42. $\displaystyle\sum_{i=1}^{6}3(5)^{i-1}$

43. $\displaystyle\sum_{i=1}^{9}8(2)^{i-1}$

44. $\displaystyle\sum_{i=1}^{5}15\left(\dfrac{2}{3}\right)^{i-1}$

45. $\displaystyle\sum_{i=1}^{7}40\left(\dfrac{1}{2}\right)^{i-1}$

46. Finance You deposit $1500 in an account that pays 7% annual interest compounded daily. Find the balance after 2 years. (See the Performance Task below for the compound interest formula.)

47. Exchange Rates The *euro* is the unit of currency for the European Union. On a certain day, the number E of euros that could be obtained for D dollars was given by this function.

$$E = 0.81419D$$

Find the inverse of the function. Then use the inverse to find the number of dollars that could be obtained for 250 euros on that day.

48. Computers Joe buys a $600 computer on layaway by making a $200 down payment and then paying $25 per month. Write a rule for the total amount of money paid on the computer after n months.

49. DVDs From 2002 to 2007, the number n (in millions) of blank DVDs a company sold can be modeled by $n = 0.42(2.47)^t$ where t is the number of years since 2002.

 a. Identify the initial amount, the growth factor, and the annual percent increase.

 b. Graph the function. Estimate the number of blank DVDs sold by the company in 2006.

50. Bike Value You buy a new mountain bike for $200. The value of the bike decreases by 25% each year.

 a. Write a model giving the mountain bike's value y (in dollars) after t years. Use the model to estimate the value of the bike after 3 years.

 b. Graph the model.

 c. Estimate when the value of the bike will be $100.

Performance Task

Vacation

You and a friend are saving money to take a trip to Europe. You deposit $1300 in a bank account that pays 4% interest compounded yearly. The amount A in the account after t years is given by the equation $A = P\left(1 + \dfrac{r}{n}\right)^{nt}$ where P is the initial principal deposited in an account that pays interest at an annual rate r (expressed as a decimal), compounded n times per year.

 a. Find the balance after 1 year.

 b. You need $1400 to take the trip. After how many years will you have enough money?

 c. Suppose you and your friend do not open a bank account. You borrow the $1400 from your parents. You give your parents a down payment of $500 and agree to pay them $50 per month. Write a rule for the total amount of money paid to them after x months.

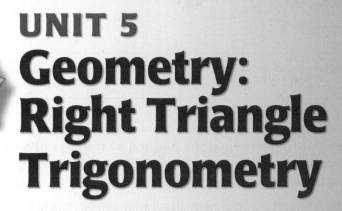

UNIT 5
Geometry: Right Triangle Trigonometry

Georgia Performance Standards

MM2G1a   Determine the lengths of sides of 30°-60°-90° triangles.

MM2G1b   Determine the lengths of sides of 45°-45°-90° triangles.

Investigating Math Activity
Special Right Triangles

Use before Lesson 5.1

Materials   metric ruler and protractor

Question

What is the relationship between the lengths of the legs of a 45°-45°-90° triangle and the length of the hypotenuse? What are the relationships among the lengths of the sides of a 30°-60°-90° triangle?

A 45°-45°-90° triangle is an isosceles right triangle that can be formed by cutting a square in half. A 30°-60°-90° triangle can be formed by dividing an equilateral triangle in half.

Explore

Investigate special right triangles.

STEP 1   Draw a 45°-45°-90° triangle

Use your metric ruler and protractor to draw a square. The side lengths should be a whole number, in centimeters. Label the vertices *A*, *B*, *C*, and *D*, and label each side with its length. Use your metric ruler to draw the diagonal $\overline{AC}$, to make two 45°-45°-90° triangles.

STEP 2   Draw a 30°-60°-90° triangle

Use your metric ruler and protractor to draw an equilateral triangle. The side lengths should be an even number, in centimeters. Label the vertices *J*, *K*, and *L*. Use your ruler to find the midpoint of side $\overline{JL}$, and label the midpoint *M*. Use your ruler to draw a segment from *K* to *M* to make two 30°-60°-90° triangles.

STEP 3   Apply Pythagorean Theorem

Apply the Pythagorean Theorem to find the length of the hypotenuse $\overline{AC}$ of $\triangle ACD$ and the length of the side $\overline{KM}$ of $\triangle JKM$. Write the lengths in simplified radical form. Do not write the lengths as decimals.

STEP 4   Complete a Table

Make a table to compare the side lengths of the special right triangles with the results of three of your classmates.

Draw Conclusions

1.   **Reasoning** What is the relationship between the lengths of the legs of a 45°-45°-90° triangle and the length of the hypotenuse?

2.   **Reasoning** What is the relationship between the lengths of the shorter leg and the hypotenuse of a 30°-60°-90° triangle? the lengths of the shorter leg and the longer leg of a 30°-60°-90° triangle?

UNIT 5

LESSON
5.1

Special Right Triangles

Georgia Performance Standards: MM2G1a, MM2G1b

Goal Use the relationships among the sides in special right triangles.

....

Vocabulary

Theorem 5.1 45°-45°-90° Triangle Theorem:
In a 45°-45°-90° triangle, the hypotenuse is $\sqrt{2}$ times as long as each leg.

Theorem 5.2 30°-60°-90° Triangle Theorem:
In a 30°-60°-90° triangle, the hypotenuse is twice as long as the shorter leg, and the longer leg is $\sqrt{3}$ times as long as the shorter leg.

Example 1 **Find lengths in a 45°-45°-90° triangle**

Find the value of x.

a. 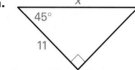   b.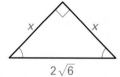

Solution

a. Because the sum of the angle measures in a triangle is 180°, the measure of the third angle is 45°. So, the triangle is a 45°-45°-90° triangle, and by Theorem 5.1, the hypotenuse is $\sqrt{2}$ times as long as each leg.

   hypotenuse = leg • $\sqrt{2}$ 45°-45°-90° Triangle Theorem

   $x = 11\sqrt{2}$ Substitute.

b. You know that each of the two congruent angles in the triangle has a measure of 45° because the sum of the angle measures in a triangle is 180°. So, the triangle is a 45°-45°-90° triangle.

   hypotenuse = leg • $\sqrt{2}$ 45°-45°-90° Triangle Theorem

   $2\sqrt{6} = x • \sqrt{2}$ Substitute.

   $2\sqrt{3} = x$ Divide each side by $\sqrt{2}$.

Guided Practice for Example 1

Find the value of x.

1.   2. 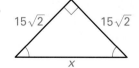   3.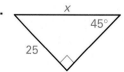

UNIT 5

Georgia Performance Standards

MM2G1a   Determine the lengths of sides of 30°–60°–90° triangles.

MM2G1b   Determine the lengths of sides of 45°–45°–90° triangles. ☑

Example 2   **Find the height of an equilateral triangle**

An equilateral triangle has side lengths of $6\sqrt{3}$. What is the height of the triangle?

Solution

Sketch the triangle. Its altitude h forms the longer leg of two 30°-60°-90° triangles.

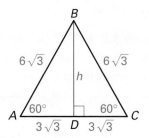

longer leg = shorter leg • $\sqrt{3}$

$\qquad h = 3\sqrt{3} \cdot \sqrt{3}$

$\qquad h = 9$

Example 3   **Find lengths in a 30°-60°-90° triangle**

Find the values of x and y.

Solution

STEP 1 **Find** the value of x.

longer leg = shorter leg • $\sqrt{3}$	30°-60°-90° Triangle Theorem
$4\sqrt{3} = x\sqrt{3}$	Substitute.
$4 = x$	Divide each side by $\sqrt{3}$.

STEP 2 **Find** the value of y.

hypotenuse = 2 • shorter leg	30°-60°-90° Triangle Theorem
$y = 2 \cdot 4$	Substitute.
$y = 8$	Simplify.

Guided Practice for Examples 2 and 3

4. An equilateral triangle has side lengths of 24. What is the height of the triangle?

5. An equilateral triangle has a height of $13\sqrt{3}$. What are the side lengths of the triangle?

Find the value of x.

6. 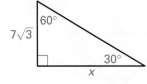   **7.** 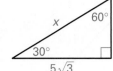   **8.**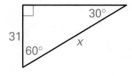

Exercise Set A

MM2G1a Determine the lengths of sides of 30°–60°–90° triangles.

MM2G1b Determine the lengths of sides of 45°–45°–90° triangles.

Find the value of *x*. Write your answer in simplest form.

1.

2.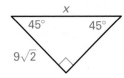

3.

4.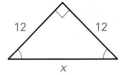

5.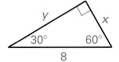

6.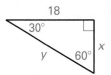

Find the value of each variable. Write your answers in simplest form.

7.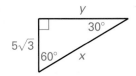

8.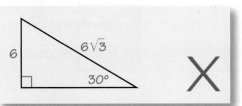

9.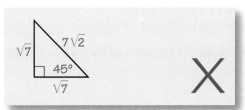

Error Analysis *Describe* and correct the error in finding the length of the hypotenuse.

10.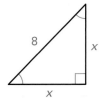

11.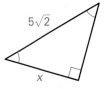

Copy and complete the table.

12.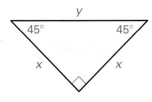

x	5	?	$\sqrt{2}$	9	?
y	?	$4\sqrt{2}$	?	?	24

13.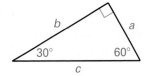

a	9	?	?	11	?
b	?	9	$5\sqrt{3}$	?	?
c	?	?	?	?	16

UNIT 5

Exercise Set A *(continued)*

Find the value of each variable. Write your answers in simplest form.

14.

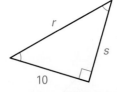

15.

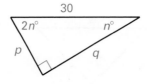

16.

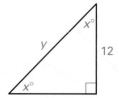

17.

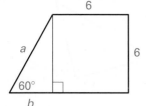

18.

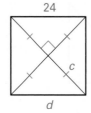

19.

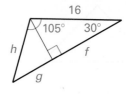

The side lengths of a triangle are given. Determine whether it is a 45°-45°-90° triangle, a 30°-60°-90° triangle, or neither.

20. $5, 10, 5\sqrt{3}$

21. $7, 7, 7\sqrt{3}$

22. $6, 6, 6\sqrt{2}$

23. **Roofing** A roofer is replacing the roof on the house shown, and needs to find the total area of the roof. The roof has a 1-1 pitch on both sides, which means that it slopes upward at a rate of 1 vertical unit for each 1 horizontal unit.

  a. Find the values of x and y in the diagram.

  b. Find the total area of the roof to the nearest square foot.

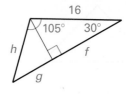

24. **Skateboard Ramp** You are using wood to build a pyramid-shaped skateboard ramp. You want each ramp surface to incline at an angle of 30° and the maximum height to be 56 centimeters as shown.

  a. Use the relationships shown in the diagram to determine the lengths a, b, c, and d to the nearest centimeter.

  b. Suppose you want to build a second pyramid ramp with a 45° angle of incline and a maximum height of 56 centimeters. You can use the diagram shown by simply changing the 30° angle to 45°. Determine the lengths a, b, c, and d to the nearest centimeter for this ramp.

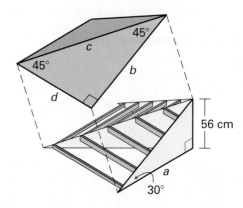

LESSON 5.1 | **Exercise Set B**

MM2G1a Determine the lengths of sides of 30°–60°–90° triangles.

MM2G1b Determine the lengths of sides of 45°–45°–90° triangles.

Find the value of each variable. Write your answers in simplest form.

1.
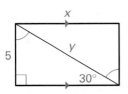

2.
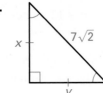

3.
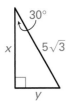

4.
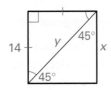

5.
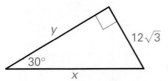

6.

7.
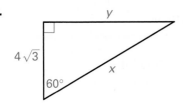

8.
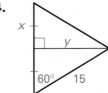

9.
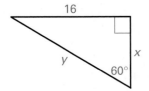

10.
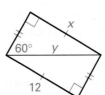

11.
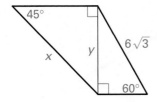

12.
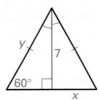

13. **Multiple Choice** In the diagrams to the right, $a = \frac{4}{3} f$. Which side length is the longest?

   A. b **B.** c

   C. d **D.** e

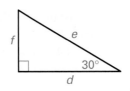

UNIT 5

Exercise Set B *(continued)*

14. Perimeter The altitude of an equilateral triangle is 12 centimeters. Find the perimeter of the triangle. Round to the nearest tenth.

15. Area The diagonal of a square is 12 inches. Find the area. Round to the nearest tenth.

16. Diagonal The perimeter of a rectangle is 32 feet. The length is three times the width. Find the length of a diagonal. Round to the nearest tenth.

17. Altitude The perimeter of an equilateral triangle is 45 meters. Find the length of an altitude. Round to the nearest tenth.

18. Distance Each figure to the right is a 30°-60°-90° triangle. Find the value of x. Round to the nearest tenth.

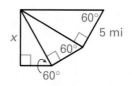

In Exercises 19–21, use the diagram and the following information.

Canyon A symmetrical canyon is 4850 feet deep. A river runs through the canyon at its deepest point. The angle of depression from each side of the canyon to the river is 60°. Round to the nearest tenth.

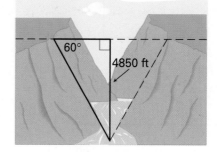

19. Find the distance across the canyon.

20. The length of the canyon wall from the edge to the river can be approximated by the length of the hypotenuse of the right triangle shown. Find this length.

21. Is it more or less than a mile across the canyon? (5280 feet = 1 mile)

In Exercises 22–24, use the diagram and the following information.

Bleachers A fan at a sporting event is sitting at point A in the bleachers. The bleacher seating has an angle of elevation of 30° and a base length of 90 feet. Round to the nearest tenth.

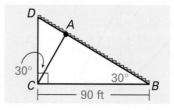

22. Find the height CD of the bleachers.

23. Find the height of the fan sitting at point A from the ground.

24. Find the distance AB that the fan is sitting from the base, point B.

Apply the Tangent Ratio

Georgia Performance Standards: MM2G2a, MM2G2b, MM2G2c

Goal Use the tangent ratio for indirect measurement.

Vocabulary

Trigonometry is a branch of mathematics that deals with the relationships between the sides and angles of triangles and the calculations based on these relationships.

A **trigonometric ratio** is a ratio of the lengths of two sides in a right triangle.

In a right triangle, the ratio of the length of the leg opposite an acute angle to the length of the leg adjacent to the angle is constant for a given angle measure. This ratio is called the **tangent** of the angle.

Tangent Ratio:
Let $\triangle ABC$ be a right triangle with acute $\angle A$. The tangent of $\angle A$ (written as $\tan A$) is defined as follows:

$$\tan A = \frac{\text{length of leg opposite } \angle A}{\text{length of leg adjacent to } \angle A} = \frac{BC}{AC}$$

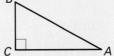

Two angles are **complementary angles** if the sum of their measures is $90°$.

Example 1 **Find tangent ratios**

Find tan X and tan Y. Write each answer as a fraction and as a decimal rounded to four places.

$$\tan X = \frac{\text{opp. } \angle X}{\text{adj. } \angle X} = \frac{YZ}{XZ} = \frac{13}{84} \approx 0.1548 \qquad \tan Y = \frac{\text{opp. } \angle Y}{\text{adj. } \angle Y} = \frac{XZ}{YZ} = \frac{84}{13} \approx 6.4615$$

Note that in the right triangle, $\triangle XYZ$, $\angle X$ and $\angle Y$ are complementary angles. You can see that the tangent ratios of the complementary angles are reciprocals.

Example 2 **Find a leg length**

Find the value of x.

Use the tangent of an acute angle to find a leg length.

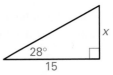

$\tan 28° = \dfrac{\text{opp.}}{\text{adj.}}$	Write ratio for tangent of $28°$.
$\tan 28° = \dfrac{x}{15}$	Substitute.
$15 \cdot \tan 28° = x$	Multiply each side by 15.
$15(0.5317) \approx x$	Use a calculator to find $\tan 28°$.
$8.0 \approx x$	Simplify.

Georgia Performance Standards

MM2G2a   Discover the relationship of the trigonometric ratios ☑
            for similar triangles.

MM2G2b   Explain the relationship between the trigonometric ☑
            ratios of complementary angles.

MM2G2c   Solve application problems using the trigonometric ☑
            ratios.

Example 3   Compare the tangent ratios for similar triangles

**Find tan *X* and tan *Y* for the similar triangles. Then compare the
tangent ratios.**

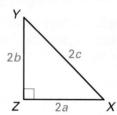

$$\tan X = \frac{b}{a}$$

$$\tan Y = \frac{a}{b}$$

$$\tan X = \frac{2b}{2a} = \frac{b}{a}$$

$$\tan Y = \frac{2a}{2b} = \frac{a}{b}$$

The values of $\tan X$ and $\tan Y$ for the similar triangles are equivalent.

Example 4   Estimate height using tangent

Find the height *h* of the lamppost to the nearest inch.

$$\tan 68° = \frac{\text{opp.}}{\text{adj.}}$$ Write ratio for tangent of 68°.

$$\tan 68° = \frac{h}{38}$$ Substitute.

$$38 \cdot \tan 68° = h$$ Multiply each side by 38.

$$94.1 \approx h$$ Use a calculator to simplify.

The lamppost is about 94 inches tall.

Guided Practice for Examples 1, 2, 3, and 4

1. Find tan *A* and tan *B*.
Round to four decimal places.

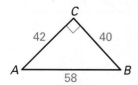

2. Find the value of *x*.
Round to the nearest tenth.

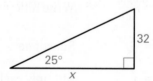

3. Find the height *h* of the lamppost in Example 4 to the nearest inch if the angle is 72°.

Exercise Set A

MM2G2a   Discover the relationship of the trigonometric ratios for similar triangles.

MM2G2b   Explain the relationship between the trigonometric ratios of complementary angles.

MM2G2c   Solve application problems using the trigonometric ratios.

Find tan *A* and tan *B*. Write each answer as a decimal rounded to four decimal places.

1.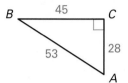

2.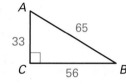

3.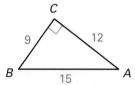

Find the value of *x* to the nearest tenth.

4.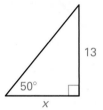

5.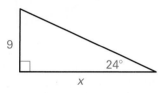

6.

7. Find tan *X* and tan *Y* for the similar triangles. Then compare the ratios.

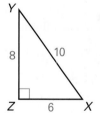

Find the value of *x* using the definition of tangent. Then find the value of *x* using the 45°-45°-90° Triangle Theorem or the 30°-60°-90° Triangle Theorem. *Compare* the results.

8.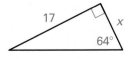

9.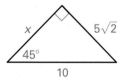

10.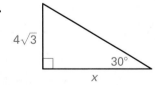

Use a tangent ratio to find the value of *x*. Round to the nearest tenth.

11.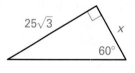

12.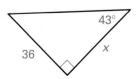

13.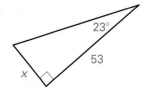

UNIT 5

Exercise Set A *(continued)*

Find the area of the triangle. Round your answer to the nearest tenth.

14.

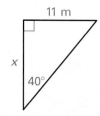

11 m

x

40°

15.

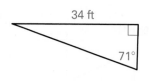

x

32°

24 ft

16.

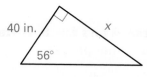

40 in.

56°

x

Find the perimeter of the triangle. Round to the nearest tenth.

17.

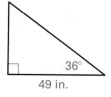

36°

49 in.

18.

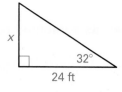

34 ft

71°

19.

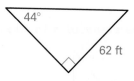

44°

62 ft

20. **Model Rockets** To calculate the height *h* reached by a model rocket, you move 100 feet from the launch point and record the angle of elevation *θ* to the rocket at its highest point. The values of *θ* for three flights are given below. Find the rocket's height to the nearest foot for the given *θ* in each flight.

   a. $\theta = 77°$

   b. $\theta = 81°$

   c. $\theta = 83°$

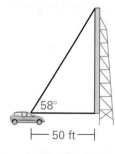

h

θ

100 ft

21. **Drive-in Movie** You are 50 feet from the screen at a drive-in movie. Your eye is on a horizontal line with the bottom of the screen and the angle of elevation to the top of the screen is 58°. How tall is the screen?

58°

50 ft

22. **Skyscraper** You are a block away from a skyscraper that is 780 feet tall. Your friend is between the skyscraper and yourself. The angle of elevation from your position to the top of the skyscraper is 42°. The angle of elevation from your friend's position to the top of the skyscraper is 71°. To the nearest foot, how far are you from your friend?

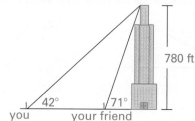

780 ft

42°   71°

you   your friend

MM2G2a Discover the relationship of the trigonometric ratios for similar triangles.

MM2G2b Explain the relationship between the trigonometric ratios of complementary angles.

MM2G2c Solve application problems using the trigonometric ratios.

Find the value of *x* to the nearest tenth.

1.
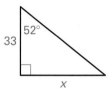

2.
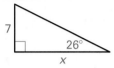

3.
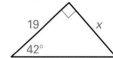

4.

5.
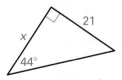

6.
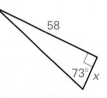

7. Find tan *X* and tan *Y* for the similar triangles.
Then compare the ratios.

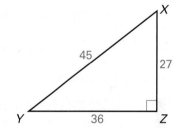

Find the value of *x* using the definition of tangent. Then find the value of *x* using the 45°-45°-90° Triangle Theorem or the 30°-60°-90° Triangle Theorem. *Compare* the results.

8.
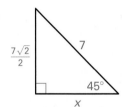

9.
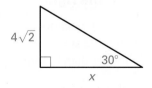

10.
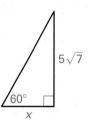

Use a tangent ratio to find the value of x. Round to the nearest tenth.

11.
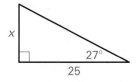

12.
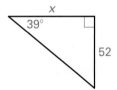

13.
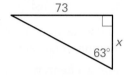

14. Show that the tangents of any two complementary angles are reciprocals of each other.
(*Hint:* Draw a right triangle whose two complementary angles are ∠*A* and ∠*B*. Let *a* and *b* be the lengths of the sides opposite ∠*A* and ∠*B*, respectively.)

UNIT 5

Exercise Set B *(continued)*

15. Perimeter What is the perimeter of an equilateral triangle with an altitude of 15 inches?

16. In the diagram to the right, $AC = 42$. What is AD? Round your answer to the nearest tenth.

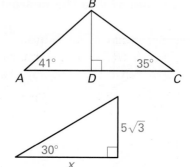

17. Multiple Representations In this exercise, you will find the value of x using two different methods.

    a. Using a Ratio Find the value of x using the definition of tangent.

    b. Using a Theorem Find the value of x using the 30°-60°-90° Triangle Theorem.

In Exercises 18–20, use the figure of the lighthouse.

18. At 2 P.M., the shadow of a lighthouse is 19 feet long and the angle of elevation is 75°. Find the height of the lighthouse.

19. At 4 P.M., the angle of elevation of the sun is 40°. Find the length of the shadow cast by the lighthouse.

20. At 6 P.M., will the length of the shadow be longer or shorter than it was at 4 P.M.? *Explain.*

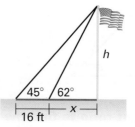

In Exercises 21 and 22, use the figure to the right.

Flagpole When the sun is shining at a 62° angle of elevation, a flagpole forms a shadow of length x feet. Later, the sun shines at an angle of 45°, and the shadow is 16 feet longer than before.

21. Write two expressions for the height h of the flagpole, in terms of x.

22. How tall is the flagpole? Round your answer to the nearest tenth of a foot.

23. Washington Monument You are on the west side of the Washington Monument which is 555 feet tall. Your friend is on the opposite (east) side. The angle of elevation from your position to the top of the monument is 42°. The angle of elevation from your friend's position to the top of the monument is 65°. To the nearest foot, how far are you from your friend?

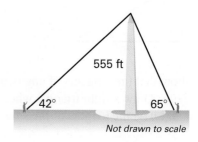

Not drawn to scale

LESSON 5.3

Apply the Sine and Cosine Ratios

Georgia Performance Standards: MM2G2a, MM2G2b, MM2G2c

Goal Use the sine and cosine ratios.

Vocabulary

The **sine** and **cosine** ratios are trigonometric ratios for acute angles that involve the lengths of a leg and the hypotenuse of a right triangle.

Sine and Cosine Ratios:
Let $\triangle ABC$ be a right triangle with acute $\angle A$. The sine of $\angle A$ and cosine of $\angle A$ (written as $\sin A$ and $\cos A$) are defined as follows:

$$\sin A = \frac{\text{length of leg opposite } \angle A}{\text{length of hypotenuse}} = \frac{BC}{AB}$$

$$\cos A = \frac{\text{length of leg adjacent to } \angle A}{\text{length of hypotenuse}} = \frac{AC}{AB}$$

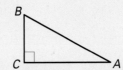

Example 1 **Find sine ratios**

Find sin X and sin Y. Write each answer as a fraction and as a decimal rounded to four places.

$$\sin X = \frac{\text{opp. } \angle X}{\text{hyp.}} = \frac{YZ}{XY}$$

$$= \frac{20}{52} \approx 0.3846$$

$$\sin Y = \frac{\text{opp. } \angle Y}{\text{hyp.}} = \frac{XZ}{XY}$$

$$= \frac{48}{52} \approx 0.9231$$

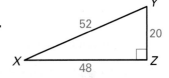

Example 2 **Find cosine ratios**

Find cos X and cos Y. Write each answer as a fraction and as a decimal rounded to four places.

$$\cos X = \frac{\text{adj. to } \angle X}{\text{hyp.}} = \frac{XZ}{XY}$$

$$= \frac{48}{52} \approx 0.9231$$

$$\cos Y = \frac{\text{adj. to } \angle Y}{\text{hyp.}} = \frac{YZ}{XY}$$

$$= \frac{20}{52} \approx 0.3846$$

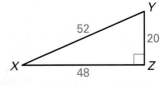

In Examples 1 and 2, $\triangle XYZ$ is a right triangle and $\angle X$ and $\angle Y$ are complementary angles. You can see that $\sin X = \cos Y$ and $\sin Y = \cos X$.

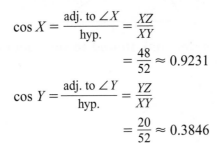

Georgia Performance Standards

MM2G2a Discover the relationship of the trigonometric ratios
for similar triangles. ☑

MM2G2b Explain the relationship between the trigonometric
ratios of complementary angles. ☑

MM2G2c Solve application problems using the trigonometric
ratios. ☑

Example 3   Sine and cosine ratios for similar triangles

Find the sine and cosine of $\angle X$, $\angle Y$, $\angle L$, and $\angle M$ of the similar triangles. Then compare the ratios.

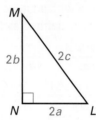

Solution

$$\sin X = \frac{b}{c} \qquad \cos X = \frac{a}{c} \qquad\qquad \sin L = \frac{2b}{2c} = \frac{b}{c} \qquad \cos L = \frac{2a}{2c} = \frac{a}{c}$$

$$\sin Y = \frac{a}{c} \qquad \cos Y = \frac{b}{c} \qquad\qquad \sin M = \frac{2a}{2c} = \frac{a}{c} \qquad \cos M = \frac{2b}{2c} = \frac{b}{c}$$

In $\triangle XYZ$, $\angle X$ and $\angle Y$ are complementary angles, so $\sin X = \cos Y$ and $\sin Y = \cos X$.

In $\triangle LMN$, $\angle L$ and $\angle M$ are complementary angles, so $\sin L = \cos M$ and $\sin M = \cos L$.

Because $\triangle XYZ$ and $\triangle LMN$ are similar triangles, $\sin X = \sin L$, $\cos X = \cos L$, $\sin Y = \sin M$, and $\cos Y = \cos M$.

Guided Practice for Examples 1, 2, and 3

Find sin *A* and sin *B*. Write each answer as a decimal. Round to four decimal places, if necessary.

1.

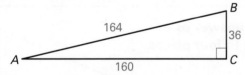

2.

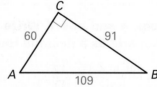

Find cos *A* and cos *B*. Write each answer as a decimal. Round to four decimal places, if necessary.

3.

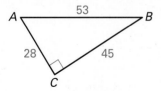

4.

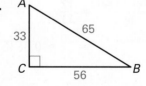

Example 4 Use trigonometric ratios to find side lengths

Use a trigonometric ratio to find the value of *x* in the diagram.
Round to the nearest tenth.

a.

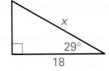

b.

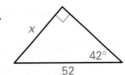

Solution

a. $\cos 29° = \dfrac{\text{adj.}}{\text{hyp.}}$

$\cos 29° = \dfrac{18}{x}$

$x = \dfrac{18}{\cos 29°}$

$x \approx \dfrac{18}{0.8746} \approx 20.6$

b. $\sin 42° = \dfrac{\text{opp.}}{\text{hyp.}}$

$\sin 42° = \dfrac{x}{52}$

$52 \sin 42° = x$

$x \approx 52(0.6691) \approx 34.8$

Example 5 Use trigonometric ratios to find side lengths

Skateboard Ramp Find the height and
length of the base of the ramp shown.

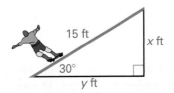

STEP 1 **Find** the height.

$\sin 30° = \dfrac{\text{opp.}}{\text{hyp.}}$

$\sin 30° = \dfrac{x}{15}$

$15 \cdot \sin 30° = x$

$7.5 = x$

STEP 2 **Find** the length of the base.

$\cos 30° = \dfrac{\text{adj.}}{\text{hyp.}}$

$\cos 30° = \dfrac{y}{15}$

$15 \cdot \cos 30° = y$

$13 \approx y$

The height is 7.5 feet and the length of the base is about 13 feet.

Guided Practice for Examples 4 and 5

Find the value of *x* in the diagram. Round to the nearest tenth.

5.

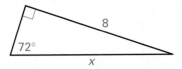

6.

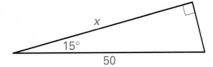

7. **What If?** In Example 5, suppose the length of the ramp is 18 feet. Find the height and
length of the base of the ramp.

Exercise Set A

MM2G2a Discover the relationship of the trigonometric ratios for similar triangles.

MM2G2b Explain the relationship between the trigonometric ratios of complementary angles.

MM2G2c Solve application problems using the trigonometric ratios.

Find sin *R* and sin *S*. Write each answer as a fraction and as a decimal. Round to four decimal places, if necessary.

1.

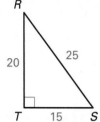

2.

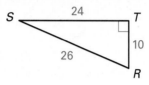

3.

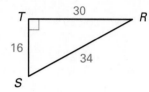

4.

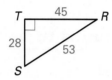

5.

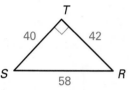

6.

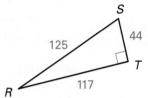

Find cos *A* and cos *B*. Write each answer as a fraction and as a decimal. Round to four decimal places, if necessary.

7.

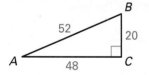

8.

9.

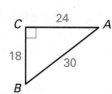

10.

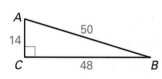

11.

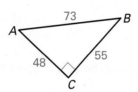

12.

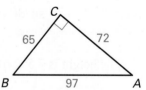

13. Find sin *X*, sin *Y*, cos *X*, and cos *Y*. Then compare the ratios

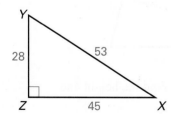

14. Find the sine and cosine of ∠*X*, ∠*Y*, ∠*L*, and ∠*M* of the similar triangles. Then compare the ratios.

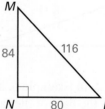

Exercise Set A *(continued)*

Use a cosine or sine ratio to find the value of each variable. Round decimals to the nearest tenth.

15.

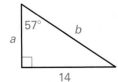

16.

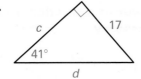

17.

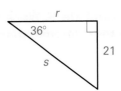

Use the 45°-45°-90° Triangle Theorem or the 30°-60°-90° Triangle Theorem to find the sine and cosine of the angle.

18. a 30° angle

19. a 45° angle

20. a 60° angle

Find the unknown side length. Then find sin *A* and cos *A*. Write each answer as a fraction in simplest form and as a decimal. Round to four decimal places, if necessary.

21.

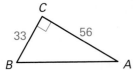

22.

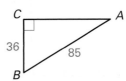

23.

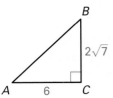

24.

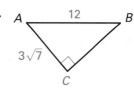

25. Ski Lift A chair lift on a ski slope has an angle of elevation of 28° and covers a total distance of 4640 feet. To the nearest foot, what is the vertical height *h* covered by the chair lift?

26. Airplane Landing A pilot is preparing to land an airplane. The airplane is on a straight line approach path that forms a 3° angle with the runway. What is the distance *d* along this approach path to the touchdown point when the airplane is 500 feet above the ground? Round your answer to the nearest foot.

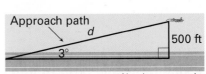

Not drawn to scale

MM2G2a   Discover the relationship of the trigonometric ratios for similar triangles.

MM2G2b   Explain the relationship between the trigonometric ratios of complementary angles.

MM2G2c   Solve application problems using the trigonometric ratios.

Find sin *R* and sin *S*. Write each answer as a fraction and as a decimal. Round to four decimal places, if necessary.

1.
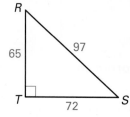

2.
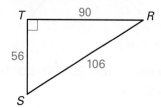

3.
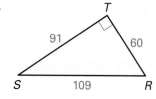

Find cos *A* and cos *B*. Write each answer as a fraction and as a decimal. Round to four decimal places, if necessary.

4.
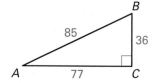

5.
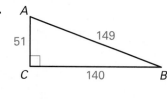

6.
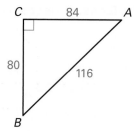

7. Find sin *X*, sin *Y*, cos *X*, and cos *Y*. Then compare the ratios.

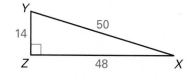

8. Find the sine and cosine of ∠*X*, ∠*Y*, ∠*L*, and ∠*M* of the similar triangles. Then compare the ratios.

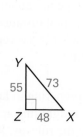

Use a sine or cosine ratio to find the value of each variable. Round decimals to the nearest tenth.

9.
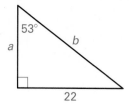

10.
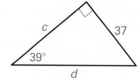

11.
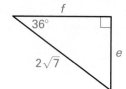

Exercise Set B (continued)

12. **Perimeter** In the diagram to the right, $BC = 110$ inches. What is the perimeter of $\triangle ABC$? Round your answer to the nearest tenth.

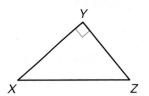

13. **Multiple Choice** In the diagram to the right, $XY \neq YZ$. Which statement about $\triangle XYZ$ *cannot* be true?

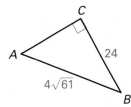

A. $\sin X = 0.6293$ **B.** $\cos Z = 0.5$

C. $\sin X = \cos Z$ **D.** $\sin X = \cos X$

Find the unknown side length. Then find sin _A_ and cos _A_. Write each answer as a fraction in simplest form and as a decimal. Round to four decimal places, if necessary.

14.

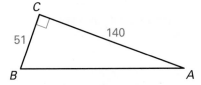

15.

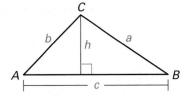

In Exercises 16–18, refer to the diagram at the right.

16. Write an expression for h using $\angle A$.

17. Write an expression for h using $\angle B$.

18. Show that $\dfrac{\sin A}{a} = \dfrac{\sin B}{b}$.

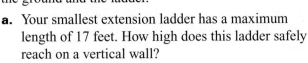

19. **Extension Ladders** You are using extension ladders to paint a chimney that is 33 feet tall. The length of an extension ladder ranges in one-foot increments from its minimum length to its maximum length. For safety, you should always use an angle of about $75.5°$ between the ground and the ladder.

a. Your smallest extension ladder has a maximum length of 17 feet. How high does this ladder safely reach on a vertical wall?

b. You place the base of the ladder 3 feet from the chimney. How many feet long should the ladder be?

c. To reach the top of the chimney, you need a ladder that reaches 30 feet high. How many feet long should the ladder be?

Technology Activity

Sine and Cosine Ratios

Use after Lesson 5.3

Question

How can you use geometry software to explore trigonometric ratios for right triangles?

Example

Construct a right triangle and calculate ratios of its side lengths.

STEP 1   Draw lines
Draw and label $\overleftrightarrow{AB}$. Draw a line perpendicular to $\overleftrightarrow{AB}$ through A. Label a point C on the perpendicular line.

STEP 2   Draw a right triangle Draw segments AB, AC, and BC. Use the *Hide* feature to hide the lines AB and AC.

STEP 3   Measure angle Measure $\angle B$. Move point C until $m\angle B$ is between 25° and 45°.

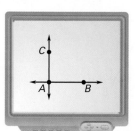

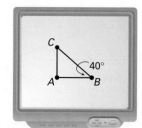

STEP 4   Measure side lengths Measure the lengths of $\overline{AB}$, $\overline{AC}$, and $\overline{BC}$.

STEP 5   Calculate ratios Find $\sin B = \dfrac{AC}{BC}$ and $\cos B = \dfrac{AB}{BC}$.

Practice

1. Move point B to make four new triangles. The measure of $\angle B$ should remain the same. Make a table. List the lengths of $\overline{AB}$, $\overline{AC}$, and $\overline{BC}$ and the ratios $\sin B = \dfrac{AC}{BC}$ and $\cos B = \dfrac{AB}{BC}$ for the five triangles.

2. Are the triangles you made in Exercise 1 congruent? Are they similar?

3. *Analyze* the table. What do you notice about the column of values for each ratio? Why should the values be equal? Does the value of a ratio depend on the particular triangle measured?

4. *Compare* your results with those of other students in the class. Does the value of a ratio depend on the measure of $\angle B$? *Explain.*

Georgia Performance Standards

MM2G2b Explain the relationship between the trigonometric ratios of complementary angles.

Investigating Math Activity
Solving Right Triangles

Use before Lesson 5.4

Materials   metric ruler, protractor, and calculator

Question

Can you solve a right triangle if you only know the measures of two sides of the triangle?

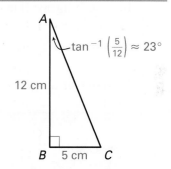

To *solve a right triangle* means to find the measures of all of its sides and angles. If you know the measures of two sides, you can find the measure of an angle by finding the *inverse* of a trigonometric ratio on a calculator. For example, to find the measure of $\angle A$, you would use a calculator to find the *inverse tangent ratio* of $\frac{5}{12}$, which is written $\tan^{-1}\left(\frac{5}{12}\right)$.

Explore

Solve a right triangle.

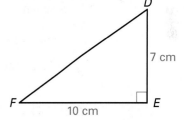

STEP 1   Draw a right triangle Use your metric ruler and protractor to draw a right triangle that has legs that are a whole number of centimeters long. Name the vertices D, E, and F, with $\angle E$ being the right angle. Write the lengths of sides $\overline{DE}$ and $\overline{EF}$ next to them.

STEP 2   Calculate hypotenuse Use the Pythagorean Theorem to find the length of the hypotenuse, $\overline{DF}$. Write the length in simplified radical form.

STEP 3   Find angle measures Use inverse trigonometric ratios to find the measures of $\angle D$ and $\angle F$.

Draw Conclusions

1. Which inverse trigonometric ratio did you use to find the measure of $\angle D$? $\angle F$? Why?

2. **Reasoning** Can you solve a right triangle if you only know the measures of two sides of the triangle? *Explain* your answer.

3. **Reasoning** For this exploration, you knew the measures of the two legs of $\triangle DEF$. Can you solve a right triangle if you know the measures of one leg and the hypotenuse? *Explain* your answer.

Solve Right Triangles

Georgia Performance Standards: MM2G2c

Goal Use inverse tangent, sine, and cosine ratios.

Vocabulary

To **solve a right triangle** means to find the measures of all of its sides and angles.

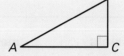

Inverse Trigonometric Ratios:
Let $\angle A$ be an acute angle.

Inverse Tangent: If $\tan A = x$, then $\tan^{-1} x = m\angle A$. $\tan^{-1} \dfrac{BC}{AC} = m\angle A$

Inverse Sine: If $\sin A = y$, then $\sin^{-1} y = m\angle A$. $\sin^{-1} \dfrac{BC}{AB} = m\angle A$

Inverse Cosine: If $\cos A = z$, then $\cos^{-1} z = m\angle A$. $\cos^{-1} \dfrac{AC}{AB} = m\angle A$

Example 1   **Use an inverse tangent to find an angle measure**

Use a calculator to approximate the measure of $\angle X$ to the nearest tenth of a degree.

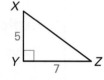

Because $\tan X = \dfrac{7}{5} = 1.4$, $\tan^{-1} 1.4 = m\angle X$. Use a calculator.

$\tan^{-1} 1.4 \approx 54.46232221 \ldots$

So, the measure of $\angle X$ is approximately $54.5°$.

Example 2   **Use an inverse sine and an inverse cosine**

Let $\angle A$ and $\angle B$ be acute angles in a right triangle. Use a calculator to approximate the measures of $\angle A$ and $\angle B$ to the nearest tenth of a degree.

   a. $\sin A = 0.19$ **b.** $\cos B = 0.56$

Solution

   a. $m\angle A = \sin^{-1} 0.19 \approx 11.0°$ **b.** $m\angle B = \cos^{-1} 0.56 \approx 55.9°$

Guided Practice for Examples 1 and 2

Let $\angle A$ be an acute angle in a right triangle. Use a calculator to approximate the measure of $\angle A$ to the nearest tenth of a degree.

  1. $\tan A = 0.95$ **2.** $\sin A = 0.23$ **3.** $\cos A = 0.12$ **4.** $\cos A = 0.67$

Example 3 Solve a right triangle

Ladder Find the missing measurements of the right triangle shown in the diagram. Round decimal answers to the nearest tenth.

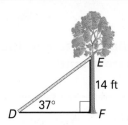

STEP 1 **Find** the measure of the angle formed by the ladder and tree by using the Triangle Sum Theorem.

$$180° = 90° + 37° + m\angle E$$

$$53° = m\angle E$$

STEP 2 **Approximate** the distance from the base of the tree to the base of the ladder by using a tangent ratio.

$\tan 37° = \dfrac{14}{DF}$	Write ratio for tangent of 37°.
$DF = \dfrac{14}{\tan 37°}$	Solve for DF.
$DF \approx \dfrac{14}{0.7536} \approx 18.6$ ft	Approximate tan 37°, simplify, and round.

STEP 3 **Approximate** the length of the ladder by using a sine ratio.

$\sin 37° = \dfrac{14}{DE}$	Write ratio for sine of 37°.
$DE = \dfrac{14}{\sin 37°}$	Solve for DE.
$DE \approx \dfrac{14}{0.6018} \approx 23.3$ ft	Approximate sin 37°, simplify, and round.

The measure of the angle formed by the ladder and tree is 53°. The distance from the base of the tree to the base of the ladder is approximately 18.6 feet. The length of the ladder is approximately 23.3 feet.

Guided Practice for Example 3

Solve the right triangle. Round decimal answers to the nearest tenth.

5.

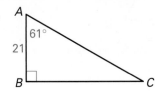

6.

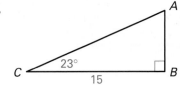

LESSON
5.4

**Exercise
Set A**

MM2G2c   Solve application problems using the trigonometric
ratios.

**Use the diagram to find the indicated measurement. Round your answer
to the nearest tenth.**

1. *MN*

2. *m∠M*

3. *m∠N*

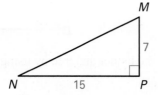

Solve the right triangle. Round decimal answers to the nearest tenth.

4.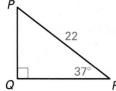

5.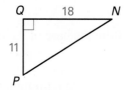

6.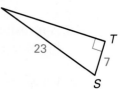

7.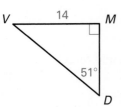

8.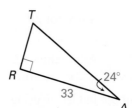

9.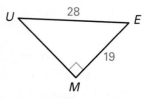

10.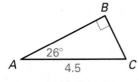

11.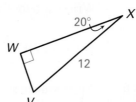

12.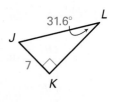

Error Analysis *Describe* **and correct the student's error in using an inverse
trigonometric ratio.**

13.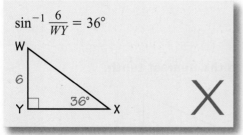

14.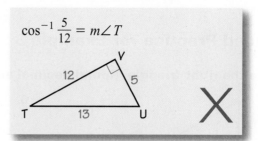

Exercise Set A *(continued)*

Let ∠A be an acute angle in a right triangle. Approximate the measure of ∠A to the nearest tenth of a degree.

15. $\sin A = 0.36$ **16.** $\tan A = 0.8$ **17.** $\sin A = 0.27$ **18.** $\cos A = 0.35$

19. $\tan A = 0.42$ **20.** $\cos A = 0.11$ **21.** $\sin A = 0.94$ **22.** $\cos A = 0.77$

23. Office Buildings The angle from the top of a 320 foot office building to the top of a 200 foot office building is 55° as shown. How far apart are the buildings?

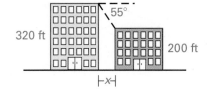

24. Suspension Bridge Use the diagram to find the distance across the suspension bridge.

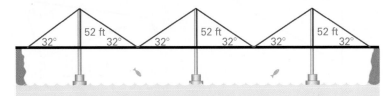

In Exercises 25 and 26, use the following information.

Ramps The Uniform Federal Accessibility Standards specify that the ramp angle used for a wheelchair ramp must be less than or equal to 4.78°.

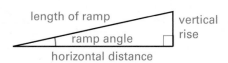

25. The length of one ramp is 16 feet. The vertical rise is 14 inches. Estimate the ramp's horizontal distance and its ramp angle. Does this ramp meet the Uniform Federal Accessibility Standards?

26. You want to build a ramp with a vertical rise of 6 inches. You want to minimize the horizontal distance taken up by the ramp but still meet the Uniform Federal Accessibility Standards. Draw a sketch showing the approximate dimensions of your ramp.

27. Hot Air Balloon You are in a hot air balloon that is 600 feet above the ground where you can see your friend. If the angle from your line of sight to your friend is 20°, how far is he from the point on the ground below the hot air balloon?

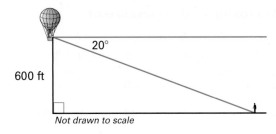

LESSON
5.4

Exercise
Set B

MM2G2c   Solve application problems using the trigonometric
ratios.

Use a calculator to approximate the measure of $\angle A$ **to the nearest tenth of a degree.**

1.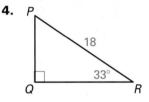

2.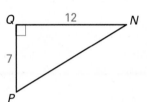

3.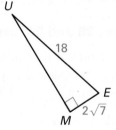

Solve the right triangle. Round decimal answers to the nearest tenth.

4.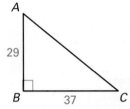

5.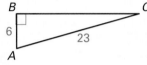

6.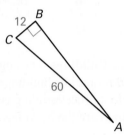

7.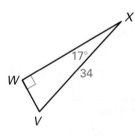

8.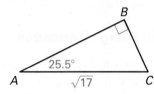

9.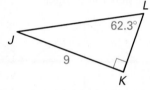

10.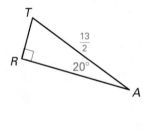

11.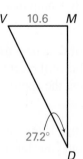

12.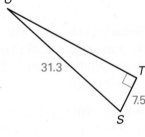

Let $\angle A$ **be an acute angle in a right triangle. Approximate the measure of** $\angle A$ **to the nearest tenth of a degree.**

13. $\sin A = 0.16$

14. $\tan A = 1.8$

15. $\sin A = 0.97$

16. $\cos A = 0.25$

17. $\tan A = 8.4$

18. $\cos A = 0.81$

19. $\sin A = 0.44$

20. $\cos A = 0.05$

21. $\tan A = 1.0$

22. $\cos A = 0.72$

23. $\sin A = 0.09$

24. $\sin A = 0.61$

Exercise Set B *(continued)*

25. Golf The angle from the tee box to the green is 10° on a par 3, 185 yard hole as shown. How much higher is the tee box than the green? Round to the nearest yard.

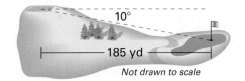

Not drawn to scale

26. Ramp You are designing a ramp where the horizontal distance is twice the vertical rise. What will be the ramp angle to the nearest tenth of a degree?

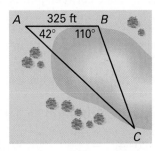

27. Bridge A surveyor needs to find the distance *BC* across a lake as part of a project to build a bridge. The distance from point *A* to point *B* is 325 feet. The measurement of angle *A* is 42° and the measurement of angle *B* is 110°. What is the distance *BC* across the lake to the nearest foot?

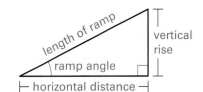

In Exercises 28–30, use the following information.

Fireworks You are watching a fireworks display where you are standing 290 feet behind the launch pad. The launch tubes are aimed directly away from you at an angle of 65° with the ground. The angle for you to see the fireworks is 40°.

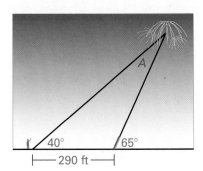

28. To the nearest foot, what is the horizontal distance from the launch pad to the point where the fireworks explode?

29. To the nearest foot, what is the height of the fireworks when they explode?

30. What is the measure of angle *A*?

Problem Solving Workshop

Problem   To find the distance d from a house on shore to a house on an island, a surveyor measures the distance between point B and point A, as shown in the diagram. An instrument called a *transit* is used to find the measure of $\angle B$. Estimate the distance d.

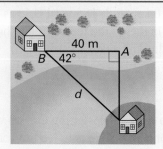

STEP 1   Read and Understand

What do you know?
The measure of angle B is 42° and angle A is 90°.
The distance between points A and B is 40 meters.

What do you want to find out?
The distance between the house on shore and the house on the island

STEP 2   Make a Plan   Use what you know to find the distance d.

STEP 3   Solve the Problem   Find the distance d by using a cosine ratio.

$$\cos 42° = \frac{\text{adj.}}{\text{hyp.}} \qquad \text{Write ratio for cosine of } 42°.$$

$$\cos 42° = \frac{40}{d} \qquad \text{Substitute.}$$

$$d \cdot \cos 42° = 40 \qquad \text{Multiply each side by } d.$$

$$d = \frac{40}{\cos 42°} \qquad \text{Divide each side by } \cos 42°.$$

$$d \approx \frac{40}{0.7431} \qquad \text{Use a calculator to find } \cos 42°.$$

$$d \approx 54 \text{ m} \qquad \text{Simplify.}$$

The distance between the house on shore and the house on the island is about 54 meters.

Practice

1. **Water Slide**   The angle from the base to the top of a water slide is about 13°. The slide extends horizontally about 58.2 meters. Estimate the height h of the slide.

2. **What If?**   In the problem above, suppose the distance between points A and B is 50 meters and the measure of angle B is 38°. Estimate the distance d.

TEST | for Unit 5

Find the value of each variable. Write your answers in simplest form.

1.
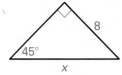
8
45°
x

2.
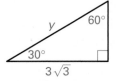
60°
y
30°
$3\sqrt{3}$

3.
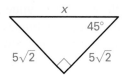
x
45°
$5\sqrt{2}$ $5\sqrt{2}$

4.
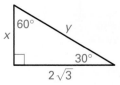
60°
y
x
30°
$2\sqrt{3}$

5.
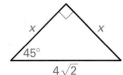
x   x
45°
$4\sqrt{2}$

6.
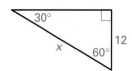
30°
x   12
60°

Find tan _A_ and tan _B_. Write each answer as a decimal rounded to four decimal places, if necessary.

7.
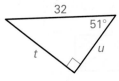
A   10   B
6   8
C

8.
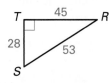
25   B
7
A   24   C

9.
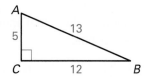
A   13
5
C   12   B

Find sin _R_, sin _S_, cos _R_, and cos _S_. Write each answer as a decimal rounded to four decimal places, if necessary.

10.
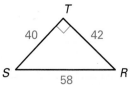
T
40   42
S   58   R

11.
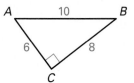
T   45   R
28   53
S

12.
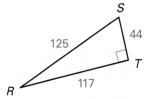
S
125   44
R   117   T

Use a cosine or sine ratio to find the value of each variable. Round decimals to the nearest tenth.

13.
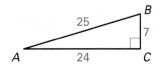
32
51°
t   u

14.
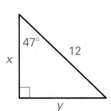
47°
x   12
y

15.
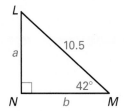
39°   g
44
h

Solve the right triangle. Round decimals to the nearest tenth.

16.
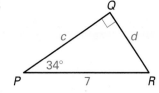
L
10.5
a
42°
N   b   M

17.
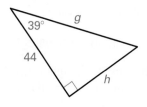
Q
c   d
34°
P   7   R

18.
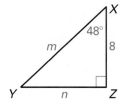
X
48°
m   8
Y   n   Z

19. Space Shuttle When the space shuttle is 6 miles from the runway, its glide angle is about 21°. Find the shuttle's altitude at this point in its descent. Round your answer to the nearest tenth.

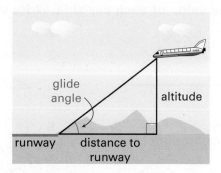

20. River You are standing on one side of a river with a friend. Your friend looks directly across the river at a tree. You stand 25 feet to the right of your friend. From where you stand, you estimate the angle between your friend and the tree to be 79°.

    a. *Explain* how to find the distance across the river from your friend to the tree. Find this distance.

    b. Suppose the actual angle measure is 74°. How far off is your estimate of the distance?

21. Slide The slide shown at the right is 6 feet long.

    a. Find the height of the slide. Round your answer to the nearest tenth, if necessary.

    b. Suppose you are standing at the bottom end of the slide. How far are you from the bottom of the ladder? Round your answer to the nearest tenth, if necessary.

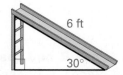

Performance Task

Step Stool

You and a friend place a wooden step stool next to the stage for an upcoming school play. Use the step stool shown to answer the following questions.

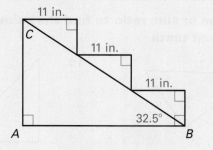

    a. Find the horizontal length of the step stool.

    b. Find the height of the step stool. Round your answer to the nearest tenth.

    c. Find the height of each step. Round your answer to the nearest tenth.

    d. Find the measure of angle C.

UNIT 6
Geometry:
Circles and Spheres

Use Properties of Tangents

Georgia Performance Standards: MM2G3a, MM2G3d

Goal Use properties of a tangent to a circle.

Vocabulary

A **circle** is the set of all points in a plane that are equidistant from a given point called the **center** of the circle.

A **radius** is a segment whose endpoints are the center and any point on the circle.

A **chord** is a segment whose endpoints are on a circle.

A **diameter** is a chord that contains the center of the circle.

A **secant** is a line that intersects a circle in two points.

A **tangent** is a line in the plane of a circle that intersects the circle in exactly one point, the point of tangency. A *tangent ray* and a *tangent segment* are also called tangents.

Theorem 6.1: In a plane, a line is tangent to a circle if and only if the line is perpendicular to a radius of the circle at its endpoint on the circle.

Theorem 6.2: Tangent segments from a common external point are congruent.

Two polygons are **similar polygons** if corresponding angles are congruent and corresponding side lengths are proportional. In the statement $\triangle ABC \sim \triangle DEF$, the symbol $\sim$ means "is similar to."

Example 1   Identify special segments and lines

Tell whether the line, ray, or segment is best described as a *radius, chord, diameter, secant,* or *tangent* of $\odot P$.

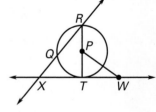

a. $\overline{RT}$ **b.** $\overrightarrow{WT}$

c. $\overline{PT}$ **d.** $\overleftrightarrow{RQ}$

Solution

a. $\overline{RT}$ is a diameter because it is a chord that contains the center P.

b. $\overrightarrow{WT}$ is a tangent ray because it is contained in a line that intersects the circle in only one point.

c. $\overline{PT}$ is a radius because P is the center and T is a point on the circle.

d. $\overleftrightarrow{RQ}$ is a secant because it is a line that intersects the circle in two points.

Guided Practice for Example 1

Use the diagram in Example 1.

1. What word best describes $\overline{QR}$? **2.** What word best describes $\overline{PR}$?

Georgia Performance Standards

MM2G3a Understand and use properties of chords, tangents, and secants as an application of triangle similarity.

MM2G3d Justify measurements and relationships in circles using geometric and algebraic properties.

Example 2 Find lengths in circles in a coordinate plane

Use the diagram to find the given lengths.

a. Diameter of $\odot P$
b. Diameter of $\odot Q$
c. Radius of $\odot P$
d. Radius of $\odot Q$

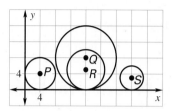

Solution

a. The diameter of $\odot P$ is 8 units.
b. The diameter of $\odot Q$ is 16 units.
c. The radius of $\odot P$ is 4 units.
d. The radius of $\odot Q$ is 8 units.

Guided Practice for Example 2

Use the diagram in Example 2.

3. Find the diameter and radius of $\odot R$ with center $R(16, 5)$.

4. Find the diameter and radius of $\odot S$ with center $S(28, 3)$.

Example 3 Draw common tangents

Tell how many common tangents the circles have and draw them.

a.

b.

c.

Solution

a. 2 common tangents
b.  4 common tangents
c. 1 common tangent

Guided Practice for Example 3

Tell how many common tangents the circles have and draw them.

5.
6.
7.

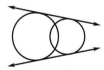

UNIT 6

Example 4 Verify a tangent to a circle

If $\overline{AB}$ is a radius of $\odot A$, show $\overline{BC}$ is tangent to $\odot A$.

Solution

Using the Converse of the Pythagorean Theorem,
$6^2 + 8^2 = 10^2$, so $\triangle ABC$ is a right triangle and $\overline{AB} \perp \overline{BC}$.
Because $\overline{BC}$ is perpendicular to a radius of $\odot A$ at its endpoint
on $\odot A$, by Theorem 6.1, $\overline{BC}$ is a tangent to $\odot A$.

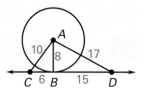

Guided Practice for Example 4

8. Using the diagram in Example 4, is $\overline{BD}$ tangent to $\odot A$?

Example 5 Find the radius of a circle

**In the diagram, B is a point of tangency.
Find the radius r of $\odot C$.**

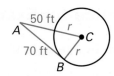

Solution

You know from Theorem 6.1 that $\overline{AB} \perp \overline{BC}$, so $\triangle ABC$
is a right triangle. You can use the Pythagorean Theorem.

$AC^2 = BC^2 + AB^2$	Pythagorean Theorem
$(r + 50)^2 = r^2 + 70^2$	Substitute.
$r^2 + 100r + 2500 = r^2 + 4900$	Multiply.
$100r = 2400$	Subtract r^2 and 2500 from each side.
$r = 24$ ft	Divide each side by 100.

The radius of $\odot C$ is 24 feet.

Example 6 Find the radius of a circle

**$\overline{RS}$ is tangent to $\odot C$ at S and $\overline{RT}$ is tangent
to $\odot C$ at T. Find the value of x.**

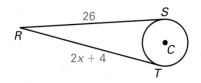

Solution

$RS = RT$	Tangent segments from the same point are $\cong$.
$26 = 2x + 4$	Substitute.
$11 = x$	Solve for x.

The value of x is 11.

UNIT 6

Triangle Similarity Postulate and Theorems

Angle-Angle (AA) Similarity Postulate: If two angles of one triangle are congruent to two angles of another triangle, then the two triangles are similar.

Theorem 6.3 Side-Side-Side (SSS) Similarity Theorem: If the corresponding side lengths of two triangles are proportional, then the triangles are similar.

Theorem 6.4 Side-Angle-Side (SAS) Similarity Theorem: If an angle of one triangle is congruent to an angle of a second triangle and the lengths of the sides including these angles are proportional, then the triangles are similar.

Example 7   Use tangents with similar triangles

A *common internal tangent* intersects the segment that joins the centers of two circles. In the diagram, $\overline{RS}$ is a common internal tangent to $\odot A$ and $\odot B$. Use similar triangles to show that $\dfrac{AC}{BC} = \dfrac{RC}{SC}$.

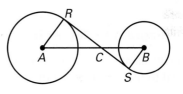

Solution

$\overline{RS} \perp \overline{AR}$ and $\overline{RS} \perp \overline{BS}$	Theorem 6.1
$\angle ARC$ and $\angle BSC$ are right angles.	Definition of perpendicular lines
$\angle ARC \cong \angle BSC$	All right angles are congruent.
$\angle ACR \cong \angle BCS$	Vertical Angles Theorem (Two angles are vertical angles if their sides form two pairs of opposite rays. The Vertical Angles Theorem states that vertical angles are congruent.)
$\triangle ARC \sim \triangle BSC$	Angle-Angle Similarity Postulate
$\dfrac{AC}{BC} = \dfrac{RC}{SC}$	Corresponding side lengths of similar triangles are proportional.

Guided Practice for Examples 5, 6, and 7

9. $\overline{ST}$ is tangent to $\odot Q$. Find the value of r.

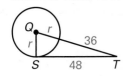

10. Find the value(s) of x.

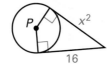

11. Find the value of r.

12. In the diagram at the right, both circles have center C. $\overline{RT}$ is tangent to the outer circle and $\overline{SU}$ is tangent to the inner circle. Use similar triangles to show that $\dfrac{RT}{SU} = \dfrac{CT}{CU}$.

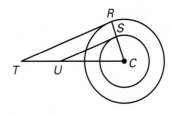

MM2G3a Understand and use properties of chords, tangents, and secants as an application of triangle similarity.

MM2G3d Justify measurements and relationships in circles using geometric and algebraic properties.

1. Tell whether the line, ray, or segment is best described as a *radius*, *chord*, *diameter*, *secant*, or *tangent* of ⊙*C*.

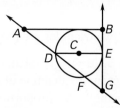

   a. $\overline{DF}$ b. $\overline{AB}$
   c. $\overline{CE}$ d. $\overline{DE}$
   e. $\overleftrightarrow{AG}$ f. $\overrightarrow{EB}$

2. Draw a circle *P*. Draw a tangent ray on the circle and label it $\overrightarrow{CD}$.

3. Draw a circle *P*. Draw a secant on the circle and label it $\overleftrightarrow{EF}$.

4. Draw a circle *P*. Draw a chord on the circle and label it $\overline{GH}$.

Use the diagram to determine if the statement is *true* or *false*.

5. The distance between the centers of the circles is equal to the length of the diameter of each circle.

6. The lines $y = 0$ and $y = 4$ represent all the common tangents of the two circles.

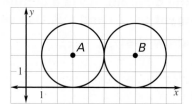

7. The circles intersect at the point (6, 3).

8. Suppose the two circles shown are inscribed in a rectangle. The perimeter of the rectangle is 36 units.

Draw two circles that have the given number of common tangents.

9. 3   10. 2   11. 0

**In Exercises 12–17, $\overline{BC}$ is a radius of ⊙*C* and $\overline{AB}$ is tangent to ⊙*C*.
Find the value of *x*.**

12.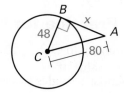

13.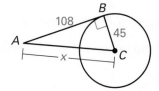

14.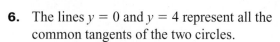

15.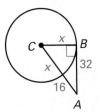

16.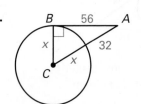

17.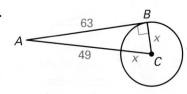

Exercise Set A *(continued)*

The points K and M are points of tangency. Find the value(s) of x.

18.

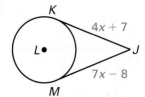

$4x + 7$

$7x - 8$

19.

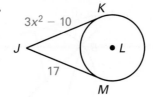

$3x^2 - 10$

17

20.

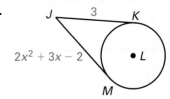

3

$2x^2 + 3x - 2$

21. Swimming Pool You are standing 36 feet from a circular swimming pool. The distance from you to a point of tangency on the pool is 48 feet as shown. What is the radius of the swimming pool?

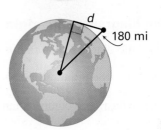

48 ft

36 ft

r r

22. Space Shuttle Suppose a space shuttle is orbiting about 180 miles above Earth. What is the distance d from the shuttle to the horizon? The radius of Earth is about 4000 miles. Round your answer to the nearest tenth.

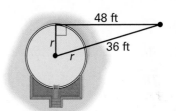

d

180 mi

In Exercises 23 and 24, use the following information.

Golf A green on a golf course is in the shape of a circle. Your golf ball is 8 feet from the edge of the green and 32 feet from a point of tangency on the green as shown in the figure.

23. Assuming the green is flat, what is the radius of the green?

24. How far is your golf ball from the cup at the center of the green?

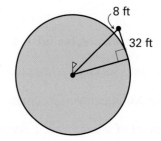

8 ft

32 ft

25. In the diagram, $\overline{SR}$ is tangent to $\odot P$ and $\odot Q$.
Use similar triangles to show that $\dfrac{QT}{PS} = \dfrac{RT}{RS}$.

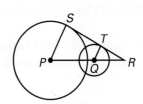

S

T

P Q R

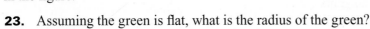

UNIT 6

LESSON
6.1

Exercise Set B

MM2G3a   Understand and use properties of chords, tangents, and secants as an application of triangle similarity.

MM2G3d   Justify measurements and relationships in circles using geometric and algebraic properties.

State the best term for the given figure in the diagram.

1. F

2. $\overleftrightarrow{FE}$

3. $\overline{HG}$

4. $\overline{DB}$

5. C

6. $\overline{BE}$

7. $\overleftrightarrow{DB}$

8. $\overrightarrow{AG}$

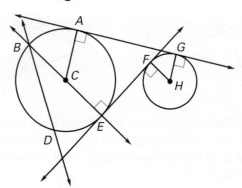

Use the diagram at the right.

9. Find the diameter and radius of $\odot A$, $\odot B$, and $\odot C$.

10. *Describe* the point of intersection of all three circles.

11. *Describe* all the common tangents of $\odot A$ and $\odot B$.

12. *Describe* the common secant of $\odot A$ and $\odot C$ that passes through both intersections of the two circles.

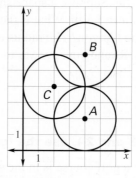

Draw a pair of circles with the characteristics described.

13. non-intersecting circles, no common tangents

14. intersecting circles, 2 common tangents

15. 1 point of intersection, 1 common tangent

16. 1 point of intersection, 3 common tangents

In the diagram, $\overline{BC}$ is a radius of $\odot C$. Determine whether $\overline{AB}$ is tangent to $\odot C$. *Explain* your reasoning.

17.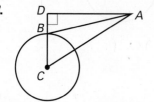

18.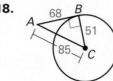

19.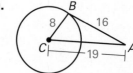

Exercise Set B (continued)

In the diagram, assume that segments are tangents if they appear to be. Find the value(s) of x.

20.

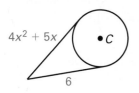

21.

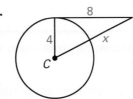

22.

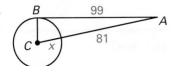

$4x^2 + 5x$

6

23.

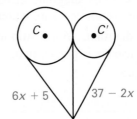

$6x + 5$ $\qquad$ $37 - 2x$

24.

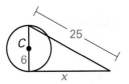

25

6

x

25.

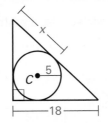

x

5

18

26. Water Tank You are standing 14 feet from the edge of a cylindrical water tank and 26 feet from a point of tangency. The tank is 10 feet tall. What is the volume of the tank in cubic feet?

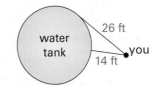

water tank — 26 ft — you — 14 ft

27. Pulleys The figure shows a pulley system in which a belt is wrapped around two pulleys so that one can drive the other. $\overline{RS}$ is tangent to $\odot Q$ at R and to $\odot P$ at S. $\overline{QT}$ is perpendicular to $\overline{SP}$, and Q and P are the centers of the circles. Let $QR = 2$ in., $PS = 8$ in., and $PQ = 12$ in.

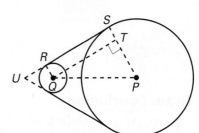

a. Write a paragraph proof to show that $QRST$ is a rectangle.

b. Find RS.

c. Find $m\angle P$.

28. In the diagram, $\overline{BZ}$ is tangent to both circles and $\overline{DZ}$ is tangent to both circles. Use similar triangles to show that $\dfrac{AC}{BD} = \dfrac{ZA}{ZB}$.

UNIT 6

Investigating Math Activity
Arcs and Central Angles

Use before Lesson 6.2

Question

What is the relationship between major arcs, minor arcs, and central angles?

A *central angle* of a circle is an angle whose vertex is the center of the circle. In the diagram, $\angle ACB$ is a central angle of $\odot C$. A *minor arc* is an arc whose measure is less than 180°. In the diagram, $\widehat{AB}$ is a minor arc. A *major arc* is an arc whose measure is greater than 180°. In the diagram, $\widehat{ADB}$ is a major arc.

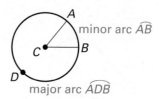

Explore

Investigate arcs and central angles.

Copy and complete the table. Use a protractor to measure the central angles in each of the diagrams below.

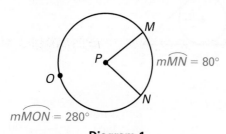

$m\widehat{MN} = 80°$

$m\widehat{MON} = 280°$

Diagram 1

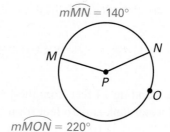

$m\widehat{MN} = 140°$

$m\widehat{MON} = 220°$

Diagram 2

	m∠MPN	**m$\widehat{MN}$**	**m$\widehat{MON}$**	**m$\widehat{MN}$ + m$\widehat{MON}$**
Diagram 1	?	?	?	?
Diagram 2	?	?	?	?

Draw Conclusions

1. Name a minor arc and a major arc of $\odot P$ in Diagram 1.

2. **Reasoning** What is the relationship between the measure of a central angle and the measure of the minor arc it intercepts?

3. In each diagram, what is the sum of $m\widehat{MN}$ and $m\widehat{MON}$?

4. **Reasoning** What is the relationship between the measure of a major arc and its corresponding minor arc?

Find Arc Measures

Georgia Performance Standards: MM2G3b, MM2G3d

Goal Use angle measures to find arc measures.

Vocabulary

A **central angle** of a circle is an angle whose vertex is the center of the circle.

A **semicircle** is an arc with endpoints that are the endpoints of a diameter.

An **arc** is an unbroken part of a circle. If $m\angle ACB$ is less than $180°$, then the points on $\odot C$ that lie in the interior of $\angle ACB$ form a **minor arc** with endpoints A and B. This minor arc is named $\overset{\frown}{AB}$. The points on $\odot C$ that do not lie on minor arc $\overset{\frown}{AB}$ form a **major arc** with the endpoints A and B. This major arc is named $\overset{\frown}{ADB}$.

The **measure of a minor arc** is the measure of its central angle.

The **measure of a major arc** is the difference between $360°$ and the measure of the related minor arc.

Arc Addition Postulate: The measure of an arc formed by two adjacent arcs is the sum of the measures of the two arcs.

Congruent circles are two circles with the same radius.

Congruent arcs are two arcs with the same measure that are arcs of the same circle or of congruent circles.

Example 1 **Find measures of arcs**

Find the measure of each arc of $\odot J$, where $\overline{KM}$ is a diameter.

a. $\overset{\frown}{LM}$ **b.** $\overset{\frown}{LMK}$ **c.** $\overset{\frown}{KLM}$

Solution

a. $\overset{\frown}{LM}$ is a minor arc, so $m\overset{\frown}{LM} = m\angle LJM = 125°$.

b. $\overset{\frown}{LMK}$ is a major arc, so $m\overset{\frown}{LMK} = 360° - 125° = 235°$.

c. $\overline{KM}$ is a diameter, so $\overset{\frown}{KLM}$ is a semicircle and $m\overset{\frown}{KLM} = 180°$.

Guided Practice for Example 1

Identify the given arc as a *major arc, minor arc,* or *semicircle* and find the measure of the arc.

1. $\overset{\frown}{AD}$ **2.** $\overset{\frown}{AB}$ **3.** $\overset{\frown}{CD}$

4. $\overset{\frown}{BDC}$ **5.** $\overset{\frown}{ACD}$ **6.** $\overset{\frown}{BC}$

UNIT 6

Example 2 Find measures of arcs

Several students were recently asked about their favorite color. The results are shown in the graph. Find the indicated arc measures.

a. $m\overarc{RT}$ b. $m\overarc{PRT}$

c. $m\overarc{RTQ}$ d. $m\overarc{STQ}$

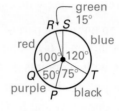

Solution

a. $m\overarc{RT} = m\overarc{RS} + m\overarc{ST} = 15° + 120° = 135°$

b. $m\overarc{PRT} = 360° - m\overarc{PT} = 360° - 75° = 285°$

c. $m\overarc{RTQ} = 360° - m\overarc{QR} = 360° - 100° = 260°$

d. $m\overarc{STQ} = m\overarc{ST} + m\overarc{TQ} = m\overarc{ST} + m\overarc{TP} + m\overarc{PQ} = 120° + 75° + 50° = 245°$

Example 3 Identify congruent arcs

Tell whether the highlighted arcs are congruent. Explain why or why not.

a.   b.   c.

Solution

a. $\overarc{AB}$ and $\overarc{CD}$ have the same measure, but are not congruent because the circles that contain them are not congruent.

b. $\overarc{JK} \cong \overarc{LM}$ because they have the same measure and are in the same circle.

c. $\overarc{PQ} \cong \overarc{RS}$ because they have the same measure and are in congruent circles.

Guided Practice for Examples 2 and 3

Find the measure of the arc.

7. $\overarc{AED}$ 8. $\overarc{AC}$ 9. $\overarc{ACE}$

10. $\overarc{BE}$ 11. $\overarc{CDE}$ 12. $\overarc{AEC}$

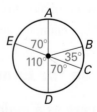

Tell whether the highlighted arcs are congruent. *Explain* why or why not.

13. 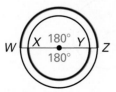   14.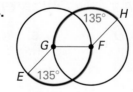

LESSON
6.2

Exercise Set A

MM2G3b Understand and use properties of central, inscribed, and related angles.

MM2G3d Justify measurements and relationships in circles using geometric and algebraic properties.

In ⊙F, determine whether the given arc is a *minor arc*, *major arc*, or *semicircle*.

1. $\overset{\frown}{AB}$

2. $\overset{\frown}{AE}$

3. $\overset{\frown}{EAC}$

4. $\overset{\frown}{ACD}$

5. $\overset{\frown}{CAD}$

6. $\overset{\frown}{DEB}$

7. $\overset{\frown}{BAE}$

8. $\overset{\frown}{DEC}$

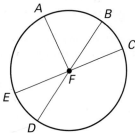

In the figure, $\overline{PR}$ and $\overline{QS}$ are diameters of ⊙U. Find the measure of the indicated arc.

9. $m\overset{\frown}{PQ}$

10. $m\overset{\frown}{ST}$

11. $m\overset{\frown}{TPS}$

12. $m\overset{\frown}{RT}$

13. $m\overset{\frown}{RQS}$

14. $m\overset{\frown}{QR}$

15. $m\overset{\frown}{PQS}$

16. $m\overset{\frown}{TQR}$

17. $m\overset{\frown}{PS}$

18. $m\overset{\frown}{PTR}$

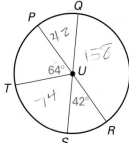

$\overset{\frown}{PQ}$ has a measure of 90° in ⊙R. Find the length of $\overline{PQ}$.

19.

20.

Find the indicated arc measure.

21. $m\overset{\frown}{AC}$

22. $m\overset{\frown}{ACB}$

23. $m\overset{\frown}{DAB}$

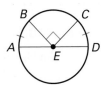

Two diameters of ⊙T are $\overline{PQ}$ and $\overline{RS}$. Find the given arc measure if $m\overset{\frown}{PR} = 35°$.

24. $m\overset{\frown}{PS}$

25. $m\overset{\frown}{PSR}$

26. $m\overset{\frown}{PRQ}$

27. $m\overset{\frown}{PRS}$

UNIT 6

Exercise Set A (continued)

Two diameters of ⊙N are $\overline{JK}$ and $\overline{LM}$. Find the given arc measure if $m\widehat{JM} = 165°$.

28. $m\widehat{JL}$ **29.** $m\widehat{JMK}$ **30.** $m\widehat{JLM}$ **31.** $m\widehat{KLM}$

Tell whether the given arcs are congruent.

32. $\widehat{JK}$ and $\widehat{QR}$

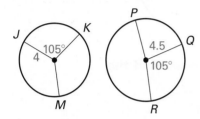

33. $\widehat{AB}$ and $\widehat{CD}$

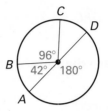

34. $\widehat{EF}$ and $\widehat{GH}$

35. $\widehat{STV}$ and $\widehat{UVT}$

Game Shows Each game show wheel shown is divided into congruent sections. Find the measure of each arc.

36. 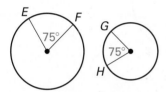   **37.** 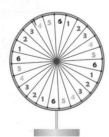   **38.**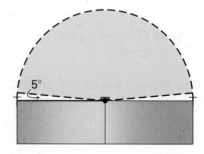

In Exercises 39 and 40, use the following information.

Sprinkler A water sprinkler covers the shaded area shown in the figure. It moves through the covered area at a rate of about 5° per second.

39. What is the measure of the arc covered by the sprinkler?

40. If the sprinkler starts at the far left position, how long will it take for the sprinkler to reach the far right position?

UNIT 6

LESSON
6.2
Exercise
Set B

MM2G3b   Understand and use properties of central, inscribed, and related angles.

MM2G3d   Justify measurements and relationships in circles using geometric and algebraic properties.

$\overline{MQ}$ and $\overline{NR}$ are diameters of $\odot O$. Determine whether the given arc is a
minor arc, major arc, or *semicircle.* Then find the measure of the arc.

1. $\overarc{MN}$

2. $\overarc{NQ}$

3. $\overarc{NQR}$

4. $\overarc{MRP}$

5. $\overarc{PN}$

6. $\overarc{MNQ}$

7. $\overarc{QR}$

8. $\overarc{MR}$

9. $\overarc{QMR}$

10. $\overarc{PQ}$

11. $\overarc{PRN}$

12. $\overarc{MQN}$

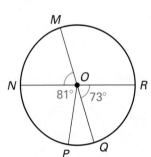

Find the indicated arc measure.

13. $m\overarc{QS}$

14. $m\overarc{LKJ}$

15. $m\overarc{DH}$

Find the value of *x*.

16.

17.

18.

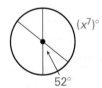

$\overline{AC}$ and $\overline{BD}$ are diameters of $\odot E$. Find the measure of the given arc if
$m\overarc{ACD} = 316°$.

19. $m\overarc{AD}$

20. $m\overarc{BC}$

21. $m\overarc{BCA}$

22. $m\overarc{DCB}$

23. $m\overarc{AB}$

24. $m\overarc{CDB}$

$\overline{RT}$ and $\overline{PS}$ are diameters of $\odot N$. Find the measure of the given arc if
$m\overarc{TP} = 47°$.

25. $m\overarc{ST}$

26. $m\overarc{PR}$

27. $m\overarc{RTP}$

28. $m\overarc{STR}$

29. $m\overarc{TPS}$

30. $m\overarc{PRT}$

UNIT 6

Exercise Set B (continued)

31. Error Analysis *Explain* what is wrong with the statement.

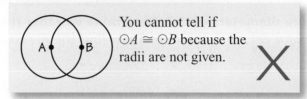

You cannot tell if $\odot A \cong \odot B$ because the radii are not given.

Tell whether $\overset{\frown}{AB} \cong \overset{\frown}{CD}$. Explain.

32.

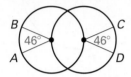

33.

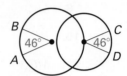

34.

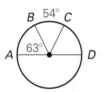

35.

36.

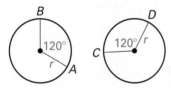

37.

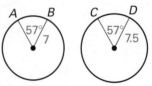

In Exercises 38–42, use the following information.

Game Timer The device shown is a 10-second game timer. The top plunger button alternatively stops and starts the timer. For game play, the timer is started at 10 (as shown) and moves counterclockwise. Players often start and stop the timer several times before it reaches 0. Give all answers to the nearest tenth.

38. What is the measure of the arc traced out by the tip of the pointer as it moves from one number to the next on the timer?

39. What is the measure of the arc traced out as the pointer moves counterclockwise from the 10 to the 0?

40. A player starts the timer at the 10 and stops it after 3.4 seconds. What is the measure of the arc generated?

41. A player stops the timer after 2.3 seconds, then after 1.2 seconds, and again after 2.5 seconds. What is the sum of the measures of the arcs?

42. How much time does it take the pointer to trace out an arc of 60°?

Problem Solving Workshop

Problem A recent survey asked teenagers to name their favorite fruit. Some of the results are shown in the circle graph. Find the indicated arc measures.

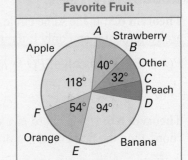

Favorite Fruit

a. $m\widehat{CD}$ b. $m\widehat{AC}$

c. $m\widehat{AFD}$ d. $m\widehat{FC}$

STEP 1 Read and Understand

What do you know?

The given arc measures in the circle

What do you want to find out?

Any missing arc measures and the measures of arcs added together

STEP 2 Make a Plan Use what you know to solve the problem.

STEP 3 Solve the Problem Use the known arc measures to solve the problem.

a. $m\widehat{CD} = 360° - m\widehat{CAD}$

$= 360° - 338°$

$= 22°$

b. $m\widehat{AC} = m\widehat{AB} + m\widehat{BC}$

$= 40° + 32°$

$= 72°$

c. $m\widehat{AFD} = m\widehat{AF} + m\widehat{FE} + m\widehat{ED}$

$= 118° + 54° + 94°$

$= 266°$

d. $m\widehat{FC} = m\widehat{FE} + m\widehat{ED} + m\widehat{DC}$

$= 54° + 94° + 22°$

$= 170°$

STEP 4 Look Back You can also solve the problem by using other arc measures.

In part (c), you can find $m\widehat{AD}$ and subtract this from 360° to find $m\widehat{AFD}$.

Practice

1. **Measuring Arcs** $\overline{KM}$ and $\overline{LN}$ are diameters of the circle. Determine whether the arc is a *minor arc*, a *major arc*, or a *semicircle*. Then find the measure of the arc.

a. $m\widehat{JK}$

b. $m\widehat{NM}$

c. $m\widehat{LM}$

d. $m\widehat{KNM}$

e. $m\widehat{NK}$

f. $m\widehat{LJM}$

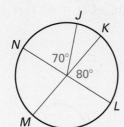

2. **Survey** A recent survey asked teenagers to name their favorite vegetable. Some of the results are shown in the circle graph below. Find the indicated arc measures.

a. $m\widehat{RS}$

b. $m\widehat{RT}$

c. $m\widehat{TQR}$

d. $m\widehat{PS}$

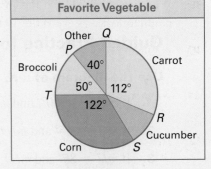

Favorite Vegetable

Apply Properties of Chords

Georgia Performance Standards: MM2G3a, MM2G3d

Goal Use relationships of arcs and chords in a circle.

Vocabulary

Theorem 6.5: In the same circle, or in congruent circles, two minor arcs are congruent if and only if their corresponding chords are congruent.

$\widehat{PQ} \cong \widehat{RS}$ if and only if $\overline{PQ} \cong \overline{RS}$.

Theorem 6.6: If one chord is a perpendicular bisector of another chord, then the first chord is a diameter.

If $\overline{BD}$ is a perpendicular bisector of $\overline{EC}$, then $\overline{BD}$ is a diameter of the circle.

Theorem 6.7: If a diameter of a circle is perpendicular to a chord, then the diameter bisects the chord and its arc.

If $\overline{WY}$ is a diameter and $\overline{WY} \perp \overline{VX}$, then $\overline{ZV} \cong \overline{ZX}$ and $\widehat{YV} \cong \widehat{YX}$.

Theorem 6.8: In the same circle, or in congruent circles, two chords are congruent if and only if they are equidistant from the center.

$\overline{FG} \cong \overline{HJ}$ if and only if $KL = KM$.

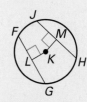

| **Example 1** | **Use congruent chords to find an arc measure** |

In the diagram, $\odot A \cong \odot B$, $\overline{CD} \cong \overline{EF}$ and $m\widehat{CD} = 140°$. Find $m\widehat{EF}$.

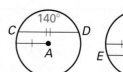

Solution

Because $\overline{CD}$ and $\overline{EF}$ are congruent chords in congruent circles, the corresponding minor arcs $\widehat{CD}$ and $\widehat{EF}$ are congruent. So, $m\widehat{CD} = m\widehat{EF} = 140°$.

Guided Practice for Example 1

Use the diagram of $\odot K$.

1. If $m\widehat{GH} = 100°$, find $m\widehat{IJ}$.

2. If $m\widehat{GI} = 55°$ and $m\widehat{HJ} = 115°$, find $m\widehat{GH}$.

3. If $m\widehat{IJ} = 85°$ and $m\widehat{HJ} = 120°$, find $m\widehat{GI}$.

Georgia Performance Standards

MM2G3a Understand and use properties of chords, tangents, and secants as an application of triangle similarity.

MM2G3d Justify measurements and relationships in circles using geometric and algebraic properties.

Example 2 **Use perpendicular bisectors**

Three baseball players stand in a field as shown. Where should a fourth player, Player *X*, stand if he wanted to throw the ball the same distance to each player?

Solution

STEP 1 **Draw** segments $\overline{RS}$ and $\overline{ST}$ as shown.

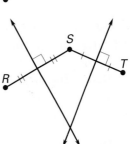

STEP 2 **Draw** the perpendicular bisectors of $\overline{RS}$ and $\overline{ST}$. By Theorem 6.6, these are diameters of the circle containing *R*, *S*, and *T*.

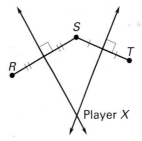

STEP 3 **Find** the point where these bisectors intersect. This is the center of the circle containing points *R*, *S*, and *T*, so it is equidistant from each point. This is where Player *X* should stand.

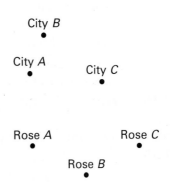

Guided Practice for Example 2

4. Three cities are located on a map as shown. A wireless communications company plans to build a relay tower to provide cell phone service to each of the cities. In order to provide the cities with a signal of equal strength, the tower must be placed equidistant from each. Show and explain how this location can be determined.

City *B*

City *A*
    City *C*

5. Three rose bushes are located in a garden as shown. You are installing an underground sprinkler system to water the garden. Where should you place the sprinkler head so that it is equidistant from each bush? Show and explain how this location can be determined.

Rose *A*   Rose *C*
    Rose *B*

Example 3 Use Theorem 6.8

In the diagram of ⊙C, QR = ST = 16. Find CU.

Solution

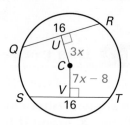

Chords $\overline{QR}$ and $\overline{ST}$ are congruent, so by Theorem 6.8 they are equidistant from C. Therefore, $CU = CV$.

$CU = CV$ By Theorem 6.8

$3x = 7x - 8$ Substitute $3x$ for CU and $7x - 8$ for CV.

$x = 2$ Solve for x.

So, $CU = 3x = 3(2) = 6$.

Example 4 Use chords with triangle similarity

In ⊙G, AJ = 26, FG = 5, HJ = 10, AH = BE = 24, and $\overline{AJ} \perp \overline{BE}$. Show that △EDG ~ △AHJ.

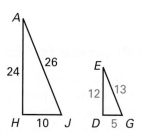

STEP 1 **Determine** the side lengths of $\triangle AHJ$.

The side lengths of $\triangle AHJ$ are $AH = 24$, $AJ = 26$, and $HJ = 10$.

STEP 2 **Determine** the side lengths of $\triangle EDG$.

$\overline{GE}$ is a radius and $\overline{AJ}$ is a diameter so $GE = \frac{1}{2}AJ = \frac{1}{2}(26) = 13$.

Diameter $\overline{AJ}$ is perpendicular to $\overline{BE}$, so by Theorem 6.7 $\overline{AJ}$ bisects $\overline{BE}$.

Therefore, $DE = \frac{1}{2}BE = \frac{1}{2}(24) = 12$. Chords $\overline{AH}$ and $\overline{BE}$ are congruent, so by Theorem 6.8, they are equidistant from G and therefore $DG = FG = 5$. The side lengths of $\triangle EDG$ are $DE = 12$, $GE = 13$, and $DG = 5$.

STEP 3 **Find** the ratios of corresponding side lengths.

$\frac{AH}{DE} = \frac{24}{12} = 2$, $\frac{AJ}{GE} = \frac{26}{13} = 2$, and $\frac{HJ}{DG} = \frac{10}{5} = 2$.

Because the side lengths are proportional, $\triangle EDG \sim \triangle AHJ$ by the Side-Side-Side Similarity Theorem.

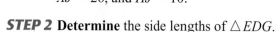

Guided Practice for Examples 3 and 4

In the diagram in Example 3, suppose ST = 24, and CU = 12. Find the given length.

6. QR **7.** QU **8.** CV

9. In Example 4, suppose $AJ = 34$, $FG = 8$, $HJ = 16$, $AH = BE = 30$, and $\overline{AJ} \perp \overline{BE}$. Show that $\triangle EDG \sim \triangle AHJ$.

LESSON
6.3

Exercise
Set A

MM2G3a Understand and use properties of chords, tangents, and secants as an application of triangle similarity.

MM2G3d Justify measurements and relationships in circles using geometric and algebraic properties.

Find the measure of the given arc or chord.

1. $m\widehat{BC}$

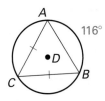

2. $m\widehat{LM}$

3. $\overline{QS}$

4. $m\widehat{AC}$

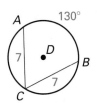

5. $m\widehat{PQR}$

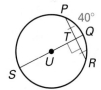

6. $m\widehat{KLM}$

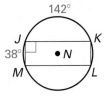

Find the value of x.

7.

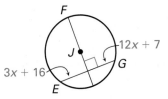

8.

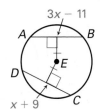

9.

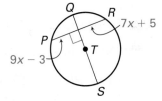

10.

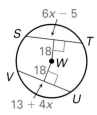

11.

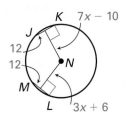

12.

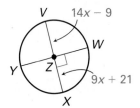

13. **Error Analysis** *Explain* what is wrong with the diagram of $\odot X$.

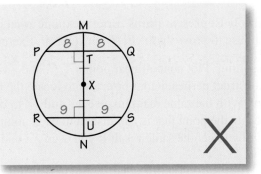

UNIT 6

Exercise Set A (continued)

14. **Proof** Copy and complete the proof.

GIVEN: $\overline{AC}$ is a diameter of $\odot F$. $\overline{AC} \perp \overline{BD}$

PROVE: $\overset{\frown}{AD} \cong \overset{\frown}{AB}$

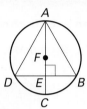

Statements	Reasons
1. $\overline{AC}$ is a diameter of $\odot F$. $\overline{AC} \perp \overline{BD}$	**1.** ?
2. ?	**2.** All right angles are congruent.
3. $\overline{DE} \cong \overline{BE}$	**3.** ?
4. $\overline{AE} \cong \overline{AE}$	**4.** ?
5. $\triangle AED \cong \triangle AEB$	**5.** ?
6. ?	**6.** Corresponding parts of congruent triangles are congruent.
7. $\overset{\frown}{AD} \cong \overset{\frown}{AB}$	**7.** ?

15. **Proof** Copy and complete the proof.

GIVEN: $\overline{PQ}$ is a diameter of $\odot U$. $\overset{\frown}{PT} \cong \overset{\frown}{QS}$

PROVE: $\triangle PUT \cong \triangle QUS$

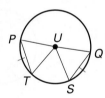

Statements	Reasons
1. $\overline{PQ}$ is a diameter of $\odot U$. $\overset{\frown}{PT} \cong \overset{\frown}{QS}$	**1.** ?
2. ?	**2.** Theorem 6.5
3. $\overline{UP} \cong \overline{UQ} \cong \overline{UT} \cong \overline{US}$	**3.** ?
4. $\triangle PUT \cong \triangle QUS$	**4.** ?

16. **Multiple Representations** Briefly explain what other congruence postulate you could use to prove that $\triangle PUT \cong \triangle QUS$ in Exercise 15.

17. **Reasoning** Plot noncollinear points X, Y, and Z on a piece of paper. Use $\overline{XY}$ and $\overline{XZ}$ to construct perpendicular bisectors to locate the point that is equidistant to each point. With the same diagram, use $\overline{XY}$ and $\overline{YZ}$ to construct perpendicular bisectors to locate the point that is equidistant to each point. Are the two points the same? Would you get the same result if you used $\overline{XZ}$ and $\overline{YZ}$? *Explain.*

UNIT 6

What can you conclude about the diagram? State a theorem that justifies your answer.

1.

2.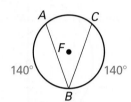

3.

P is the center of the circle. Use the given information to find XY.

4. $ZY = 3$

5. $ZY = 6, XW = 4$

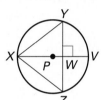

6. $CA = 3$

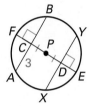

Find the measure of $\overparen{MN}$.

7.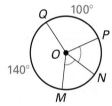

8.

9.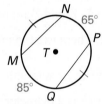

10.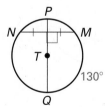

11.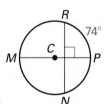

12.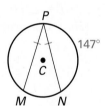

13.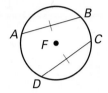

14.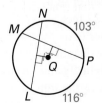

15.

Exercise Set B *(continued)*

Use the figure to match the chord or arc with a congruent arc or chord.

16. $\overset{\frown}{FB}$ **A.** $\overset{\frown}{FE}$

17. $\overline{AF}$ **B.** $\overset{\frown}{ED}$

18. $\overset{\frown}{BC}$ **C.** $\overset{\frown}{EC}$

19. $\overline{EC}$ **D.** $\overline{AB}$

20. $\overset{\frown}{DC}$ **E.** $\overline{BF}$

21. $\overline{PD}$ **F.** $\overline{PA}$

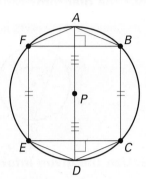

22. In $\odot F$, $\overline{BG}$ is perpendicular to $\overline{AC}$. *Explain* why $\triangle ABD \sim \triangle EDF$.

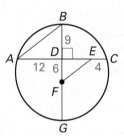

23. **Proof** Write a paragraph proof.

   GIVEN: X, Y, and Z are noncollinear points.

   PROVE: There exists a circle that contains X, Y, and Z.

24. **Proof** Write a paragraph proof.

   GIVEN: $\overline{IF}$ is a diameter and $\overline{DG} \cong \overline{EH}$.

   PROVE: $\angle DJI \cong \angle HJI$
   (Hint: Construct perpendicular bisectors.)

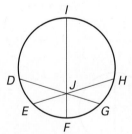

25. **Pool** You challenge a friend to find a way to use three 10-foot boards to mark the location of the center of a circular swimming pool with a diameter of 12 feet. Your friend centers the top board on the other two boards and makes sure its ends are the same distance from the edge of the pool as shown at the right. Then your friend marks a spot on the exact center of the top board. Is this the center of the pool? *Explain.*

Use Inscribed Angles and Polygons

Georgia Performance Standards: MM2G3b, MM2G3d

Goal Use inscribed angles of circles.

Vocabulary

An **inscribed angle** is an angle whose vertex is on a circle and whose sides contain chords of the circle.

The arc that lies in the interior of an inscribed angle and has endpoints on the angle is called the **intercepted arc** of the angle.

Theorem 6.9 Measure of an Inscribed Angle Theorem: The measure of an inscribed angle is one half the measure of its intercepted arc.

Theorem 6.10: If two inscribed angles of a circle intercept the same arc, then the angles are congruent.

A polygon is an **inscribed polygon** if all of its vertices lie on a circle. The circle that contains the vertices is a **circumscribed circle.**

Theorem 6.11: If a right triangle is inscribed in a circle, then the hypotenuse is a diameter of the circle. Conversely, if one side of an inscribed triangle is a diameter of the circle, then the triangle is a right triangle and the angle opposite the diameter is the right angle.

Theorem 6.12: A quadrilateral can be inscribed in a circle if and only if its opposite angles are supplementary.

UNIT 6

Example 1   Use inscribed angles

Find (a) $m\overset{\frown}{YZ}$ and (b) $m\angle YWZ$.

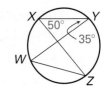

a. $\angle YXZ$ intercepts $\overset{\frown}{YZ}$. So the measure of $\angle YXZ$ is one half the measure of $\overset{\frown}{YZ}$ or the measure of $\overset{\frown}{YZ}$ is twice the measure of $\angle YXZ$.

$$m\overset{\frown}{YZ} = 2m\angle YXZ \qquad \text{Theorem 6.9}$$
$$= 2(50°) \qquad \text{Substitute } 50° \text{ for } m\angle YXZ.$$
$$= 100° \qquad \text{Multiply.}$$

b. $\angle YXZ$ and $\angle YWZ$ both intercept $\overset{\frown}{YZ}$.

$$\angle YWZ \cong \angle YXZ \qquad \text{Theorem 6.10}$$
$$m\angle YWZ = m\angle YXZ \qquad \text{Congruent angles have equal measures.}$$
$$m\angle YWZ = 50° \qquad \text{Substitute } 50° \text{ for } m\angle YXZ.$$

Guided Practice for Example 1

Use the diagram in Example 1 to find the given measure.

1. $m\overset{\frown}{WX}$

2. $m\angle WZX$

Georgia Performance Standards

MM2G3b Understand and use properties of central, inscribed, and related angles.

MM2G3d Justify measurements and relationships in circles using geometric and algebraic properties.

Example 2 Use a circumscribed circle

Home Security You want to illuminate the front exterior of your house with spotlights that have a 90° range of projection. You position one spotlight as shown to maximize efficiency. However, it's not quite bright enough, so you want to add additional lights. Where else can you place the spotlights in order to get the brightest results?

Solution

From Theorem 6.11, if a right triangle is inscribed in a circle, then the hypotenuse of the triangle is the diameter of the circle. Draw a circle that has the front of the house as the diameter. Place a spotlight anywhere on the semicircle so that the entire front of the house is within the 90° range.

Guided Practice for Example 2

3. In Example 2, explain how you would position the spotlight if you wanted to illuminate both the front and right side of the house.

Example 3 Use Theorem 6.12

Find the value of each variable.

Solution

Quadrilateral $ABCD$ is inscribed in a circle. So, by Theorem 6.12, opposite angles are supplementary.

$m\angle A + m\angle C = 180°$ $\qquad$ $m\angle B + m\angle D = 180°$

$\quad 95° + q° = 180°$ $\qquad$ $\quad 110° + p° = 180°$

$\qquad q = 85$ $\qquad\qquad\qquad\quad p = 70$

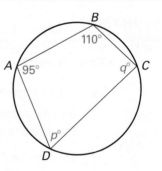

Guided Practice for Example 3

4. Find the measure of each interior angle of the quadrilateral.

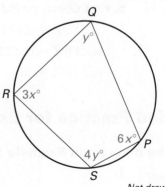

Not drawn to scale

MM2G3b Understand and use properties of central, inscribed, and related angles.

MM2G3d Justify measurements and relationships in circles using geometric and algebraic properties.

1. **Multiple Choice** In the figure shown, which statement is true?

   A. $\angle SPR \cong \angle PSQ$ **B.** $\angle RQS \cong \angle RPS$

   C. $\angle RPS \cong \angle PRQ$ **D.** $\angle PRQ \cong \angle SQR$

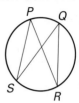

Find the measure of the indicated angle or arc in $\odot P$.

2. $m\widehat{ST}$

3. $m\widehat{AB}$

4. $m\angle JLM$

5. $m\angle A$

6. $m\angle K$

7. $m\widehat{VST}$

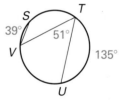

Find the measure of the indicated angle or arc in $\odot P$, given $m\widehat{LM} = 84°$ and $m\widehat{KN} = 116°$.

8. $m\angle JKL$ 9. $m\angle MKL$

10. $m\angle KMN$ 11. $m\angle JKM$

12. $m\angle KLN$ 13. $m\angle LNM$

14. $m\widehat{MJ}$ 15. $m\widehat{LKJ}$

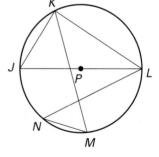

In Exercises 16–18, find the values of the variables.

16.

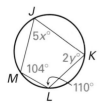

17.

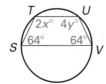

18.

UNIT 6

Exercise Set B (continued)

Determine whether a circle can be circumscribed about the figure.

18.

19.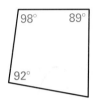

20.

Find the value(s) of the variable(s). (In Exercise 22, $\overline{AB}$ is a diameter of $\odot O$.)

21.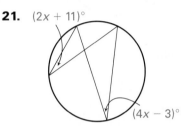

22.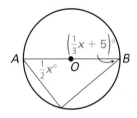

23.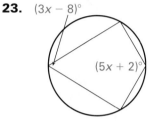

24.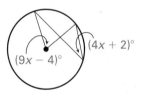

25.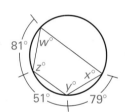

26.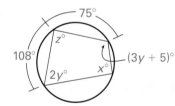

27. **Proof** Write a paragraph proof.

    GIVEN: $\odot C$, $\overline{FG} \cong \overline{GE}$

    PROVE: $\triangle DEF$ is isosceles.
          (*Hint:* Draw an additional segment.)

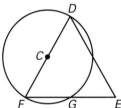

28. **Proof** Write a paragraph proof.

    GIVEN: $\odot Q$ and $\odot P$ are tangent at R.

    PROVE: $\overline{RS} \cong \overline{ST}$

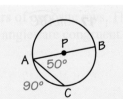

29. **Error Analysis** *Describe* the error in the diagram of $\odot C$. Find two ways to correct the error.

Investigating Math Activity
Arcs and Angles

Use before Lesson 6.5

Question

What is the relationship between an inscribed angle and the arc it intercepts when the angle is formed by a tangent line and a chord?

Explore

Investigate angles formed by chords and tangent lines.

Copy and complete the table below. Use your protractor to measure ∠1 and ∠2 in each of the diagrams below.

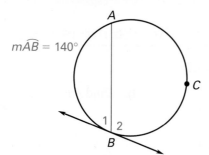

Diagram 1

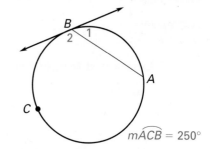

Diagram 2

	$m\widehat{AB}$	$m\angle 1$	$m\widehat{ACB}$	$m\angle 2$
Diagram 1	?	?	?	?
Diagram 2	?	?	?	?

Draw Conclusions

1. In diagrams 1 and 2, what is the relationship between the measure of ∠1 and the measure of $\widehat{AB}$?

2. In diagrams 1 and 2, what is the relationship between the measure of ∠2 and the measure of $\widehat{ACB}$?

3. **Reasoning** In general, what is the relationship between an inscribed angle and the arc it intercepts when the angle is formed by a tangent line and a chord?

4. **Writing** Without using your protractor, find $m\angle 1$, $m\angle 2$, and $m\widehat{PRQ}$ of the circle at the right. *Explain* how you found each of the measures.

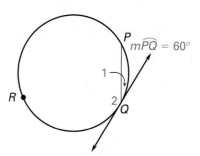

LESSON
6.5
Georgia Performance Standards: MM2G3b, MM2G3d

Apply Other Angle Relationships in Circles

Goal Find the measures of angles inside or outside a circle.

Vocabulary

Theorem 6.13: If a tangent and a chord intersect at a point on the circle, then the measure of each angle formed is one half the measure of its intercepted arc.

Theorem 6.14 Angles Inside the Circle Theorem: If two chords intersect *inside* a circle, then the measure of each angle is one half the *sum* of the measures of the arcs intercepted by the angle and its vertical angle.

Theorem 6.15 Angles Outside the Circle Theorem: If a tangent and a secant, two tangents, or two secants intersect *outside* a circle, then the measure of the angle formed is one half the *difference* of the measures of the intercepted arcs.

Example 1   **Find the angle and the arc measures**

Line *x* is a tangent to the circle.

a. Find $m\angle 1$.

b. Find $m\widehat{EFG}$.

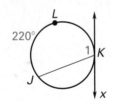
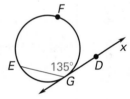

Solution

a. $m\angle 1 = \frac{1}{2}m\widehat{JLK}$ Theorem 6.13

$= \frac{1}{2}(220°)$ Substitute 220° for $m\widehat{JLK}$.

$= 110°$ Multiply.

b. $m\widehat{EFG} = 2(m\angle EGD)$ Theorem 6.13

$= 2(135°)$ Substitute 135° for $\angle EGD$.

$= 270°$ Multiply.

Guided Practice for Example 1

The line shown is a tangent to the circle. Find the indicated measure.

1. $m\widehat{PRQ}$

2. $m\angle 1$

3. $m\widehat{XZ}$

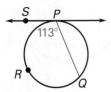

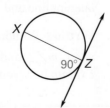

Example 2 Find an angle measure inside a circle

Find the value of x.

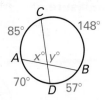

Solution

The chords $\overline{AB}$ and $\overline{CD}$ intersect inside the circle. By Theorem 6.14:

$$x° = \frac{1}{2}\left(m\widehat{AC} + m\widehat{BD}\right) = \frac{1}{2}(85° + 57°) = 71°$$

$$x = 71$$

Example 3 Find an angle measure outside a circle

Find the value of x.

a.

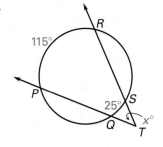

b.

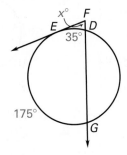

Solution

a. The secants $\overrightarrow{TR}$ and $\overrightarrow{TP}$ intersect outside the circle. By Theorem 6.15:

$$x° = \frac{1}{2}\left(m\widehat{PR} - m\widehat{QS}\right) = \frac{1}{2}(115° - 25°) = 45°$$

$$x = 45$$

b. The secant $\overrightarrow{FG}$ and the tangent $\overrightarrow{FE}$ intersect outside the circle. By Theorem 6.15:

$$x° = \frac{1}{2}\left(m\widehat{EG} - m\widehat{ED}\right) = \frac{1}{2}(175° - 35°) = 70°$$

$$x = 70$$

Guided Practice for Examples 2 and 3

4. Using the diagram in Example 2, find the value of y.

5. Find $m\angle 1$.

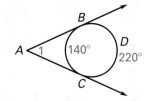

UNIT 6

LESSON
6.5

Exercise
Set A

MM2G3b Understand and use properties of central, inscribed, and related angles.

MM2G3d Justify measurements and relationships in circles using geometric and algebraic properties.

Find the indicated arc measure.

1. $m\widehat{AB}$

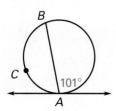

2. $m\widehat{FH}$

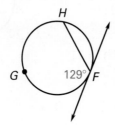

3. $m\widehat{JKL}$

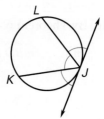

Find $m\angle 1$.

4.

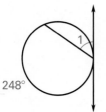

5.

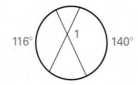

6.

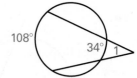

7.

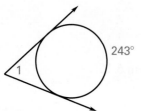

8.

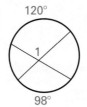

9.

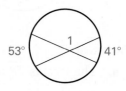

10.

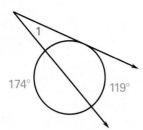

11.

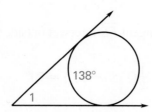

12.

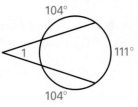

In Exercises 13–15, find the value of x.

13.

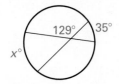

14.

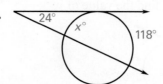

15.

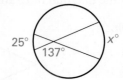

Exercise Set A (continued)

In Exercises 16–18, find the value of x.

16.

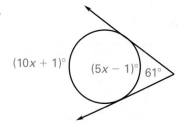

$(10x + 1)°$ $(5x − 1)°$ $61°$

17.

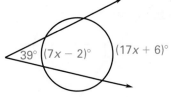

$39°$ $(7x − 2)°$ $(17x + 6)°$

18.

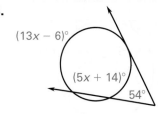

$(13x − 6)°$ $(5x + 14)°$ $54°$

19. Angle Measures In the diagram shown, *m* is tangent to the circle at the point *S*. Find the measures of all the numbered angles.

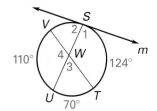

Use the diagram shown to find the measure of the angle.

20. $m\angle CAF$ **21.** $m\angle AFB$

22. $m\angle CEF$ **23.** $m\angle CFB$

24. $m\angle DCF$ **25.** $m\angle BCD$

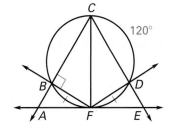

In Exercises 26 and 27, the circles have center P. Find the value of x.

26.

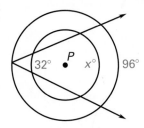

$32°$ P $x°$ $96°$

27.

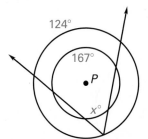

$124°$ $167°$ P $x°$

28. Transportation A plane is flying at an altitude of about 7 miles above Earth as shown in the diagram. What is the measure of arc *TV* that represents the part of Earth you can see? The radius of Earth is about 4000 miles.

29. Mountain Climbing A mountain climber is standing on top of a mountain that is about 4.75 miles above sea level. Use the information from Exercise 28 to find the measure of the arc that represents the part of Earth the mountain climber can see.

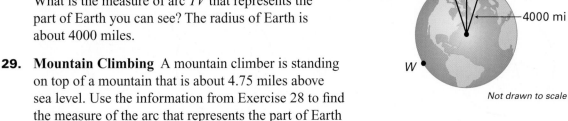

4007 mi   4000 mi

Not drawn to scale

UNIT 6

Exercise Set B

MM2G3b Understand and use properties of central, inscribed, and related angles.

MM2G3d Justify measurements and relationships in circles using geometric and algebraic properties.

Find the measure of ∠1.

1.

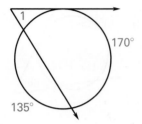

170°

135°

2.

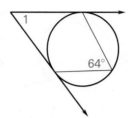

64°

3.

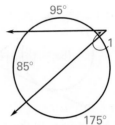

95°

85°

175°

4.

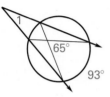

65°

93°

5.

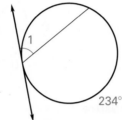

234°

6.

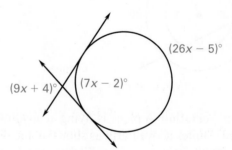

142°

93°

Use the information given in the diagram to find the measure.

7. $m\widehat{TV}$

8. $m\widehat{SV}$

9. $m\angle STU$

10. $m\angle VWU$

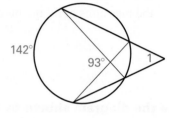

124°

Find the value of x.

11.

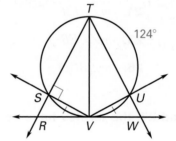

$x°$

$(2x - 20)°$

$(3x + 17)°$

12.

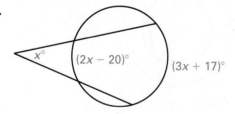

$(26x - 5)°$

$(9x + 4)°$ $(7x - 2)°$

13.

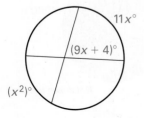

$11x°$

$(9x + 4)°$

$(x^2)°$

14.

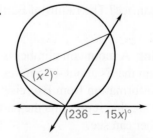

$(x^2)°$

$(236 - 15x)°$

UNIT 6

Exercise Set B *(continued)*

Use the given information to find the indicated quantity.

15. **GIVEN:** $\overline{AB} \cong \overline{CD}$, $m\widehat{ACD} = 200°$

   FIND: $m\angle P$

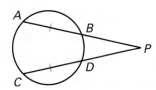

16. **GIVEN:** The two circles intersect at A and B;
   $m\angle AXB = 70°$, $m\widehat{CD} = 20°$,
   $m\widehat{EF} = 160°$

   FIND: The difference between the measures of
   $\widehat{AB}$ of the smaller circle and $\widehat{AB}$ of the
   larger circle

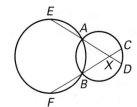

17. **Proof** Write a paragraph proof.

   GIVEN: In the diagram, line m is tangent to both
   circles at T, line j is tangent to the small
   circle at U, and line k is tangent to the large
   circle at V.

   PROVE: $m\angle TJU = m\angle TKV$

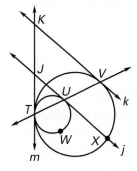

18. **Proof** Write a paragraph proof.

   GIVEN: $m\widehat{AG} = 2 \cdot m\widehat{CE}$
   PROVE: $m\widehat{CE} + 2 \cdot m\widehat{BF} = 360°$

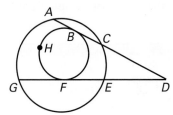

19. **Multiple Representations** Points X and Y are on a circle and t is a tangent line
   containing X and another point Z.

   a. **Drawing a Diagram** Draw two different diagrams that illustrate this situation.
   b. **Writing an Equation** Write an equation for $m\widehat{XY}$ in terms of $m\angle YXZ$ for
   each diagram.
   c. **Solving an Equation** When will these equations give the same value for $m\widehat{XY}$?

20. **Reasoning** Use the diagram to show that
   $m\widehat{VY} = r° - s°$.

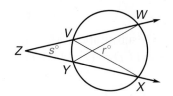

Find Segment Lengths in Circles

Georgia Performance Standards: MM2G3a, MM2G3d

Goal Find segment lengths in circles.

Vocabulary

When two chords intersect in the interior of a circle, each chord is divided into two segments that are called **segments of a chord.**

Theorem 6.16 Segments of Chords Theorem:
If two chords intersect in the interior of a circle, then the product of the lengths of the segments of one chord is equal to the product of the lengths of the segments of the other chord.

$$EA \cdot EB = EC \cdot ED$$

A **secant segment** is a segment that contains a chord of a circle, and has exactly one endpoint outside the circle. The part of the secant segment that is outside the circle is called an **external segment.**

Theorem 6.17 Segments of Secants Theorem:
If two secant segments share the same endpoint outside a circle, then the product of the lengths of one secant segment and its external segment equals the product of the lengths of the other secant segment and its external segment.

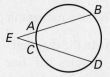

$$EA \cdot EB = EC \cdot ED$$

Theorem 6.18 Segments of Secants and Tangents Theorem:
If a secant segment and a tangent segment share an endpoint outside a circle, then the product of the lengths of the secant segment and its external segment equals the square of the length of the tangent segment.

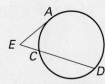

$$EA^2 = EC \cdot ED$$

Example 1   **Find lengths using Theorem 6.16**

Find *AB* and *CD*.

Solution

By Theorem 6.16, $EA \cdot EB = EC \cdot ED$.

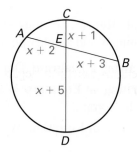

$$(x + 2)(x + 3) = (x + 1)(x + 5)$$

$$x^2 + 5x + 6 = x^2 + 6x + 5$$

$$5x + 6 = 6x + 5$$

$$1 = x$$

By substitution, $AB = (x + 2) + (x + 3) = (1 + 2) + (1 + 3) = 7$
and $CD = (x + 1) + (x + 5) = (1 + 1) + (1 + 5) = 8$.

Georgia Performance Standards

MM2G3a Understand and use properties of chords, tangents, and secants as an application of triangle similarity.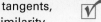

MM2G3d Justify measurements and relationships in circles using geometric and algebraic properties.

In Example 1, suppose segments $\overline{AD}$ and $\overline{CB}$ are drawn to create two triangles. Using the Segments of Chords Theorem, you can reason that $\dfrac{EC}{EA} = \dfrac{EB}{ED}$. You also know that $\angle AED \cong \angle CEB$ by the Vertical Angles Theorem. So, $\triangle AED \sim \triangle CEB$ by the SAS Triangle Similarity Theorem. Similar triangles can also be seen in Example 2.

Example 2 **Find lengths using Theorem 6.17**

Find **EB** and **ED**.

Solution

By Theorem 6.17, $EA \cdot EB = EC \cdot ED$.

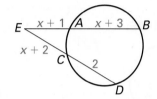

$$(x + 1)[(x + 1) + (x + 3)] = (x + 2)[(x + 2) + 2]$$

$$(x + 1)(2x + 4) = (x + 2)(x + 4)$$

$$2x^2 + 6x + 4 = x^2 + 6x + 8$$

$$x^2 = 4$$

$$x = \pm 2$$

Lengths cannot be negative so use the positive solution. By substitution,
$EB = (x + 1) + (x + 3) = (2 + 1) + (2 + 3) = 8$ and
$ED = (x + 2) + 2 = (2 + 2) + 2 = 6$.

Example 3 **Find lengths using Theorem 6.18**

Find **ED**.

By Theorem 6.18, $(EA)^2 = EC \cdot ED$.

$$(6)^2 = x(x + 9)$$

$$36 = x^2 + 9x$$

$$0 = x^2 + 9x - 36$$

$$0 = (x + 12)(x - 3)$$

$$x = -12 \text{ or } 3$$

Lengths cannot be negative so use the positive solution. By substitution,
$ED = x + 9 = 3 + 9 = 12$.

Guided Practice for Examples 1, 2, and 3

Find the value(s) of x.

1.

2.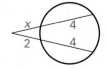

3.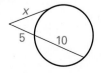

LESSON 6.6

Exercise Set A

MM2G3a   Understand and use properties of chords, tangents, and secants as an application of triangle similarity.

MM2G3d   Justify measurements and relationships in circles using geometric and algebraic properties.

Find the value of *x*.

1.

2.

3.

Find *AB* and *DE*.

4.

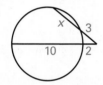

5.

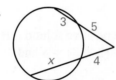

6.

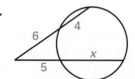

Find the value of *x*.

7.

8.

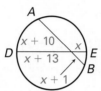

9.

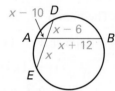

Find *RT* and *TV*.

10.

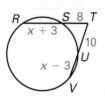

11.

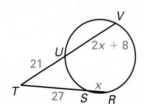

12.

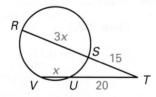

Find the value of *x*.

13.

14.

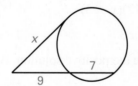

15.

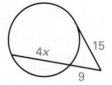

Find *PQ*.

16.

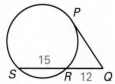

17.

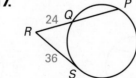

18.

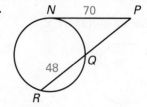

Exercise Set A *(continued)*

Find the value of x.

19.
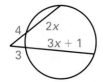
4
2x
3x + 1
3

20.
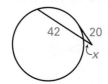
42
20
x

21.
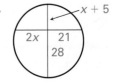
x + 5
2x   21
      28

22.
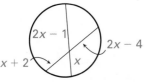
2x − 1
2x − 4
x + 2
x

23.
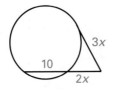
3x
10
2x

24.
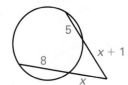
5
x + 1
8
x

25. In the diagram, $\overline{RS}$ is a tangent segment, $MP = 6$, $NP = \sqrt{30}$, $QP = 10$, and $RS = 6$. Show that $\triangle MNP \sim \triangle SRP$.

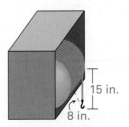

Q   S
N
M   P
      R

Not drawn to scale

26. Winch A large industrial winch is enclosed as shown. There are 15 inches of the cable hanging free off of the winch's spool and the distance from the end of the cable to the spool is 8 inches. What is the diameter of the spool?

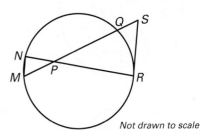

15 in.
8 in.

27. Storm Drain The diagram shows a cross-section of a large storm drain pipe with a small amount of standing water. The distance across the surface of the water is 48 inches and the water is 4.25 inches deep at its deepest point. To the nearest inch, what is the diameter of the storm drain pipe?

4.25 in.
48 in.

28. Basketball The Xs show the positions of two basketball teammates relative to the circular "key" on a basketball court. The player outside the key passes the ball to the player on the key. To the nearest tenth of a foot, how long is the pass?

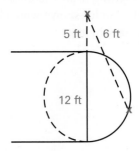

5 ft   6 ft
12 ft

UNIT 6

LESSON
6.6

**Exercise
Set B**

MM2G3a   Understand and use properties of chords, tangents,
and secants as an application of triangle similarity.

MM2G3d   Justify measurements and relationships in circles
using geometric and algebraic properties.

Find the value of x. Round decimal answers to the nearest tenth.

1.

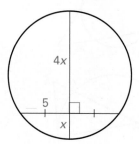

6
4
7
x

2.

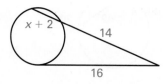

x + 2
14
16

3.

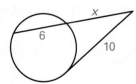

x
6
10

4.

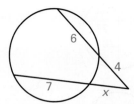

4x
5
x

5.

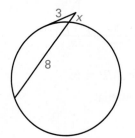

3 x
8

6.

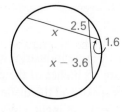

6
x
x + 3
4x

7.

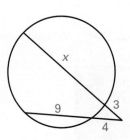

x
9
3
4

8.

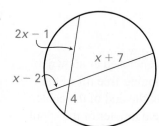

2x − 1
x + 7
x − 2
4

9.

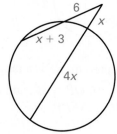

2.5
x
1.6
x − 3.6

Find all the possible values of x.

10.

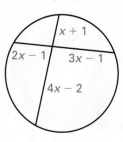

x + 1
2x − 1
3x − 1
4x − 2

11.

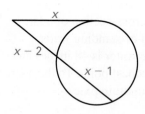

x
x − 2
x − 1

12.

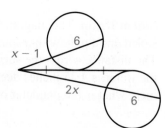

6
x − 1
2x
6

13. Reasoning Can Theorem 6.16 be used to solve for x and y
in the circles shown which have the same center? *Explain*
why or why not.

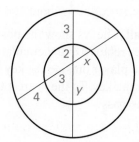

3
2
x
3
y
4

Exercise Set B (continued)

14. In the figure at the right, let $AP = x$, $PQ = x + 2$, $QB = x + 4$, $CP = 2$, $PD = 6x$, $EQ = y$, and $QD = 14$. Find AP, PQ, QB, PD, and EQ.

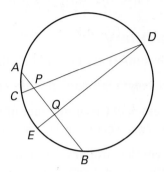

In Exercises 15 and 16, use the diagram at the right.

15. Find $m\angle PQR$.

16. **Multiple Representations** Using the Geometric Mean Theorem, you can relate the sides of $\triangle PQR$ using the proportion $\dfrac{OP}{OQ} = \dfrac{OQ}{OR}$. *Explain* how the theorem involving segments of chords can be used instead of the Geometric Mean Theorem to obtain the proportion.

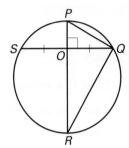

17. **Proof** Use the diagram at the right to write a paragraph proof.

   GIVEN: $\overrightarrow{OT}$ is tangent to both circles at T.
   PROVE: $OP \cdot OQ = OR \cdot OS$

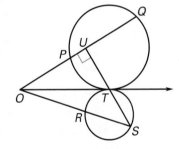

18. **Water Tank** You want to estimate the diameter of a circular water tank. You stand at a location 10.5 feet from the edge of the circular tank. From this position, your distance to a point of tangency on the tank is 23 feet.

   a. Draw a diagram of the situation. Label your position as C and the radius of the tank as r.

   b. Find the length of the radius to the nearest tenth of a foot.

19. **Satellite** A satellite is about 100 miles above Earth's surface. The satellite is taking photographs of Earth. Earth's diameter is about 8000 miles.

   a. Draw a diagram of the situation, representing Earth as a circle.

   b. In the diagram, draw a segment to show one of the farthest possible points on Earth that can be photographed from the satellite. What type of geometric figure is the segment?

   c. Find the length of the segment drawn in part (b).

Circumference and Arc Length

Georgia Performance Standards: MM2G3c

Goal Find arc lengths and other measures of circles.

Vocabulary

The **circumference** of a circle is the distance around the circle.

An **arc length** is a portion of the circumference of a circle.

Theorem 6.19 Circumference of a Circle: The circumference C of a circle is $C = \pi d$ or $C = 2\pi r$, where d is the diameter of the circle and r is the radius of the circle.

Arc Length Corollary: In a circle, the ratio of the length of a given arc to the circumference is equal to the ratio of the measure of the arc to 360°.

Example 1 — Use the formula for circumference

Find the indicated measure.

  a. Circumference of a circle with radius 11 feet

  b. Diameter of a circle with circumference 75 meters

Solution

a. $C = 2\pi r$ Write circumference formula.

     $= 2 \cdot \pi \cdot 11$ Substitute 11 for r.

     $= 22\pi$ Simplify.

     ≈ 69.12 Use a calculator.

The circumference is about 69.08 feet.

b. $C = \pi d$ Write circumference formula.

     $75 = \pi d$ Substitute 75 for C.

     $\dfrac{75}{\pi} = d$ Divide each side by π.

     $23.87 \approx d$ Use a calculator.

The diameter is about 23.87 meters.

Guided Practice for Example 1

Use the diagram to find the indicated measure.

  1. Circumference   **2.** Radius   **3.** Circumference

16 in.

$C = 35$ yd

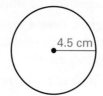

4.5 cm

Example 2 | Find arc lengths

Find the length of $\overset{\frown}{AB}$.

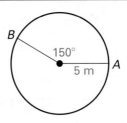

Solution

Arc length of $\overset{\frown}{AB} = \dfrac{150°}{360°} \cdot 2\pi(5) \approx 13.09$ meters.

Guided Practice for Example 2

Find the length of $\overset{\frown}{AB}$.

4.

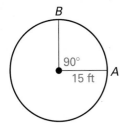

5.

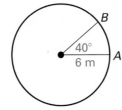

6.

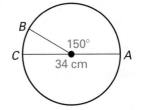

Example 3 | Use arc lengths to find measures

Find the circumference of $\odot Q$.

Solution

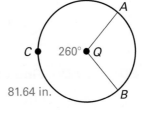

$$\dfrac{\text{Arc length of } \overset{\frown}{ACB}}{C} = \dfrac{m\overset{\frown}{ACB}}{360°}$$

$$\dfrac{81.64}{C} = \dfrac{260°}{360°}$$

$$113.04 = C$$

The circumference of $\odot Q$ is 113.04 inches.

Guided Practice for Example 3

Find the indicated measure.

7. $m\overset{\frown}{AB}$

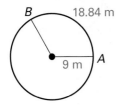

8. Radius of $\odot N$

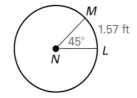

9. Circumference of $\odot Q$

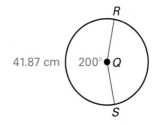

UNIT 6

LESSON
6.7

MM2G3c   Use the properties of circles to solve problems
involving the length of an arc and the area of a sector.

Exercise Set A

1. Find the circumference.

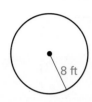

8 ft

2. Find the circumference.

13 in.

3. Find the radius.

r

$C = 65.98$ cm

Find the indicated measure.

4. The exact radius of a circle with circumference 42 meters

5. The exact diameter of a circle with circumference 39 centimeters

6. The exact circumference of a circle with diameter 15 inches

7. The exact circumference of a circle with radius 27 feet

Find the length of $\overset{\frown}{AB}$.

8.

6 cm
60°
P   B
A

9.

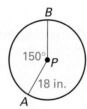

B
150°
P
18 in.
A

10.

A
B
30°
P
28 ft
C

In ⊙D shown below, ∠EDF ≅ ∠FDG. Find the indicated measure.

11. $m\overset{\frown}{EFG}$

12. $m\overset{\frown}{EHG}$

13. Length of $\overset{\frown}{EFG}$

14. Length of $\overset{\frown}{EHG}$

15. $m\overset{\frown}{EHF}$

16. Length of $\overset{\frown}{FEG}$

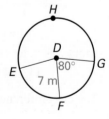

H
D
E   80°   G
7 m
F

Find the indicated measure.

17. $m\overset{\frown}{AB}$

18. Circumference of ⊙F

19. Radius of ⊙J

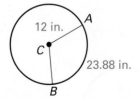

12 in.
A
C
23.88 in.
B

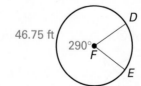

46.75 ft
290°
F
D
E

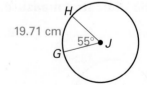

H
19.71 cm
55° J
G

UNIT 6

Exercise Set A *(continued)*

Find the perimeter of the region.

20.

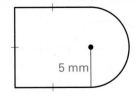

5 mm

21.

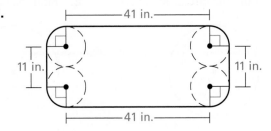

41 in.

11 in.

11 in.

41 in.

22. In the table below, $\overset{\frown}{AB}$ refers to the arc of a circle. Complete the table.

Radius	4	11	?	?	9.5	10.7
$m\overset{\frown}{AB}$	30°	?	105°	75°	?	270°
Length of $\overset{\frown}{AB}$	?	8.26	17.94	6.3	14.63	?

23. Bicycles The chain of a bicycle travels along the front and rear sprockets, as shown. The circumference of each sprocket is given.

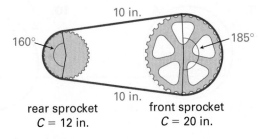

10 in.

160°

185°

10 in.

rear sprocket
C = 12 in.

front sprocket
C = 20 in.

a. About how long is the chain?

b. On a chain, the teeth are spaced in $\frac{1}{2}$ inch intervals. About how many teeth are there on this chain?

24. Enclosing a Garden You have planted a circular garden with its center at one of the corners of your garage, as shown. You want to fence in your garden. About how much fencing do you need?

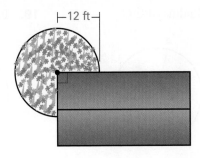

12 ft

MM2G3c   Use the properties of circles to solve problems
involving the length of an arc and the area of a sector.

1. Find the circumference.

r = 5.7cm

2. Find the circumference.

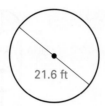

21.6 ft

3. Find the radius.

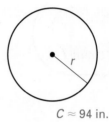

C ≈ 94 in.

Find the indicated measure.

4. The exact radius of a circle with circumference 74 centimeters

5. The exact diameter of a circle with circumference 58 feet

6. The exact circumference of a circle with diameter 26.3 inches

7. The exact circumference of a circle with radius 31.9 meters

Find the length of $\overarc{AB}$.

8.

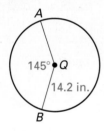

145° Q
14.2 in.

9.

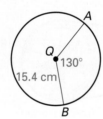

Q 130°
15.4 cm

10.

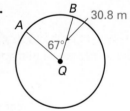

A
67°
B 30.8 m
Q

In ⊙D shown below, ∠ADC ≅ ∠BDC. Find the indicated measure.

11. $m\overarc{ACB}$

12. $m\overarc{CB}$

13. Length of $\overarc{ACB}$

14. Length of $\overarc{CB}$

15. $m\overarc{ABC}$

16. Length of $\overarc{BAC}$

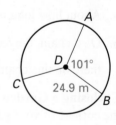

A
D 101°
C
24.9 m
B

Find the indicated measure.

17. Circumference of ⊙Q

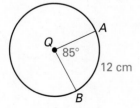

Q 85°
A
12 cm
B

18. Radius of ⊙Q

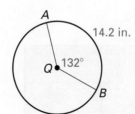

A
14.2 in.
Q 132°
B

19. Length of $\overarc{AB}$

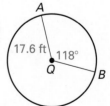

A
17.6 ft 118°
Q
B

Exercise Set B *(continued)*

Find the perimeter of the region.

20.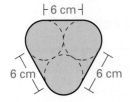

21.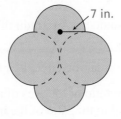

22.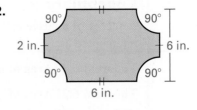

23. In the table below, $\overset{\frown}{AB}$ refers to the arc of a circle. Copy and complete the table.

Radius	6.7	11.4	?	?	25.8	19.3
$m\overset{\frown}{AB}$	103°	?	25°	261°	?	332°
Length of $\overset{\frown}{AB}$	?	15.72	7.46	61.95	64.39	?

24. **Thread** A spool of thread contains 150 revolutions of thread. The diameter of the spool is 3 centimeters. Find the length of the thread to the nearest centimeter.

25. **Go-Cart Track** Find the distance around the track on the inside lane and on the outside lane.

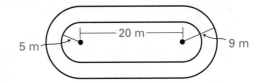

26. **Pendulum** Find the distance traveled in one back and forth swing by the weight of a 16 inch pendulum that swings through a 70° angle.

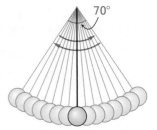

27. **Turntable** Two belt-driven gears for a turntable are shown. What is the total length of the belt?

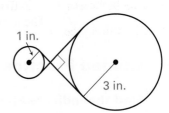

Areas of Circles and Sectors

Goal Find the areas of circles and sectors.

Vocabulary

A **sector of a circle** is the region bounded by two radii of the circle and their intercepted arc.

Theorem 6.20 Area of a circle: The area of a circle is π times the square of the radius.

Theorem 6.21 Area of a sector: The ratio of the area of a sector of a circle to the area of the whole circle (πr^2) is equal to the ratio of the measure of the intercepted arc to 360°.

Example 1 Use the formula for area of a circle

Find the indicated measure.

a. Radius

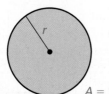

$A = 201$ ft^2

b. Area

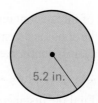

5.2 in.

Solution

a.

$$A = \pi r^2$$ Write the formula for area of a circle.

$$201 = \pi r^2$$ Substitute 201 for A.

$$\frac{201}{\pi} = r^2$$ Divide each side by π.

$$8 \approx r$$ Find the positive square root of each side.

The radius of the circle is about 8 feet.

b.

$$A = \pi r^2$$ Write the formula for area of a circle.

$$= \pi \cdot (5.2)^2$$ Substitute 5.2 for r.

$$= 27.04\pi$$ Simplify.

$$\approx 84.9$$ Use a calculator.

The area of the circle is about 84.9 square inches.

Guided Practice for Example 1

Find the indicated measure.

1. The diameter of the circle is 11 centimeters. Find the area.

2. The area of the circle is 158.3 square yards. Find the radius.

3. The area of circle is 1024π square meters. Find the diameter.

Georgia Performance Standards

MM2G3c Use the properties of circles to solve problems
involving the length of an arc and the area of a sector.

MM2G3d Justify measurements and relationships in circles
using geometric and algebraic properties. ✓

Example 2 **Find the areas of sectors**

Find the areas of the sectors formed by $\angle PQR$.

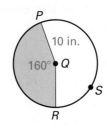

Solution

STEP 1 Find the measures of the minor and major arcs.

Because $m\angle PQR = 160°$, $m\overset{\frown}{PR} = 160°$ and
$m\overset{\frown}{PSR} = 360° - 160° = 200°$.

STEP 2 Find the areas of the small and large sectors.

$$\text{Area of small sector} = \frac{160°}{360°} \cdot \pi \cdot 10^2 \approx 139.62$$

$$\text{Area of large sector} = \frac{200°}{360°} \cdot \pi \cdot 10^2 \approx 174.54$$

So, the areas of the small and large sectors are about 139.62 square inches and
174.54 square inches, respectively.

Example 3 **Use the Area of a Sector Theorem**

Use the diagram to find the area of $\odot Y$.

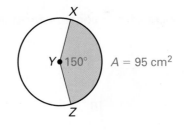

Solution

$$\frac{\text{Area of sector } XYZ}{\text{Area of } \odot Y} = \frac{m\overset{\frown}{XY}}{360°}$$

$$\text{Area of sector } XYZ = \frac{m\overset{\frown}{XY}}{360°} \cdot \text{Area of } \odot Y$$

$$95 = \frac{150°}{360°} \cdot \text{Area of } \odot Y$$

$$228 = \text{Area of } \odot Y$$

The area of $\odot Y$ is 228 square centimeters.

Guided Practice for Examples 2 and 3

4. Find the areas of the sectors
formed by $\angle ABC$.

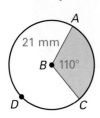

5. Find the area of $\odot H$.

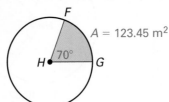

UNIT 6

LESSON
6.8

Exercise Set A

MM2G3c Use the properties of circles to solve problems involving the length of an arc and the area of a sector.

MM2G3d Justify measurements and relationships in circles using geometric and algebraic properties.

Find the exact area of the circle. Then find the area to the nearest hundredth.

1.

6 in.

2.

10.5 ft

3.

24.8 cm

Find the indicated measure.

4. The area of a circle is 173 square inches. Find the radius.

5. The area of a circle is 290 square meters. Find the radius.

6. The area of a circle is 52 square millimeters. Find the radius.

7. The area of a circle is 342 square yards. Find the diameter.

8. The area of a circle is 654 square centimeters. Find the diameter.

9. The area of a circle is 528 square feet. Find the diameter.

Find the areas of the sectors formed by $\angle ACB$.

10.

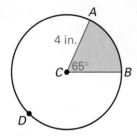

4 in.
65°
A
B
C
D

11.

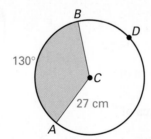

130°
27 cm
B
D
C
A

12.

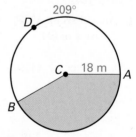

209°
18 m
D
C
A
B

Use the diagram to find the indicated measure.

13. Find the area of $\odot H$.

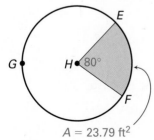

E
G
H 80°
F
$A = 23.79$ ft²

14. Find the radius of $\odot H$.

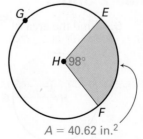

G
E
H 98°
F
$A = 40.62$ in.²

15. Find the diameter of $\odot H$.

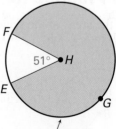

F
51° H
E
G
$A = 31.47$ m²

UNIT 6

Exercise Set A *(continued)*

The area of ⊙*R* is 295.52 square inches. The area of sector *PRQ* is 55 square inches. Find the indicated measure.

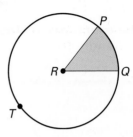

16. Radius of ⊙*R*

17. Circumference of ⊙*R*

18. $m\widehat{PQ}$

19. Length of $\widehat{PQ}$

20. Perimeter of shaded region

21. Perimeter of unshaded region

Find the area of the shaded region.

22.

6 cm 43°

23.

13 in.

24.

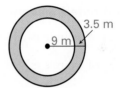

3.5 m
9 m

25.

10 ft 2 ft

26.

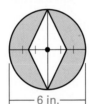

6 in.

27.

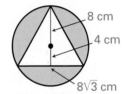

8 cm
4 cm
8√3 cm

28. **Fountain** A circular water fountain has a diameter of 42 feet. Find the area of the fountain.

29. **Landscaping** The diagram below shows the area of a lawn covered by a water sprinkler.

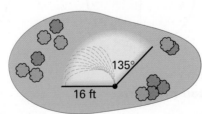

135°
16 ft

   a. What is the area of the lawn that is covered by the sprinkler?

   b. The water pressure is lowered so that the radius is 10 feet. What is the area of lawn that will be covered?

30. **Window Design** The window shown is in the shape of a semicircle. Find the area of the glass in the shaded region.

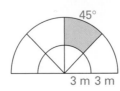

45°
3 m 3 m

Exercise Set B

MM2G3c Use the properties of circles to solve problems involving the length of an arc and the area of a sector.

MM2G3d Justify measurements and relationships in circles using geometric and algebraic properties.

Find the exact area of the circle. Then find the area to the nearest hundredth.

1.

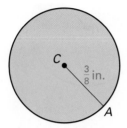

$\frac{3}{8}$ in.

2.

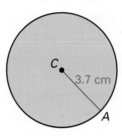

3.7 cm

3.

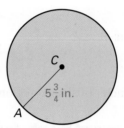

$5\frac{3}{4}$ in.

Find the indicated measure.

4. The area of a circle is 236 square inches. Find the radius.

5. The area of a circle is 390 square meters. Find the radius.

6. The area of a circle is 36.5 square millimeters. Find the radius.

7. The area of a circle is 186 square yards. Find the diameter.

8. The area of a circle is 857 square centimeters. Find the diameter.

9. The area of a circle is 714 square feet. Find the diameter.

Find the areas of the sectors formed by ∠ACB.

10.

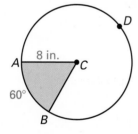

8 in.

60°

11.

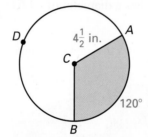

$4\frac{1}{2}$ in.

120°

12.

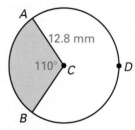

12.8 mm

110°

Use the diagram to find the indicated measure.

13. Find the area of ⊙M.

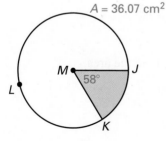

A = 36.07 cm²

58°

14. Find the radius of ⊙M.

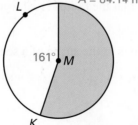

A = 84.14 m²

161°

15. Find the diameter of ⊙M.

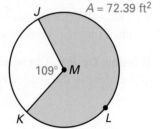

A = 72.39 ft²

109°

Exercise Set B (continued)

**The area of ⊙*V* is 624.36 square meters. The area of
sector *SVT* is 64.17 square meters. Find the indicated
measure.**

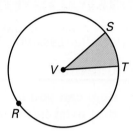

16. Radius of ⊙*V* **17.** Circumference of ⊙*V*

18. $m\widehat{ST}$ **19.** Length of $\widehat{ST}$

20. Perimeter of shaded region **21.** Perimeter of unshaded region

Find the area of the shaded region.

22.

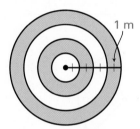

1 m

23.

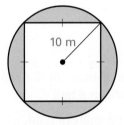

10 m

24.

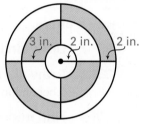

3 in. 2 in. 2 in.

25.

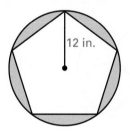

12 in.

26.

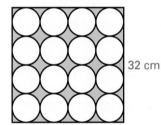

32 cm

32 cm

27.

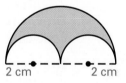

2 cm 2 cm

28. Pizza Three pizzas of the given diameter are cut. Which cut produces the largest pieces?

  A. An 8-inch pizza cut into 6 congruent slices

  B. A 12-inch pizza cut into 8 congruent slices

  C. A 16-inch pizza cut into 10 congruent slices

29. Error Analysis *Describe* and correct the error in finding the area of the shaded sector.

Area of the sector $RST = \dfrac{240°}{360°} \cdot \pi \cdot 5^2$

  $\approx 78.5 \text{ m}^2$

240°

X

UNIT 6

Georgia Performance Standards

MM2G3d Justify measurements and relationships in circles using geometric and algebraic properties.

Technology Activity
Relationships in Circles

Use after Lesson 6.8

Question

How can you use geometry drawing software to determine relationships that exist between a circle and special regions in the circle?

The formulas for the circumference and area of a circle are $C = 2\pi r$ and $A = \pi r^2$ where C is the circumference, A is the area, and r is the radius of the circle.

Example

Draw a circle.

STEP 1 **Draw circle** Draw $\odot A$.

STEP 2 **Draw diameter** Draw a diameter in $\odot A$ and label endpoints of the diameter B and C.

STEP 3 **Find midpoints** Find midpoints of radii $\overline{AB}$ and $\overline{AC}$. Label the midpoints D and E.

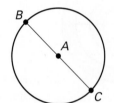

STEP 4 **Draw circle** Draw $\odot D$ with radius $\overline{AD}$ and centered at D.

STEP 5 **Draw circle** Draw $\odot E$ with radius $\overline{AE}$ and centered at E.

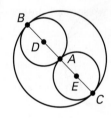

STEP 6 **Measure areas** Measure the areas of $\odot A$, $\odot D$, and $\odot E$.

STEP 7 **Measure circumferences** Measure the circumferences of $\odot A$, $\odot D$, and $\odot E$.

STEP 8 **Calculate area ratio** Use the *calculate* feature to divide the area of $\odot A$ by the sum of the areas of $\odot D$ and $\odot E$.

STEP 9 **Calculate circumference ratio** Use the *calculate* feature to divide the circumference of $\odot A$ by the sum of the circumferences of $\odot D$ and $\odot E$.

STEP 10 **Change the size** Change the size of $\odot A$ and observe the results.

Practice

1. In Step 8, the area of $\odot A$ was shown to be twice that of the sum of the areas of $\odot D$ and $\odot E$. Show why this is true algebraically. (*Hint:* Let r be the radius of $\odot A$ and $\frac{1}{2}r$ be the radius for both $\odot D$ and $\odot E$.)

2. In Step 9, the circumference of $\odot A$ was shown to be the same as that of the sum of the circumferences of $\odot D$ and $\odot E$. Briefly explain why this is true.

UNIT 6

Surface Area and Volume of Spheres

Georgia Performance Standards: MM2G4a, MM2G4b

Goal Find surface areas and volumes of spheres.

Vocabulary

A **sphere** is the set of all points in space equidistant from a given point. This point is called the **center** of the sphere.

A **radius** of a sphere is a segment from the center to a point on the sphere.

A **chord** of a sphere is a segment whose endpoints are on the sphere.

A **diameter** of a sphere is a chord that contains the center.

A **great circle** is the intersection of a sphere and a plane passing through the center of the sphere. The circumference of a great circle is the circumference of the sphere.

A **hemisphere** is half of a sphere, formed when a great circle separates a sphere into two congruent halves.

Theorem 6.22: Surface Area of a Sphere: The surface area S of a sphere is $S = 4\pi r^2$, where r is the radius of the sphere.

Theorem 6.23: Volume of a Sphere: The volume V of a sphere is $V = \frac{4}{3}\pi r^3$, where r is the radius of the sphere.

Example 1 **Find the surface area of a sphere**

Find the surface area of the sphere.

Solution

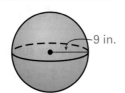
9 in.

$$S = 4\pi r^2 \qquad \text{Formula for surface area of a sphere}$$

$$= 4\pi(9)^2 \qquad \text{Substitute 9 for } r.$$

$$\approx 1017.88 \qquad \text{Use a calculator.}$$

The surface area of the sphere is about 1017.88 square inches.

Example 2 **Use the circumference of a sphere**

In the diagram, the circumference of the outer ball is 8π feet. Find the surface area of the outer ball.

Solution

$$C = 2\pi r \qquad\qquad \text{Formula for circumference}$$

$$8\pi = 2\pi r \qquad\qquad \text{Substitute } 8\pi \text{ for } C.$$

$$4 = r \qquad\qquad \text{Divide each side by } 2\pi.$$

$$S = 4\pi r^2 = 4\pi(4)^2 \approx 201.06 \qquad \text{Use the radius in the formula for surface area.}$$

The surface area of the outer ball is 64π, or about 201.06 square feet.

UNIT 6

25. Satellites A satellite is taking pictures of Earth from 2000 miles above its surface. What is the measure of Earth's surface $\overset{\frown}{RT}$ that can be photographed from the satellite?

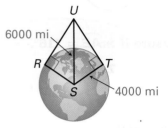

6000 mi

R   T

S   4000 mi

Not drawn to scale

26. Spinach Quiche A spinach quiche is sliced into 8 equal pieces. The arc length of one piece of quiche is 6.28 inches as shown. Find the diameter of the quiche.

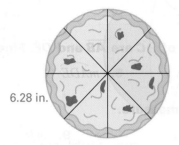

6.28 in.

In Exercises 27–29, use the following information.

Softball A softball has a surface area of about 38.52 square inches. Round your answers to two decimal places.

27. Find the radius of the softball.

28. Find the circumference of a great circle of the softball.

29. Find the volume of the softball.

Performance Task

Picnic

Four friends are sitting around a circular picnic table. $\odot P$ represents the table. Adele is sitting at point A, Bryant is sitting at point B, Curtis is sitting at point C, and Denise is sitting at point D. Use the diagram to answer the following questions.

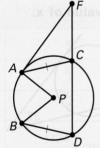

a. A flagpole is located at point F. If $m\angle FAP = 90°$, what word best describes $\overline{AF}$?

b. If $m\angle APB = 75°$, find the distance, in degrees, along the edge of the table between Adele and Bryant. In other words, find $m\overset{\frown}{AB}$.

c. The distance across the table from Adele to Curtis is equal to the distance across the table from Bryant to Denise. If $m\overset{\frown}{AC} = 88°$, what is $m\overset{\frown}{BD}$?

d. Use your answers from parts (b) and (c) to find $m\angle AFD$.

e. If $AF = 14.2$ feet and $CF = 10$ feet, find the distance between Curtis and Denise.

f. If $BP = 7$ feet, what is the circumference of the picnic table?

UNIT 7
Data Analysis and Probability

MM2D2a   Gather and plot data that can be modeled with linear
         and quadratic functions.

MM2D2b   Examine the issues of curve fitting by finding good
         linear fits to data using simple methods such as the
         median-median line and "eyeballing."

Investigating Math Activity
Fitting a Line to Data

Use before Lesson 7.1

Question

How can you approximate the *best-fitting line* for a set of data?

Explore

Collect and record data.

STEP 1   Set up
Position an overhead projector a convenient
distance from a projection screen. Draw a
line segment 6 inches long on a transparency
and place the transparency on the projector.

STEP 2   Collect data
Measure the distance, in inches, from the
projector to the screen and the length of
the line segment as it appears on the screen.
Reposition the projector several times,
each time taking these measurements.

STEP 3   Record data
Record your measurements from Step 2 in
a table like the one shown at the right.

Distance from projector to screen (in.), x	Length of line segment on screen (in.), y
80	?
85	?
90	?
95	?
100	?
105	?
110	?
115	?
120	?
125	?

Draw Conclusions

1. Graph the data pairs (x, y). What pattern do you observe?

2. Use a ruler to draw a line that lies as close as possible to all of the points on the
   graph. The line does not have to pass through any of the points. There should be
   about as many points above the line as below it

3. Estimate the coordinates of two points on your line. Use your points to write an
   equation of the line.

4. Using your equation from Exercise 3, predict the length of the line segment on the
   screen for a particular projector-to-screen distance less than those in your table
   and for a particular projector-to-screen distance greater than those in your table.

5. **Writing** Test your predictions from Exercise 4. How accurate were they?
   Explain why your predictions were accurate or not accurate.

Draw Scatter Plots and Best-Fitting Lines

Georgia Performance Standards: MM2D2a, MM2D2b, MM2D2d

Goal Fit lines to data in scatter plots.

Vocabulary

A **scatter plot** is a graph of a set of data pairs (x, y).

If y tends to increase as x increases, then the data have a **positive correlation**.

If y tends to decrease as x increases, then the data have a **negative correlation**.

A **correlation coefficient**, denoted by r, is a number from -1 to 1 that measures how well a line fits a set of data pairs (x, y). If r is near 1, the points lie close to a line with a positive slope. If r is near -1, the points lie close to a line with a negative slope. If r is near 0, the points do not lie close to any line.

The **best-fitting line** is the line that lies as close as possible to all the data points. **Linear regression** is a method for finding the equation of the best-fitting line, or regression line, which expresses the linear relationship between the independent variable x and the dependent variable y, e.g., $y = ax + b$.

A **median-median line** is a linear model used to fit a line to a data set. The line is fit only to summary points, key points calculated using medians.

An **algebraic model** is an expression, equation, or function that represents data or a real-world situation.

An **inference** is a logical conclusion that is derived from known data.

| Example 1 | Describe and estimate correlation coefficients |

Describe the data as having a *positive correlation*, a *negative correlation*, or *approximately no correlation*. Tell whether the correlation coefficient for the data is closest to −1, −0.5, 0, 0.5, or 1.

Solution

The scatter plot shows a strong negative correlation. So the best estimate given is $r = -1$.

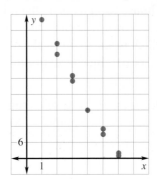

Correlation and Causation The fact that two variables are strongly correlated does not in itself imply a cause-and-effect relationship between the variables. Further study is usually needed to determine that x causes y (or reversely, that y causes x). It is possible that the relationship between x and y is simply a coincidence or that it may be caused by one or more additional factors.

Georgia Performance Standards

MM2D2a	Gather and plot data that can be modeled with linear and quadratic functions.
MM2D2b	Examine the issues of curve fitting by finding good linear fits to data using simple methods such as the median-median line and "eyeballing."
MM2D2d	Investigate issues that arise when using data to explore the relationship between two variables, including confusion between correlation and causation.

Guided Practice for Example 1

For each scatter plot, (a) tell whether the data have a *positive correlation*, a *negative correlation*, or *approximately no correlation*, and (b) tell whether the correlation is closest to −1, −0.5, 0, 0.5, or 1.

1.

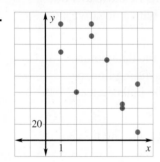

2.

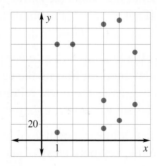

Example 2 Approximate the best-fitting line

The ordered pairs (*x, y*) give the height *y* in feet of a young tree *x* years after 2000. Approximate the best-fitting line for the data.

(0, 5.1), (1, 6.4), (2, 7.7), (3, 9), (4, 10.3), (5, 11.6), (6, 12.9)

STEP 1 **Draw** a scatter plot of the data.

STEP 2 **Sketch** the line that appears to best fit the data. One possibility is shown.

STEP 3 **Choose** two points on the line. For the line shown, you can choose (0, 5), which is not an original data point, and (5, 11.6) which is an original data point.

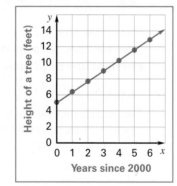

Years since 2000

STEP 4 **Write** an equation of the line. Find the slope using the points (0, 5) and (5, 11.6).

$$m = \frac{11.6 - 5}{5 - 0} = \frac{6.6}{5} = 1.32$$

Use point-slope form to write the equation.

$y - y_1 = m(x - x_1)$	Point-slope form
$y - 5 = 1.32(x - 0)$	Substitute for m, x_1, and y_1.
$y = 1.32x + 5$	Simplify.

An approximation of the best-fitting line is $y = 1.32x + 5$.

Example 3 Find a median-median line

Find the equation of the median-median line for the data.

(1, 48), (2, 42), (2, 50), (4, 45), (5, 69), (6, 44), (7, 82), (7, 93), (8, 96)

STEP 1 **Organize** the data so that the *x*-values are in order from least to greatest. Then separate the coordinates into three equal sized groups. If the number of coordinates is not divisible by three, make sure the first and last group have an equal number of coordinates (e.g., groupings of 3-2-3 or 4-3-4).

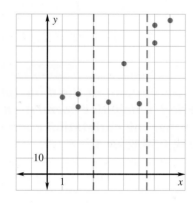

STEP 2 **Find** the median *x*-value and the median *y*-value for each group.

Group	*x*-values	*y*-values	Median *x*-value	Median *y*-value
1	1, 2, 2	42, 48, 50	2	48
2	4, 5, 6	44, 45, 69	5	45
3	7, 7, 8	82, 93, 96	7	93

STEP 3 **Create** a summary point for each group by combining the median *x*-value and the median *y*-value into an ordered pair.

Group 1: (2, 48)   Group 2: (5, 45)   Group 3: (7, 93)

STEP 4 **Determine** the equation of the line between the two outer points by finding *m* and using point-slope form to write the equation.

$$m = \frac{93 - 48}{7 - 2} = 9 \rightarrow y - 48 = 9(x - 2) \rightarrow y = 9x + 30$$

STEP 5 **Move** the equation one-third of the way toward the middle summary point.
Middle summary point: (5, 45)
Predicted value at $x = 5$: $y = 9(5) + 30 = 75$

One-third of difference between $y = 45$ and
$y = 75$: $\frac{1}{3}(45 - 75) = -10$

New equation: $y = 9x + 30 - 10 = 9x + 20$

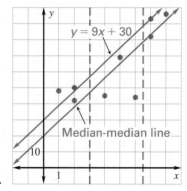

The equation of the median-median line is $y = 9x + 20$.

Guided Practice for Examples 2 and 3

3. Draw a scatter plot and approximate the best-fitting line for the following data:
(1, 22), (2, 30), (3, 33), (4, 39), (5, 45)

4. Find the equation of the median-median line for the data: (1, 22), (2, 27), (2, 20), (3, 15), (4, 19), (5, 10), (5, 14), (6, 9), (8, 7), (8, 11), (8, 13), (9, 5)

MM2D2a   Gather and plot data that can be modeled with linear and quadratic functions.

MM2D2b   Examine the issues of curve fitting by finding good linear fits to data using simple methods such as the median-median line and "eyeballing."

MM2D2d   Investigate issues that arise when using data to explore the relationship between two variables, including confusion between correlation and causation.

Draw a scatter plot of the data. Tell whether the data have a *positive correlation*, a *negative correlation*, or *approximately no correlation*. Tell whether the correlation coefficient for the data is closest to −1, −0.5, 0, 0.5, or 1.

1.

x	0	0.5	1.25	2.75	3
y	−3.5	−2	−0.75	1.25	2.5
x	3.5	4.25	4.75	5.25	6
y	3.25	5.5	7	8.25	9.5

2.

x	−1.5	−1	−0.75	0	1.5
y	−5.25	−2.5	4	5.75	−1.75
x	2	2.25	3	3.5	4
y	−3	4.25	5.5	1.75	−1.25

3. **Football Game Attendance** You found a strong positive correlation between the numbers of home-game wins for your school's football team and attendance at home games. Can you say that a high number of home-game wins causes a high home-game attendance? *Explain.*

4. **Test Scores** You found a strong negative correlation between the number of hours students in your class watch television and test scores of the same students in your class. Can you say that a high number of hours watching television causes lower test scores? *Explain.*

Approximate the best-fitting line for the data.

5.

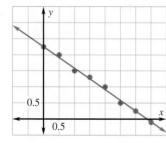

6.

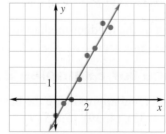

Exercise Set A *(continued)*

Draw a scatter plot of the data. Approximate the best-fitting line for the data.

7.

x	0.5	1	1.5	2	2.5
y	−2.25	−2.75	−1.7	−0.5	0
x	3	3.5	4	4.5	5
y	−0.6	1.2	1.9	2.5	2.3

8.

x	−4	−3	−2	−1	0
y	2	−0.5	0	−1.5	−4.2
x	1	2	3	4	
y	−5.8	−8.8	−9.5	−11.4	

9.

x	−4	−3	−2	−1	0
y	2.5	3	1.5	2	1
x	1	2	3	4	
y	2	3.5	0.5	2.5	

In Exercises 10–12, use the following information.

Softball The table shows the number of adult softball teams for the years 1999 to 2003.

Year	1999	2000	2001	2002	2003
Number of teams (in thousands)	163	155	149	143	119

10. Draw a scatter plot for the data. Let t represent the number of years since 1999.

11. Use the *linear regression* feature of a graphing calculator to approximate the best-fitting line for the data.

12. Using this model, predict the number of adult softball teams in 2010.

13. Find the equation of the median-median line for the data.

x	5	5	7	8	9	11	12	12	14
y	3	8	5	7	11	10	15	19	20

Exercise Set B

MM2D2a Gather and plot data that can be modeled with linear and quadratic functions.

MM2D2b Examine the issues of curve fitting by finding good linear fits to data using simple methods such as the median-median line and "eyeballing."

MM2D2d Investigate issues that arise when using data to explore the relationship between two variables, including confusion between correlation and causation.

1. **Test Scores** You found a strong positive correlation between the numbers of hours students in your class study and test scores of the same students in your class. Can you say that a high number of hours studying causes higher test scores? *Explain.*

2. **Hockey Game Attendance** You found a strong negative correlation between the numbers of home-game losses for your town's hockey team and attendance at home games. Can you say that a high number of home-game losses causes a low home-game attendance? *Explain.*

Approximate the best-fitting line for the data.

3.
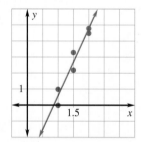

4.
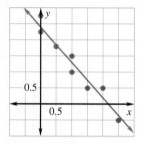

Draw a scatter plot of the data. Approximate the best-fitting line for the data.

5.

x	1	2	4	7	8
y	0.5	1.2	2.6	3.3	3.7

6.

x	2	3	5	6	8
y	8.2	6.0	1.5	0	−4.5

7. **Reasoning** In addition to drawing a scatter plot, the type of correlation between data sets can also be determined by examining the data in a table format. *Explain* how this can be done.

In Exercises 8 and 9, use the following information.

Florida The table shows the population p (in millions) of Florida over a four year span.

Year	2002	2003	2004	2005
Population (in millions)	16.4	17.0	17.4	17.8

8. Approximate the best-fitting line for the data.

9. Using this model, what will be the population in 2010?

UNIT 7

Exercise Set B *(continued)*

10. Find the equation of the median-median line for the data.

x	2	4	4	5	7	9	10	11
y	16	20	21	7	15	1	2	5

In Exercises 11 and 12, use the following information.

Carbon Dioxide The table shows the U.S. residential carbon dioxide emissions from 1993 to 2002. Emissions are measured in million metric tons.

Year	1993	1994	1995	1996	1997
Emissions (in million metric tons)	1027.6	1020.9	1026.5	1086.1	1077.5

Year	1998	1999	2000	2001	2002
Emissions (in million metric tons)	1083.3	1107.1	1170.4	1163.3	1193.9

11. Use the *linear regression* feature of a graphing calculator to approximate the best-fitting line for the data.

12. Using this model, how many residential tons were emitted in 1990? How many will be emitted in 2010?

In Exercises 13 and 14, use the following information.

Planets The table shows the average distance in millions of miles from the sun and the maximum surface temperature in degrees Fahrenheit of each planet.

	Mercury	Venus	Earth	Mars
Distance (in millions of miles)	36.0	67.2	92.9	141.6
Maximum surface temperature (in degrees Fahrenheit)	801	864	136	23

	Jupiter	Saturn	Uranus	Neptune
Distance (in millions of miles)	483.7	885.9	1783.9	2795.1
Maximum surface temperature (in degrees Fahrenheit)	−234	−288	−357	−353

13. What type of correlation does the data have?

14. Based on your observations, do you think a linear model is the best fit for the given data? *Explain.*

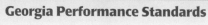

Georgia Performance Standards

MM2D2a	Gather and plot data that can be modeled with linear and quadratic functions	
MM2D2c	Understand and apply the processes of linear and quadratic regression for curve fitting using appropriate technology.	

Investigating Math Activity

Modeling Data with a Quadratic Function

Use before Lesson 7.2

Materials compass, 60 nickels, graphing calculator

Question

How can you fit a quadratic function to a set of data?

Explore

Collect and model quadratic data.

STEP 1 Collect data
Draw five circles using a compass. Use diameters of 2 inches, 4 inches, 6 inches, 8 inches, and 10 inches. Place as many nickels as you can in each circle, making sure that each nickel is completely within the circle.

Diameter of circle (in.), x	Number of nickels, y
0	?
2	?
4	?
6	?
8	?
10	?

STEP 2 Record data
Record your results from Step 1 in a table like the one shown at the right. Also, record the number of nickels that would fit in a circle with a diameter of 0 inch.

STEP 3 Enter data
Enter the data you collected into two lists of a graphing calculator.

STEP 4 Display data
Display the data in a scatter plot. Notice that the points appear to lie on a parabola.

STEP 5 Find model
Use the *quadratic regression* feature to find a quadratic model for the data.

Draw Conclusions

1. **Writing** Graph your model from Step 5 on the same screen as the scatter plot. *Describe* how well the model fits the data.

2. Use your model from Step 5 to predict the number of nickels that will fit in a circle with a diameter of 12 inches. Check your prediction by drawing another circle.

3. **Reasoning** *Explain* why you would expect the number of nickels that fit inside a circle to be a quadratic function of the circle's diameter?

Write Quadratic Functions and Models

Georgia Performance Standards: MM2D2a, MM2D2c

Goal Write quadratic functions and models.

Vocabulary

Quadratic regression is the process of finding the **best-fitting quadratic model** for a set of data.

Finding a line or curve that matches a set of data points is called **curve fitting**.

Example 1   Write a quadratic function in vertex form

Write a quadratic function whose graph has vertex (−2, 3) and passes through the point (−1, 1).

$$y = a(x - h)^2 + k \qquad \text{Vertex form}$$
$$y = a(x + 2)^2 + 3 \qquad \text{Substitute } -2 \text{ for } h \text{ and } 3 \text{ for } k.$$

Use the point $(-1, 1)$ to find a.

$$1 = a(-1 + 2)^2 + 3$$
$$1 = a + 3$$
$$-2 = a$$

A quadratic function for the parabola is $y = -2(x + 2)^2 + 3$.

Example 2   Write a quadratic function in intercept form

Write a quadratic function whose graph has *x*-intercepts −2 and 1, and point (−1, −4).

$$y = a(x - p)(x - q) \qquad \text{Intercept form}$$
$$y = a(x + 2)(x - 1) \qquad \text{Substitute } -2 \text{ for } p \text{ and } 1 \text{ for } q.$$
$$-4 = a(-1 + 2)(-1 - 1) \qquad \text{Substitute } -1 \text{ for } x \text{ and } -4 \text{ for } y.$$
$$-4 = -2a \qquad \text{Simplify coefficient of } a.$$
$$2 = a \qquad \text{Solve for } a.$$

A quadratic function for the parabola is $y = 2(x + 2)(x - 1)$.

Guided Practice for Examples 1 and 2

Write a quadratic function whose graph has the given characteristics.

1. vertex: $(1, -4)$
point on graph: $(0, -3)$

2. vertex: $(-2, 1)$
point on graph: $(-1, 0)$

3. *x*-intercepts: $-3, 1$
point on graph: $(-2, -6)$

4. *x*-intercepts: $-4, 2$
point on graph: $(-2, 16)$

MM2D2a Gather and plot data that can be modeled with linear and quadratic functions.

MM2D2c Understand and apply the processes of linear and quadratic regression for curve fitting using appropriate technology.

Write a quadratic function in vertex form whose graph has the given vertex and passes through the given point.

1. vertex: $(1, 2)$
   point: $(2, 4)$

2. vertex: $(-3, -2)$
   point: $(1, 14)$

3. vertex: $\left(\frac{3}{4}, 2\right)$
   point: $\left(2, \frac{41}{8}\right)$

4. vertex: $\left(-\frac{1}{2}, \frac{2}{3}\right)$
   point: $\left(\frac{3}{2}, \frac{14}{3}\right)$

Write a quadratic function in intercept form whose graph has the given x-intercepts and passes through the given point.

5. x-intercepts: $-3, 7$
   point: $(6, -9)$

6. x-intercepts: $4, 6$
   point: $(5, -2)$

7. x-intercepts: $-2, 1.5$
   point: $(4, 7.5)$

8. x-intercepts: $-\frac{2}{3}, \frac{1}{6}$
   point: $\left(\frac{7}{3}, \frac{13}{2}\right)$

9. x-intercepts: $-2, \frac{5}{4}$
   point: $\left(\frac{9}{4}, -\frac{51}{32}\right)$

10. x-intercepts: $-\frac{16}{3}, -\frac{5}{2}$
    point: $\left(-\frac{9}{2}, -\frac{25}{18}\right)$

Write a quadratic function in standard form whose graph passes through the given points.

11. $(1, 2), (-2, 5), (3, -20)$

12. $(2, -7), (-2, 21), (1, -3)$

13. $\left(1, -\frac{1}{2}\right), (0, -3), (2, 3)$

14. $\left(\frac{1}{2}, -\frac{3}{16}\right), \left(3, -\frac{17}{4}\right), \left(4, -\frac{17}{2}\right)$

15. $(3, 15), \left(-4, \frac{121}{2}\right), \left(\frac{1}{3}, -\frac{7}{3}\right)$

16. $\left(\frac{1}{2}, -\frac{3}{10}\right), \left(1, \frac{6}{5}\right), \left(\frac{1}{4}, -\frac{3}{10}\right)$

17. **Multiple Representations** The following table shows the number of scrap parts P produced by a large manufacturing company from 1999 to 2007. Quality control is working to eliminate the production of scrap. Assume that t is the number of years since 1999 and P is measured in thousands.

Year, t	0	1	2	3	4	5	6	7	8
Scrap parts, P	10.1	9.9	9.7	9.5	9.1	8.9	8.2	7.4	6.7

a. **Write a Model** Using a system of equations and the data from 2000, 2003, and 2005, write a quadratic model for the data. Then use a graphing calculator to find the best-fitting quadratic model for the data.

b. **Calculate a Value** Using the graphing calculator model, in what year will the number of scrap parts theoretically be zero?

Find Measures of Central Tendency and Dispersion

Georgia Performance Standards: MM2D1b, MM2D1c

Goal Describe data using statistical measures.

Vocabulary

Statistics are numerical values used to summarize and compare sets of data.

A **measure of central tendency** is a number used to represent the center or middle of a set of data values. The **mean**, or average, of n numbers is the sum of the numbers divided by n. The mean is denoted by $\bar{x}$, which is read as "x-bar." For the data set $x_1, x_2, \ldots, x_n$, the mean is $\bar{x} = \dfrac{x_1 + x_2 + \cdots + x_n}{n}$. The **median** of n numbers is the middle number when the numbers are written in order. (If n is even, the median is the mean of the two middle numbers.) The **mode** of n numbers is the number or numbers that occur most frequently. There may be one mode, no mode, or more than one mode.

A **measure of dispersion** is a statistic that tells you how dispersed, or spread out, data values are. One simple measure of dispersion is the **range**, which is the difference between the greatest and least data values. The **standard deviation** σ (read as "sigma") of $x_1, x_2, \ldots, x_n$ is $\sigma = \sqrt{\dfrac{(x_1 - \bar{x})^2 + (x_2 - \bar{x})^2 + \cdots + (x_n - \bar{x})^2}{n}}$.

Example 1   Find measures of central tendency

Find the mean, median, and mode of the data set.

Test Scores
42, 72, 81, 95, 98, 58, 77, 75, 83, 97, 45, 89, 93, 57, 82, 97, 52, 75

Solution

To find the mean, divide the sum of the scores by the number of scores.

Mean: $\bar{x} = \dfrac{42 + 72 + \cdots + 75}{18} = 76$

To find the median, first order the test scores:

42, 45, 52, 57, 58, 72, 75, 75, 77, 81, 82, 83, 89, 93, 95, 97, 97, 98

Because there is an even number of scores, the median is the average of the two middle scores.

Median: $\dfrac{77 + 81}{2} = 79$

There are two modes, 75 and 97, because these numbers occur most frequently.

Guided Practice for Example 1

1. Find the mean, median, and mode of 15, 11, 19, 15, 14, 14, 13, 17, 11, 12, 17, 15, 14, 15.

Georgia Performance Standards

MM2D1b	Understand and calculate the means and standard deviations of sets of data.	☑
MM2D1c	Use means and standard deviations to compare data sets.	☑

Example 2 **Find measures of dispersion**

Find the range and standard deviation of the test scores in Example 1.

Solution

To find the range, subtract the least data value from the greatest data value.

Range: $98 - 42 = 56$

To find the standard deviation, substitute the scores and the mean into the formula.

Std. Dev.: $\sigma = \sqrt{\dfrac{(42 - 76)^2 + (72 - 76)^2 + \cdots + (75 - 76)^2}{18}} = \sqrt{\dfrac{5692}{18}} \approx 17.8$

Example 3 **Compare data sets**

The lists show the number of cars sold each month for one year by two competing car dealers. Compare the mean and standard deviation for the numbers of cars sold by the two car dealers.

Dealer A: 8, 9, 15, 25, 28, 16, 24, 18, 21, 14, 16, 10

Dealer B: 7, 4, 10, 18, 21, 30, 27, 20, 16, 18, 12, 9

Solution

A: Mean: $\bar{x} = \dfrac{8 + 9 + \cdots + 10}{12} = 17$

Std. Dev.: $\sigma = \sqrt{\dfrac{(8 - 17)^2 + (9 - 17)^2 + \cdots + (10 - 17)^2}{12}} = \sqrt{\dfrac{460}{112}} \approx 6.2$

B: Mean: $\bar{x} = \dfrac{7 + 4 + \cdots + 9}{12} = 16$

Std. Dev.: $\sigma = \sqrt{\dfrac{(7 - 16)^2 + (4 - 16)^2 + \cdots + (9 - 16)^2}{12}} = \sqrt{\dfrac{692}{12}} \approx 7.6$

Dealer A has a greater mean and Dealer B has a greater standard deviation. The average number of cars sold per month by Dealer A is greater than the average number of cars sold per month by Dealer B. The standard deviations show that the data given for Dealer A vary less than the data given for Dealer B.

Guided Practice for Examples 2 and 3

2. Find the range and standard deviation of the data set in Exercise 1.

3. *Compare* the means and standard deviations of Set A and Set B.

Set A	7	3	4	9	2
Set B	5	8	7	6	4

LESSON 7.3 **Exercise Set A**

MM2D1b	Understand and calculate the means and standard deviations of sets of data.
MM2D1c	Use means and standard deviations to compare data sets.

Find the mean, median, and mode of the data set.

1. 6, 22, 4, 15, 10, 8, 8, 7, 14, 20

2. 10, 15, 12, 20, 25, 22, 28, 24, 22, 26

3. 53, 52, 48, 44, 60, 48, 44, 57, 44

4. 100, 150, 100, 130, 125, 135, 140, 145, 100

5. 0.12, 0.54, 0.36, 0.17, 0.36, 0.94, 0.88

6. 1.3, 4.5, 18.7, 22.3, 1.9, 15.6, 17.6, 7.9

Find the range and standard deviation of the data set.

7. 47, 18, 65, 28, 43, 18

8. 70, 27, 41, 30, 10, 47, 11

9. 31, 33, 35, 37, 32, 34, 39

10. 6, 49, 87, 23, 51, 15, 32

11. 29.4, 22.9, 15.7, 26.9, 24.0, 27.5, 11.4

12. 35.8, 29.4, 32.1, 24.9, 30.5, 20.3

13. Error Analysis *Describe* and correct the error in finding the median.

> The median of the data set below is 10 because 10 is the middle number.
> 15, 7, 11, 10, 16, 9, 14

In Exercises 14–17, find the mean, median, mode, range, and standard deviation of the data set.

14. Cordless Phones The data set below gives the prices (in dollars) of cordless phones at an electronics store.

35, 50, 60, 60, 75, 65, 80

15. Baseball The data set below gives the numbers of home runs for the 10 batters who hit the most home runs during the 2005 Major League Baseball regular season.

51, 48, 47, 46, 45, 43, 41, 40, 40, 39

16. Department of Motor Vehicles The data set below gives the waiting times (in minutes) of several people at a department of motor vehicles service center.

11, 7, 14, 2, 8, 13, 3, 6, 10, 3, 8, 4, 8, 4, 7

17. Cereal The data set below gives the calories in a 1-ounce serving of several breakfast cereals.

135, 115, 120, 110, 110, 100, 105, 110, 125

18. High Temperatures The data sets below give the high temperatures (in degrees Fahrenheit) for two cities during a 15-day period. *Compare* the mean and standard deviation for the temperatures of the two cities.

City A: 36, 37, 36, 34, 39, 33, 30, 30, 32, 31, 31, 32, 32, 33, 35
City B: 41, 35, 28, 29, 25, 36, 36, 32, 38, 40, 40, 34, 31, 28, 30

UNIT 7

MM2D1b Understand and calculate the means and standard deviations of sets of data.

MM2D1c Use means and standard deviations to compare data sets.

Find the mean, median, and mode of the data set.

1. 12, 15, 17, 11, 8, 14, 7, 14

2. 58, 56, 57, 59, 56, 61, 54, 53

3. 105, 99, 106, 109, 97, 108, 109, 96, 101, 102

4. 4.7, 3.9, 4.2, 5.3, 5.6, 5.5, 4.2, 3.7, 5.5, 5.2

5. 0.3, 8.9, 7.6, 3.7, 1.5, 4.2, 7.6, 8.1

6. 100, 175, 200, 150, 350, 425, 250, 300, 175, 425

Find the range and standard deviation of the data set.

7. 22, 18, 19, 25, 27, 21, 24

8. 38, 46, 37, 42, 39, 40, 48, 42

9. 8.4, 7.7, 8.6, 7.5, 8.9, 7.8, 8.6, 9.1, 8.0

10. 1.25, 3.69, 5.67, 4.89, 0.12, 4.35, 2.78

11. 515, 720, 635, 895, 585, 690, 770, 840

12. 116, 105, 117, 124, 107, 112, 117, 125, 110, 113

13. **Basketball** The data set below gives the points per game averages for the 10 players who had the highest averages (minimum 70 games or 1400 points) during the 2004−2005 National Basketball Association regular season. Find the mean, median, mode, range, and standard deviation of the data set.

30.7, 27.6, 27.2, 26.1, 26.0, 25.7, 25.5, 24.5, 24.1, 23.9

In Exercises 14–18, use the following information.

Manufacturing Tubes A company that manufactures plastic tubes takes ten samples from one machine and ten samples from another machine. The outside diameter of each sample is measured with a digital caliper. The company's goal is to produce tubes that have an outside diameter of exactly 1 inch. The results of the measurements are shown below.

Machine 1: 1.000, 0.998, 1.001, 1.000, 0.997, 1.001, 1.002, 0.996, 0.998, 1.000

Machine 2: 0.997, 1.000, 0.998, 0.996, 1.000, 0.998, 1.000, 0.998, 1.001, 0.999

14. Find the mean diameter of the samples for each machine.

15. Find the standard deviation of the samples for each machine.

16. Which machine produces an average closest to the company's goal?

17. Which machine produces the more consistent diameter?

18. Suppose that the last measurement for Machine 2 above was 0.989 instead of 0.999. What affect does this new measurement have on the mean and standard deviation?

Georgia Performance Standards

MM2D1b   Understand and calculate the means and standard deviations of sets of data.

LESSON 7.3

Problem Solving Workshop

Problem   In Examples 1 and 2 on pages 259 and 260, you saw how to find measures of central tendency and dispersion by hand. You can also find the measures by *using a graphing calculator*. Find the mean, median, mode, range, and standard deviation of the test scores.

> **Test Scores**
>
> 42, 72, 81, 95, 98, 58,
> 77, 75, 83, 97, 45, 89,
> 93, 57, 82, 97, 52, 75

STEP 1   Enter the data in list L_1. Then press the ![STAT] button, choose the ![CALC] menu, and select *1-Var Stats*.

```
1-Var Stats
  x̄=76
  Σx=1368
  Σx²=109660
  Sx=18.29818377
  σx=17.78263822
↓ n=18
```

STEP 2   The screen shows a list of statistics.

The mean is $\bar{x} = 76$. The standard deviation is $\sigma x \approx 17.8$.

Scroll down to see the rest of the statistics. The median (Med) is 79. The range is maxX − minX, or 56.

The calculator does not give the mode. By looking at the data, the modes are 75 and 97.

```
1-Var Stats
  n=18
  minX=42
  Q₁=58
  Med=79
  Q₃=93
  maxX=98
```

Practice

1. **Real Estate**   In the past month, a real estate agent has sold six homes priced at $118,700, $145,300, $174,000, $155,900, $133,500, and $158,000. Find the mean, median, mode, range, and standard deviation of the selling prices.

2. **What If?**   Exercise 1, suppose the real estate agent also sold another home during the month priced at $245,000. How does this price affect the mean? What effect does this price have on the range and standard deviation?

3. **Fat Content**   The fat contents of seven different sandwiches available at a restaurant are 42, 61, 13, 17, 25, 45, and 30. Find the mean, median, mode, range, and standard deviation of the fat contents.

4. **Fat Content**   The fat contents of seven similar sandwiches at a competing restaurant are 25, 40, 9, 12, 9, 16, and 18. Find the mean, median, mode, range, and standard deviation of the fat contents. *Compare* the fat contents of this restaurant and the one in Exercise 3 using the mean, median, and standard deviation.

UNIT 7

Use Normal Distributions

Georgia Performance Standards: MM2D1d

Goal Study normal distributions.

Vocabulary

A **normal distribution** is modeled by a bell-shaped curve called a **normal curve** that is symmetric about the mean. The total area under the related curve is 1. The percentage of the area covered by each standard deviation from the mean is shown in the graph.

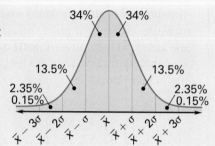

The **standard normal distribution** is the normal distribution with mean 0 and standard deviation 1. The formula below can be used to transform x-values from a normal distribution with mean $\bar{x}$ and standard deviation σ into z-values having a standard normal distribution.

$$z = \frac{x - \bar{x}}{\sigma}$$

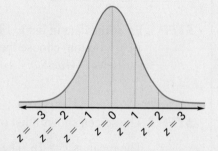

The z-value for a particular x-value is called the **z-score** for the x-value and is the number of standard deviations the x-value lies above or below the mean $\bar{x}$.

Example 1 Find a normal probability

A normal distribution has mean $\bar{x}$ and standard deviation σ. For a randomly selected x-value from the distribution, find $P(\bar{x} \le x \le \bar{x} + 2\sigma)$.

Solution

The probability that a randomly selected x-value lies between $\bar{x}$ and $\bar{x} + 2\sigma$ is the shaded area under the normal curve shown.

$P(\bar{x} \le x \le \bar{x} + 2\sigma) = 0.34 + 0.135$

$\hspace{3.5cm} = 0.475$

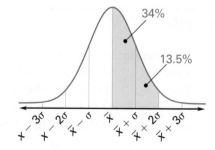

Guided Practice for Example 1

A normal distribution has mean $\bar{x}$ and standard deviation σ. Find the indicated probability for a randomly selected x-value from the distribution.

1. $P(x \le \bar{x} + \sigma)$ **2.** $P(x \ge \bar{x} + \sigma)$ **3.** $P(\bar{x} \le x \le \bar{x} + \sigma)$

Georgia Performance Standards

MM2D1d Compare the means and standard deviations of random samples with the corresponding population parameters, including those population parameters for normal distributions. Observe that the different sample means vary from one sample to the next. Observe that the distribution of the sample means has less variability than the population distribution.

Example 2 Interpret normally distributed data

Oak Trees The heights (in feet) of fully grown white oak trees are normally distributed with a mean of 90 feet and a standard deviation of 3.5 feet. About what percent of white oak trees have heights between 86.5 feet and 93.5 feet?

Solution

The heights of 86.5 feet and 93.5 feet represent one standard deviation on either side of the mean, as shown. So, 68% of the trees have heights between 86.5 feet and 93.5 feet.

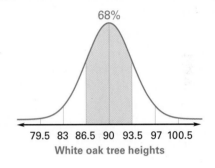

White oak tree heights

Example 3 Use a z-score and the standard normal table

In Example 2, find the probability that a randomly selected white oak tree has a height of at most 94 feet.

Solution

STEP 1 **Find** the z-score corresponding to an x-value of 94.

$$z = \frac{x - \bar{x}}{\sigma} = \frac{94 - 90}{3.5} \approx 1.1$$

STEP 2 **Use** the standard normal table on page 296 to find $P(x \le 94) \approx P(z \le 1.1)$.

The table shows that $P(z \le 1.1) = 0.8643$. So, the probability that a randomly selected white oak tree has a height of at most 94 feet is about 0.8643.

z	.0	.1	.2
−3	.0013	.0010	.0007
−2	.0228	.0179	.0139
−1	.1587	.1357	.1151
−0	.5000	.4602	.4207
0	.5000	.5398	.5793
1	.8413	.8643	.8849

Guided Practice for Examples 2 and 3

In the following exercises, refer to Example 2.

4. About what percent of white oak trees have heights less than 97 feet?

5. About what percent of white oak trees have heights between 83 feet and 90 feet?

6. Find the probability that a randomly selected white oak tree has a height of at most 85 feet.

**Exercise
Set A**

MM2D1d Compare the means and standard deviations of random samples with the corresponding population parameters, including those population parameters for normal distributions. Observe that the different sample means vary from one sample to the next. Observe that the distribution of the sample means has less variability than the population distribution.

A normal distribution has mean $\bar{x}$ and standard deviation σ. Find the indicated probability for a randomly selected x-value from the distribution.

1. $P(x \geq \bar{x} + \sigma)$ **2.** $P(x \leq \bar{x} + 2\sigma)$ **3.** $P(x \geq \bar{x} - 3\sigma)$

Give the percent of the area under the normal curve represented by the shaded region.

4.

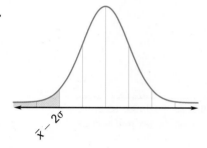

5.

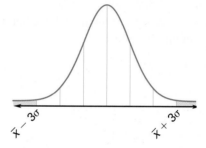

A normal distribution has a mean of 27 and a standard deviation of 5. Find the probability that a randomly selected x-value from the distribution is in the given interval.

6. Between 22 and 32 **7.** Between 12 and 27 **8.** Between 17 and 37

9. At least 22 **10.** At least 37 **11.** At most 32

A normal distribution has a mean of 75 and a standard deviation of 10. Use the standard normal table on page 296 to find the indicated probability for a randomly selected x-value from the distribution.

12. $P(x \leq 70)$ **13.** $P(x \leq 52)$ **14.** $P(x \leq 78)$

15. $P(x \leq 96)$ **16.** $P(x \leq 44)$ **17.** $P(x \leq 106)$

18. **Biology** The weights of adult male rhesus monkeys are normally distributed with a mean of 17 pounds and a standard deviation of 3 pounds. What is the probability that a randomly selected adult male rhesus monkey has a weight less than 14 pounds?

19. **Error Analysis** A survey was conducted to measure the number of hours per week that adults in the United States spend on home computers. In the survey, the numbers of hours were normally distributed with a mean of 7 hours and a standard deviation of 1 hour. *Describe* and correct the error in finding the probability that a participant spends at most 6.5 hours per week on the home computer.

$$z = \frac{x - \bar{x}}{\sigma} = \frac{7 - 6.5}{1} = 0.5$$

From the standard normal table, $P(x \leq 0.5) = 0.6915$. So, the probability that an adult spends at most 6.5 hours per week on the home computer is 0.6915.

UNIT 7

Exercise Set B

MM2D1d Compare the means and standard deviations of random samples with the corresponding population parameters, including those population parameters for normal distributions. Observe that the different sample means vary from one sample to the next. Observe that the distribution of the sample means has less variability than the population distribution.

A normal distribution has mean $\bar{x}$ and standard deviation σ. Find the indicated probability for a randomly selected x-value from the distribution.

1. $P(x \geq \bar{x} + 3\sigma)$

2. $P(x \leq \bar{x} - 3\sigma)$

3. $P(x \leq \bar{x} + 2\sigma)$

Give the percent of the area under the normal curve represented by the shaded region.

4.

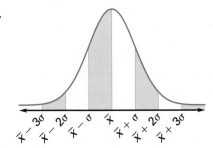

5.

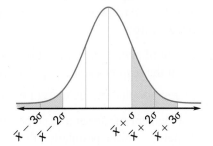

A normal distribution has a mean of 63.7 and a standard deviation of 2.9. Find the probability that a randomly selected x-value from the distribution is in the given interval.

6. Between 63.7 and 69.5

7. Between 60.8 and 72.4

8. Between 57.9 and 66.6

9. At least 66.6

10. At least 57.9

11. At most 69.5

A normal distribution has a mean of 125.8 and a standard deviation of 10.4. Use the standard normal table on page 296 to find the indicated probability for a randomly selected x-value from the distribution.

12. $P(x \leq 117.3)$

13. $P(x \leq 92.6)$

14. $P(x \leq 140.1)$

15. $P(124 \leq x \leq 145.6)$

16. $P(99.8 \leq x \leq 112.3)$

17. $P(136.1 \leq x \leq 165.3)$

In Exercises 18–20, use the following information.

Obstacle Course Two different obstacle courses were set up for gym class. The times to complete Course A are normally distributed with a mean of 54 seconds and a standard deviation of 6.1 seconds. The times to complete Course B are normally distributed with a mean of 1 minute, 25 seconds and a standard deviation of 8.7 seconds. Matt completed Course A in 59 seconds. John completed Course B in 1 minute, 31 seconds.

18. Find the z-score for Matt's time.

19. Find the z-score for John's time.

20. Which student had the better time? *Explain.*

UNIT 7

Select and Draw Conclusions from Samples

Georgia Performance Standards: MM2D1a

Goal Study different sampling methods for collecting data.

Vocabulary

A **population** is a group of people or objects that you want information about.

A **sample** is a subset of the population. In a *self-selected sample*, members of a population can volunteer to be in the sample. In a *systematic sample*, a rule is used to select members of a population, such as selecting every other person. In a *convenience sample*, easy-to-reach members of a population are selected, such as those in the first row. In a *random sample*, each member of a population has an equal chance of being selected.

An **unbiased sample** is representative of the population you want information about. A sample that overrepresents the population or underrepresents part of the population is a **biased sample**.

The **margin of error** gives a limit on how much the responses of a sample would differ from the responses of a population. When a random sample of size n is taken from a large population, the margin of error is approximated as $\pm\dfrac{1}{\sqrt{n}}$. This means that if the percent of the sample responding a certain way is p (expressed as a decimal), then the percent of the population that would respond the same way is likely to be between $p - \dfrac{1}{\sqrt{n}}$ and $p + \dfrac{1}{\sqrt{n}}$.

Example 1   Classify samples

Lunch Habits A business reporter wants to survey workers about where they eat lunch during a typical work week. Identify the type of sample described as a *self-selected sample*, a *systematic sample*, a *convenience sample*, or a *random sample*.

a. The reporter writes a column asking workers to call a special phone number and identify where they eat lunch during a typical work week.

b. The reporter asks everyone in the newsroom where they eat lunch during a typical work week.

Solution

a. The workers can choose whether or not to respond. So, the sample is a self-selected sample.

b. The reporter selected workers that are easily accessible. So, the sample is a convenience sample.

Georgia Performance Standards

MM2D1a   Pose a question and collect sample data from at least two different populations.

Example 2 Identify biased samples

Tell whether each sample in Example 1 is *biased* or *unbiased*. Explain your reasoning.

a. The sample is biased because the sample is self-selected and it may not be representative of the population the reporter wants information about.

b. The sample is biased because a convenience sample is not representative of the population the reporter wants information about.

Example 3 Find a margin of error

Lunch Habits In a survey of 990 workers, 30% said they eat at home during a typical work week.

a. What is the margin of error for the survey?

b. Give an interval that is likely to contain the exact percent of all workers who eat at home during a typical work week.

Solution

a. Use the margin of error formula.

$$\text{Margin of error} = \pm \frac{1}{\sqrt{n}} \qquad \text{Write margin of error formula.}$$

$$= \pm \frac{1}{\sqrt{990}} \qquad \text{Substitute 990 for } n.$$

$$\approx \pm 0.032 \qquad \text{Use a calculator.}$$

The margin of error for the survey is about ±3.2%.

b. To find the interval, subtract and add 3.2% to the percent of workers surveyed who eat at home during a typical work week.

$$30\% - 3.2\% = 26.8\% \qquad\qquad 30\% + 3.2\% = 33.2\%$$

It is likely that the exact percent of all workers who eat at home during a typical work week is between 26.8% and 33.2%.

Guided Practice for Examples 1, 2, and 3

1. A real estate agent wants to know if first-time home buyers used the Internet to research home listings. The real-estate agent calls every fifth first-time home buyer and asks them if they used the Internet to research home listings. Identify the type of sample described.

2. Tell whether the sample in Exercise 1 is *biased* or *unbiased*. *Explain* your reasoning.

3. In a survey of 1200 first-time home buyers, 41% said they used the Internet to research home listings. What is the margin of error? Give an interval that is likely to contain the exact percent of all first-time home buyers who used the Internet to research home listings.

4. In Example 3, 29% of the 990 workers surveyed said they eat at their desks during a typical work week. Give an interval that is likely to contain the exact percent of all workers who eat at their desks during a typical work week.

UNIT 7

MM2D1a   Pose a question and collect sample data from at least two different populations.

Identify the type of sample described. Then tell if the sample is biased.
Explain **your reasoning.**

1. A consumer advocacy group wants to know if car owners believe their car is reliable. The group randomly selects 1020 car owners and mails out a survey to each one.

2. A grocery store wants to know which day of the week consumers prefer to do their grocery shopping. Everyone who shops at the store on Friday is asked which day of the week they prefer to do their grocery shopping.

3. A survey of students' favorite school subjects is being conducted. Every other student in the math club is asked "Which school subject is your favorite?"

Find the margin of error for a survey that has the given sample size. Round your answer to the nearest tenth of a percent.

4. 200   5. 350   6. 1100   7. 2600

8. 5200   9. 495   10. 280   11. 9000

Find the sample size required to achieve the given margin of error. Round your answer to the nearest whole number.

12. $\pm 2\%$ 13. $\pm 4\%$ 14. $\pm 9.5\%$ 15. $\pm 2.7\%$

16. $\pm 4.5\%$ 17. $\pm 0.5\%$ 18. $\pm 3.6\%$ 19. $\pm 7.5\%$

In Exercises 20 and 21, use the following information.

Technology Survey In a survey of 504 people in the United States, about 11% said that the influx of new technologies such as computers has left them feeling overwhelmed.

20. What is the margin of error for the survey? Round your answer to the nearest tenth of a percent.

21. Give an interval that is likely to contain the exact percent of all people in the United States who feel overwhelmed by the influx of new technologies.

In Exercises 22–25, use the following information.

TV in the Bedroom A survey reported that 510 kids ages 8 to 18, or 68% of those surveyed, have a TV in their bedroom.

22. How many kids ages 8 to 18 were surveyed?

23. What is the margin of error for the survey? Round your answer to the nearest tenth of a percent.

24. Give an interval that is likely to contain the exact percent of all kids ages 8 to 18 who have a TV in their bedroom

25. About how many kids ages 8 to 18 should be surveyed to have a margin of error of $\pm 2.5\%$?

LESSON 7.5

Exercise Set B

MM2D1a   Pose a question and collect sample data from at least two different populations.

Identify the type of sample described. Then tell if the sample is biased. *Explain* **your reasoning.**

1. A team wants to know who the fans think was the team's most valuable player during the season. Fans can vote on the team's website.

2. The managers of a movie theater chain want to find the number of movies people in the community usually see in a theater each month. The managers have the ticket sellers at each theater survey customers when they purchase their tickets.

3. The managers of a company with 500 employees want to know how the employees feel about some proposed changes. The managers use a computer to generate a list of 50 employees to survey from a database that includes all of the employees.

Find the margin of error for a survey that has the given sample size. Round your answer to the nearest tenth of a percent.

4. 586	5. 817	6. 935	7. 642
8. 5700	9. 8968	10. 7103	11. 12,000

Find the sample size required to achieve the given margin of error. Round your answer to the nearest whole number.

12. $\pm 2.4\%$	13. $\pm 5.1\%$	14. $\pm 3.8\%$	15. $\pm 1.2\%$
16. $\pm 5.9\%$	17. $\pm 3.3\%$	18. $\pm 4.6\%$	19. $\pm 0.7\%$

In Exercises 20 and 21, use the following information.

Wheelchair A new medically approved wheelchair was considered to be an improvement over a standard wheelchair by 325 out of 450 patients in a survey.

20. What is the margin of error for the survey? Round your answer to the nearest tenth of a percent.

21. Give an interval that is likely to contain the exact percent of all patients who would consider the new wheelchair an improvement.

In Exercises 22 and 23, use the following information.

City Park A survey claims that the percent of an entire population that agrees with redeveloping the city park is likely between 49.1% and 57.5%. The remainder of the people in the survey were against redevelopment.

22. How many people were surveyed? Find the interval that is likely to contain the exact percent of people in the population against redevelopment.

23. How many people in the survey would need to agree with redevelopment in order for you to be confident that the majority of the population agrees with redevelopment?

Technology Activity
Use a Calculator for Random Sampling

Use after Lesson 7.5

Question

How can you use a graphing calculator to select a random sample?

A *population* is a group of people or objects that you want information about. When it is too difficult, time-consuming, or expensive to survey everyone in a population, information is gathered from a *sample*, or subset, of the population. In a *random sample*, each member of a population has an equal chance of being selected.

Example

Select a random sample.

The cafeteria staff wants to survey the students in each grade who purchase school lunches to determine their favorite lunch items. There are 427 students who purchase a school lunch. Describe a method for selecting a random sample of 20 students from each grade.

Grade level	10th	11th	12th
Number of students	150	140	137

STEP 1 **Make** a list of the 150 tenth graders who purchase school lunches, and assign each of these students a different number from 1 to 150.

STEP 2 **Use** the TI-83 Plus graphing calculator to generate 20 unique random integers from 1 to 150. (*Note:* the Casio CFX-9850GC Plus does not have a random integer function.) To randomly generate an integer between 1 and 150 use the following keystrokes.

[MATH] [▶] [▶] [▶] 5 1 [,] 150 [)] [ENTER]

For each integer that is generated, circle the corresponding student on your list. Press [ENTER] to generate the next random integer. If a number is repeated, simply discard it. Continue to generate integers until 20 students are chosen.

Choose 20 students from the 11th grade by repeating steps 1 and 2 and replacing 150 with 140. Then choose 20 students from the 12th grade by repeating steps 1 and 2 and replacing 150 with 137.

Practice

1. Split the class into two groups. Assign each student in the group a number. Use a graphing calculator to generate a random sample from each group. Ask each student in the sample, "How many pets do you have?" Calculate the mean and standard deviation for each group and compare the results.

Sample Data and Populations

Georgia Performance Standards: MM2D1a, MM2D1d

Goal Collect sample data from populations.

Vocabulary

A **statistic** is a numerical description of a *sample* characteristic.

A *parameter* is a numerical description of a *population* characteristic. The mean of a population is an example of a population parameter.

The **population mean** is the true mean of the entire population.

Example 1 **Collect data by randomly sampling**

A country club has 345 social members and 876 golf members. The president of the country club wants to form a random sample of 20 social members and a separate random sample of 50 golf members to answer some survey questions. Each social member has a membership number from 1 to 345 and each golf member has a membership number from 1001 to 1876. Use a graphing calculator to select the members who will participate in each random sample.

Solution

Random sample of social members:

Use the random integer feature of a graphing calculator to generate 20 random integers between 1 and 345. Use the arrows to scroll over and see the rest of the random values.

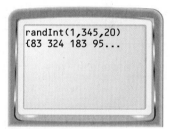

The social members with membership numbers 83, 324, 183, 95, ... make up the random sample of social members.

Random sample of golf members:

Use the random integer feature of a graphing calculator to generate 50 random integers between 1001 and 1876. Use the arrows to scroll over and see the rest of the random values.

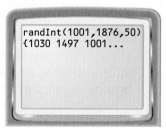

The golf members with membership numbers 1030, 1497, 1001, ... make up the random sample of golf members.

Guided Practice for Example 1

1. In Example 1, suppose there are 221 social members and 384 golf members. The president wants to form a random sample of 15 social members and a separate random sample of 25 golf members. Use a graphing calculator to select the members who will participate in each random sample.

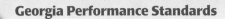
Example 2   Compare statistics and parameters

A school's math club wants to know how many hours students spend on math homework each week. Savannah and Miguel, two students in the math club, collect separate random samples. Their results are displayed below. The population mean is 11.9 and the population standard deviation is about 6.7. Compare the means and standard deviations of the random samples to the population parameters.

Savannah	Miguel
8, 5, 12, 8, 10, 10, 6, 4, 8, 17, 14, 14, 16, 9, 10, 7, 10, 7, 12, 15, 5, 9, 14, 10, 5	12, 14, 14, 7, 6, 16, 8, 18, 10, 8, 20, 7, 10, 16, 18, 14, 7, 12, 18, 17, 16, 7, 20, 10, 12, 11, 9, 18, 14, 12

Solution

Savannah: $\bar{x} = \dfrac{8 + 5 + \cdots + 5}{25} = \dfrac{245}{25} = 9.8$

Miguel: $\bar{x} = \dfrac{12 + 14 + \cdots + 12}{30} = \dfrac{381}{90} = 12.7$

Savannah: $\sigma = \sqrt{\dfrac{(8 - 9.8)^2 + (5 - 9.8)^2 + \cdots + (5 - 9.8)^2}{25}}$

$ = 3.6$

Miguel: $\sigma = \sqrt{\dfrac{(12 - 12.7)^2 + (14 - 12.7)^2 + \cdots + (12 - 12.7)^2}{30}}$

$ \approx 4.2$

The mean of Savannah's sample is less than the population mean while the mean of Miguel's sample is greater than the population mean. The standard deviations of both samples are less than the population standard deviation, which indicates that the samples are less varied than the entire population.

Guided Practice for Example 2

2. For a large population, the mean is 4.8 and the standard deviation is about 3.6. One random sample produced data values of 5, 1, 3, 4, 7, 6, 8, 2, 1, and 3. Another random sample produced data values of 8, 7, 5, 3, 4, 2, 2, 9, 7, and 3. *Compare* the means and standard deviations of the random samples to the population parameters.

UNIT 7

**Exercise
Set A**

MM2D1a Pose a question and collect sample data from at least two different populations.

MM2D1d Compare the means and standard deviations of random samples with the corresponding population parameters, including those population parameters for normal distributions. Observe that the different sample means vary from one sample to the next. Observe that the distribution of the sample means has less variability than the population distribution.

In Exercises 1–4, use a graphing calculator to generate five random integers in the given range.

1. 1 to 125   **2.** 200 to 800   **3.** 55 to 95   **4.** 101 to 150

5. Error Analysis A school's pep club wants to know the favorite sports of students. Ethan, a member of the pep club, offers to conduct the survey. He decides to survey the members of the football team and claims that the sample is representative of the entire school. *Describe* the error in his claim and suggest a better method for selecting a random sample.

For a large population, the mean is 13.7 and the standard deviation is about 8.9. *Compare* **the mean and standard deviation of the random sample to the population parameters.**

6.

Random Sample A
19, 8, 12, 17, 16, 25, 5, 18, 21, 7

7.

Random Sample B
12, 15, 17, 20, 13, 11, 18, 9, 15, 14

8.

Random Sample C
4, 15, 3, 11, 24, 19, 8, 7, 11, 17, 10, 15

9. Reasoning From Exercises 6–8, what conclusion can you draw about the standard deviation of a sample versus the standard deviation of the population?

10. Student Survey At Central High School, there are 137 juniors and 163 seniors. The principal of the school wants to form a random sample of 25 juniors and a separate random sample of 25 seniors to answer some survey questions. Each junior has a student identification number from 11001 to 11137 and each senior has a student identification number from 12001 to 12163. Use a graphing calculator to select the students who will participate in each random sample.

11. Number of Pets A pet store wants to know the number of pets owned by each household in their small town. Two employees, Chandra and Xavier, collect separate random samples. The population mean is 2.4 and the population standard deviation is about 2.2. *Compare* the means and standard deviations of the random samples to the population parameters.

Chandra
0, 1, 5, 4, 2, 2, 3, 0, 1, 1, 0, 0, 4, 3, 0, 1, 0, 4, 6, 2, 2, 2, 5, 3, 0, 3, 4, 0, 2, 1, 2

Xavier
2, 1, 4, 3, 3, 1, 0, 5, 6, 3, 8, 2, 1, 0, 4, 2, 1, 5, 7, 2, 2, 1, 5, 2, 5

UNIT 7

MM2D1a Pose a question and collect sample data from at least two different populations.

MM2D1d Compare the means and standard deviations of random samples with the corresponding population parameters, including those population parameters for normal distributions. Observe that the different sample means vary from one sample to the next. Observe that the distribution of the sample means has less variability than the population distribution.

You are conducting a survey to determine how students in your school spend their summer vacation. In Exercises 1 and 2, tell whether the sampling method is representative of the entire student population.

1. Survey members of the sailing club.

2. Assign a number to each student in the school and generate random numbers. Then survey each student whose number is randomly selected.

3. **Random Integers** Use a graphing calculator to generate 12 random integers in the range 525 to 675.

For a large population, the mean is 1.5 and the standard deviation is about 1.1. *Compare* the mean and standard deviation of the random sample to the population parameters.

4.

Random Sample A
0.4, 0.9, 1.4, 0.8, 2.4, 1.3, 0.5, 0.8, 1.6, 2.3

5.

Random Sample B
1.3, 2.0, 0.6, 0.8, 2.1, 1.4, 1.6, 0.9

6.

Random Sample C
0.8, 1.9, 2.5, 0.3, 1.6, 0.4, 2.2, 2.8, 2.3, 0.5

7. **Reasoning** From Exercises 4–6, what conclusion can you draw about the means of different samples from the same population?

8. **Student Survey** At Parkside High School, there are 567 juniors and 515 seniors. The principal of the school wants to form a random sample of 22 juniors and a separate random sample of 27 seniors to answer some survey questions. Each junior has a student identification number from 11001 to 11567 and each senior has a student identification number from 12001 to 12515. Use a graphing calculator to select the students who will participate in each random sample.

9. **Number of Cell Phones** An electronics store wants to know the number of cell phones currently used by each family in their town. The store manager and the cashier collect separate random samples. The population mean is 2.9 and the population standard deviation is about 2.1. *Compare* the means and standard deviations of the random samples to the population parameters.

Store Manager
2, 5, 4, 3, 3, 2, 1, 1, 4, 0, 3, 5, 6, 4, 2, 1, 0, 2, 3, 1, 1, 1, 2, 4, 5, 5, 3

Cashier
3, 0, 2, 5, 7, 3, 2, 2, 4, 2, 3, 0, 4, 5, 8, 4, 3, 4, 3, 1, 2, 3, 4, 2, 4, 3, 3, 3, 1, 7, 4

Georgia Performance Standards

MM2D1d   Compare the means and standard deviations of random samples with the corresponding population parameters, including those population parameters for normal distributions. Observe that the different sample means vary from one sample to the next. Observe that the distribution of the sample means has less variability than the population distribution.

Technology Activity
Compare Sample and Population Variability

Use after Lesson 7.6

Question

How can you use a graphing calculator to generate and compare samples?

When given the mean and the standard deviation of a normal distribution, you can use a graphing calculator to generate random samples and find the mean and standard deviation of each sample.

Example 1

Generate samples and find statistics.

The heights of male students at a school are normally distributed with a mean of 166 centimeters and a standard deviation of 8 centimeters. Generate 5 samples of the data that each have a sample size of 5. Then calculate the mean and standard deviation of each sample.

STEP 1   Generate samples

Use the *random Normal* feature to generate one sample. Press **MATH**, choose the PRB menu, select randNorm), and type 166,8,5). Use the **STO+** key to store the sample in L_1.

STEP 2   Calculate statistics

Press **STAT**, choose the CALC menu, select 1-Var Stats, and type L_1.

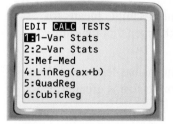

STEP 3   Read statistics

The screen shows a list of statistics. For this sample, the mean is $\overline{x} \approx 168.2$ and the standard deviation is $\sigma \approx 6.292$.

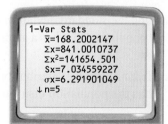

STEP 4   **Repeat** Steps 1–3 four more times storing the samples in L_2, L_3, L_4, and L_5.

Example 2

Compare samples with population.

Find the standard deviation of the sample means calculated in Example 1. Then compare the sample means standard deviation with the population standard deviation.

STEP 1 **Enter data**

Enter the five sample means from Example 1 in L_6. (They may differ from the ones shown below.)

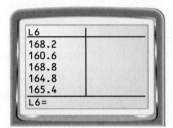

STEP 2 **Calculate statistics**

Press **STAT**, choose the CALC menu, select 1-Var Stats, and type L_6. The standard deviation for the sample means is $\sigma \approx 2.921$.

STEP 3 **Compare statistics**

The standard deviation of the sample means, 2.921, is less than the standard deviation of the population, 8.

Practice

1. The heights of female students at a school are normally distributed with a mean of 162 centimeters and a standard deviation of 7.6 centimeters. Generate 6 samples that each have a sample size of 6. Then calculate the mean and standard deviation of each sample.

2. Find the standard deviation of the sample means calculated in Exercise 1. Then compare the sample means standard deviation with the population standard deviation.

3. For a population that is normally distributed, the means of samples of the population are normally distributed. The standard deviation of the distribution of sample means, $\sigma_{\bar{x}}$, is given by the formula below where σ is the standard deviation of the population and n is the sample size.

$$\sigma_{\bar{x}} = \frac{\sigma}{\sqrt{n}}$$

   a. Find the standard deviation of the distribution of sample means for a population that has a standard deviation of 8 given that the sample size is 5.

   b. *Explain* why the distribution of the sample means has less variability than the population distribution when the sample size is greater than 1.

Choose the Best Model for Two-Variable Data

Georgia Performance Standards: MM2D2a, MM2D2c

Goal Choose the best model to represent a set of data.

The functions in the table at the right have been used to model sets of data. To determine the best model to use for a set of data pairs (x, y), make a scatter plot of the data and choose the type of function suggested by the pattern of the data points. Use the *regression* feature of a graphing calculator to find a model for the data.

Function	General Form
Linear	$y = ax + b$
Quadratic	$y = ax^2 + bx + c$
Cubic	$y = ax^3 + bx^2 + cx + d$
Exponential	$y = ab^x$
Power	$y = ax^b$

Example 1   Use a linear model

Use a graphing calculator to find a model for the data.

x	3	4	5	6	7	8	9	10
y	7931	8306	8800	9206	9588	10,076	10,444	10,876

STEP 1 Make a scatter plot. The points lie approximately on a line. This suggests a linear model.

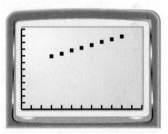

STEP 2 Use the *linear regression* feature to find an equation of the model.

LinReg
  y=ax+b
  a=422.797619
  b=6655.190476

STEP 3 Graph the model along with the data to verify that the model fits the data well.

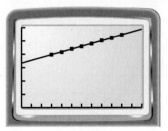

A model for the data is $y = 423x + 6655$.

Georgia Performance Standards

MM2D2a Gather and plot data that can be modeled with linear and quadratic functions. ☑

MM2D2c Understand and apply the processes of linear and quadratic regression for curve fitting using appropriate technology. ☑

Example 2 Use a quadratic model

Use a graphing calculator to find a model for the data.

x	3	4	5	6	7	8	9	10
y	15	30	40	50	45	42	31	18

STEP 1 **Make** a scatter plot. The points form an inverted U-shape. This suggests a quadratic model.

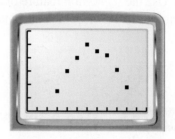

STEP 2 **Use** the *quadratic regression* feature to find an equation of the model.

```
QuadReg
 y=ax²+bx+c
 a=-2.553571429
 b=33.51785714
 c=-62.69642857
```

STEP 3 **Graph** the model along with the data to verify that the model fits the data well.

A model for the data is $y = -2.55x^2 + 33.5x - 63$.

Guided Practice for Examples 1 and 2

Use a graphing calculator to find a linear, quadratic, or exponential model for the data. Then graph the model and the data in the same coordinate plane.

1.

x	4	8	12	16	20	24	28	32
y	24	28	30	32	36	39	43	45

2.

x	3	4	5	6	7	8	9	10
y	1.6	3	6	13	26	51	102	205

3.

x	2	7	9	13	17	20	25
y	34	37	38	37	36	32	26

LESSON
7.7

**Exercise
Set A**

MM2D2a   Gather and plot data that can be modeled with linear
and quadratic functions.

MM2D2c   Understand and apply the processes of linear and
quadratic regression for curve fitting using appropriate
technology.

Determine which type of function best models the data points. *Explain.*

1.

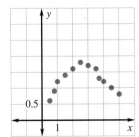

2.

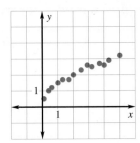

3.

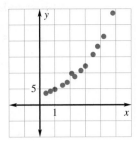

Multiple Choice Determine the equation that best models the data.

4.

x	2	6	9	15	17	23	27
y	5	2	1	2	4	9	15

A. $y = 1.54x^{0.37}$

B. $y = 0.4x - 0.28$

C. $y = 0.05x^2 - 1.06x + 6.69$

D. $y = 1.44(1.07)^x$

5.

x	2	5	7	10	13	15	19
y	24	14	10	6	4	3	1

A. $y = 35.3(0.84)^x$

B. $y = -1.24x + 21.48$

C. $y = 86.46x^{-1.27}$

D. $y = 0.095x^2 - 3.22x + 28.91$

6.

x	3	6	9	12	15	18	21	24
y	26	37	49	56	67	74	83	96

A. $y = 25.86(1.06)^x$

B. $y = 3.2x + 17.82$

C. $y = 12.63x^{0.62}$

D. $y = 0.01x^3 - 0.2x^2 + 5.6x + 10.4$

7. **Black Bears** The table shows the weight w (in kilograms) and the chest-girth circumference
c (in centimeters) for 9 male black bears in West Virginia. Use the *regression* feature of
a graphing calculator to find a function that models the data. What is the weight of a male
black bear that has a chest-girth circumference of 119 centimeters?

w	82	90	101	112	125	136	144	152	160
c	91	94	99	103	108	112	116	119	122

Exercise Set B

MM2D2a   Gather and plot data that can be modeled with linear and quadratic functions.

MM2D2c   Understand and apply the processes of linear and quadratic regression for curve fitting using appropriate technology.

Determine which type of function best models the data points. *Explain*.

1.
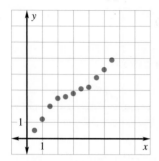

2.
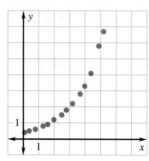

3.
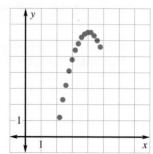

Use a graphing calculator to find the equation that best models the data. *Explain* your choice.

4.

x	3	6	9	12	15	18	21
y	7	13	21	30	35	40	51

5.

x	0.1	0.5	0.8	1.2	1.6	2.3	2.7	3.4
y	1.97	2.61	3.33	4.47	6.02	10.34	13.98	23.75

6.

x	1.2	1.8	2.3	2.7	3.1	3.6	4.4	4.9	5.5
y	0.79	6.62	12.64	19.43	27.18	38.48	60.2	76.21	97.77

7. Multiple Representations The graph below shows the height (in inches) of a boy during the years 1997 to 2006 (ages 3 to 12). Use a graphing calculator to find a model for the data. Then graph the model and the data in the same coordinate plane.

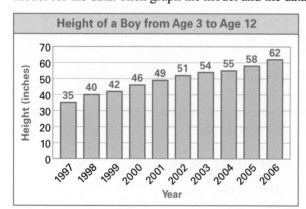

TEST | for Unit 7

1. Draw a scatter plot of the data. Tell whether the data have a *positive correlation*, a *negative correlation*, or *approximately no correlation*. Then approximate the best-fitting line for the data.

x	−4	−3	−2	−1	0	1	2	3	4
y	−2.7	−3.1	−1.1	1.5	1.2	2.9	4.8	3.9	5.7

Write a quadratic function in vertex form whose graph has the given vertex and passes through the given point.

2. vertex: $(0, 5)$
   point: $(−1, 8)$

3. vertex: $(−2, −22)$
   point: $(2, −18)$

4. vertex: $(4, 1)$
   point: $(8, 17)$

Find the mean, median, mode, range, and standard deviation of the data set.

5. 8, 12, 5, 11, 8, 3, 15, 9, 21, 16

6. 25, 42, 48, 31, 50, 29, 36, 43, 29, 52

A normal distribution has a mean of 52 and a standard deviation of 14. Use the standard normal table on page 296 to find the indicated probability for a randomly selected *x*-value from the distribution.

7. $P(x \le 17)$

8. $P(x \le 70.2)$

9. $P(x \le 57.6)$

In Exercises 10–12, identify the type of sample described as a *self-selected sample*, a *systematic sample*, a *convenience sample*, or a *random sample*. Then tell if the sample is biased. *Explain* your reasoning.

10. For quality assurance, every twentieth engine part is selected from an assembly line and tested for durability.

11. City council wants to know how citizens feel about a proposed new ordinance. They mail out surveys to all of the citizens and use the surveys that are returned.

12. A band director wants to know how many students in the school can play the saxophone. He collects a sample by asking students during marching band practice.

For a large population, the mean is 92 and the standard deviation is about 14.7. *Compare* the mean and standard deviation of the random sample to the population parameters.

13. Random Sample A: 85, 76, 91, 95, 101, 75, 86, 94, 79, 77, 87, 95, 100, 96, 88, 85, 91, 98, 84, 95, 75

14. Random Sample B: 94, 103, 75, 99, 105, 87, 101, 91, 84, 93, 81, 110, 96, 99, 102, 78, 105, 92, 83, 100, 96, 84, 99

In Exercises 15 and 16, use a graphing calculator to find the linear, exponential, or quadratic equation that best models the data. *Explain* your choice.

15.

x	0	2	4	6	8	10	12
y	22	20	19	14	15	10	7

16.

x	0.5	1.1	1.6	2.2	2.7	3.4	3.9	4.5	5.1
y	0.7	5.4	12.1	21.6	32.4	44.8	60.3	78.4	95.1

17. Monthly Sales The table shows the monthly sales for a new hair salon since its grand opening in March. Assume that t is the number of months since March and S is the total sales in thousands of dollars. Use a graphing calculator to find the best-fitting quadratic model for the data. Using the model, what will be the total sales in September?

Month, t	0	1	2	3	4	5
Sales, S	5.6	5.8	6.2	6.9	7.9	9.0

18. Apples The annual per person consumption of apples in the United States is normally distributed with a mean of 16 pounds and a standard deviation of 4 pounds. Find the z-score for an annual per person consumption of 22 pounds of apples. What is the probability that a randomly selected person in the United States has an annual consumption of at most 22 pounds of apples?

Performance Task

Summer Reading

A school's book club wants to know how many books were read by students during summer vacation.

a. Melinda says that she will survey the students in the book club. What type of sampling is this? Will the sample be biased? *Explain* your reasoning and suggest a better sampling method.

b. José suggests that they select students to survey by randomly choosing student identification numbers. There are 875 students in the school with identification numbers from 1 to 875. Use a graphing calculator to generate 25 random student identification numbers.

c. The population mean is 5 and the standard deviation is about 3.9. *Compare* the means and standard deviations of the random samples below to the population parameters.

Dakota's Sample: 1, 0, 5, 2, 12, 4, 1, 0, 0, 3, 5, 4, 2, 1, 2, 0

Hong's Sample: 4, 6, 7, 15, 5, 8, 0, 1, 4, 7, 6, 4, 3, 3, 4

d. The table shows the average number of books y read by students who are x years of age. Draw a scatter plot of the data and describe the correlation. Then use a graphing calculator to find a model for the data. Graph the model and the data in the same coordinate plane.

x	13	14	15	16	17	18
y	2.1	3.4	4.9	6.1	6.9	7.3

Student Resources

Tables

Table of Symbols

Symbol	Meaning	Page
i	imaginary unit equal to $\sqrt{-1}$	2
$\sqrt{a}$	the nonnegative square root of a	2
$\cdot$	multiplication, times	2
$-a$	opposite of a	2
π	pi, equal to irrational number about 3.14	2
$|z|$	absolute value of complex number z	17
$\approx$	is approximately equal to	24
$|x|$	absolute value of x	28
$\neq$	is not equal to	28
$>$	is greater than	29
$<$	is less than	29
$\leq$	is less than or equal to	29
$\geq$	is greater than or equal to	29
(x, y)	ordered pair	33
$f(x)$	the value of the function f at x	33
$\pm$	plus or minus	83
f^{-1}	inverse of function f	116
$\sqrt[n]{a}$	nth root of a	116
Σ	summation	133
$\cdots$	and so on	133
$\circ$	degree(s)	150

Symbol	Meaning	Page
$\overline{AB}$	segment AB	150
$\triangle ABC$	triangle ABC	150
$\llcorner$	right angle symbol	151
$\angle$	angle	157
$\tan$	tangent	157
$\sin$	sine	163
$\cos$	cosine	163
$\overleftrightarrow{AB}$	line AB	170
$m\angle A$	measure of angle A	170
$\tan^{-1}$	inverse tangent	171
$\sin^{-1}$	inverse sine	172
$\cos^{-1}$	inverse cosine	172
$\sim$	is similar to	182
$\odot P$	circle with center P	182
$\overrightarrow{AB}$	ray AB	182
$\perp$	is perpendicular to	184
$\cong$	is congruent to	185
$m\overgroup{AB}$	measure of minor arc AB	190
$m\overgroup{ABC}$	measure of major arc ABC	190
$\overline{x}$	x-bar, the mean of a data set	259
σ	sigma, the standard deviation of a data set	259
$P(A)$	the probability of an event A	264

Time

60 seconds (sec) = 1 minute (min)
60 minutes = 1 hour (h)
24 hours = 1 day
7 days = 1 week
4 weeks (approx.) = 1 month

$\left.\begin{array}{l}\text{365 days}\\\text{52 weeks (approx.)}\\\text{12 months}\end{array}\right\}$ = 1 year

10 years = 1 decade
100 years = 1 century

Measures

Metric	United States Customary
Length	**Length**
10 millimeters (mm) = 1 centimeter (cm)	12 inches (in.) = 1 foot (ft)
$\left.\begin{array}{l}\text{100 cm}\\\text{1000 mm}\end{array}\right\}$ = 1 meter (m)	$\left.\begin{array}{l}\text{36 in.}\\\text{3 ft}\end{array}\right\}$ = 1 yard (yd)
1000 m = 1 kilometer (km)	$\left.\begin{array}{l}\text{5280 ft}\\\text{1760 yd}\end{array}\right\}$ = 1 mile (mi)
Area	**Area**
100 square millimeters = 1 square centimeter (mm^2) (cm^2)	144 square inches (in.^{2}) = 1 square foot (ft^2)
10,000 cm^2 = 1 square meter (m^2)	9 ft^2 = 1 square yard (yd^2)
10,000 m^2 = 1 hectare (ha)	$\left.\begin{array}{l}\text{43,560 ft}^2\\\text{4840 yd}^2\end{array}\right\}$ = 1 acre (A)
Volume	**Volume**
1000 cubic millimeters = 1 cubic centimeter (mm^3) (cm^3)	1728 cubic inches (in.^{3}) = 1 cubic foot (ft^3)
1,000,000 cm^3 = 1 cubic meter (m^3)	27 ft^3 = 1 cubic yard (yd^3)
Liquid Capacity	**Liquid Capacity**
$\left.\begin{array}{l}\text{1000 milliliters (mL)}\\\text{1000 cubic centimeters (cm}^3\text{)}\end{array}\right\}$ = 1 liter (L)	8 fluid ounces (fl oz) = 1 cup (c)
1000 L = 1 kiloliter (kL)	2 c = 1 pint (pt)
	2 pt = 1 quart (qt)
	4 qt = 1 gallon (gal)
Mass	**Weight**
1000 milligrams (mg) = 1 gram (g)	16 ounces (oz) = 1 pound (lb)
1000 g = 1 kilogram (kg)	2000 lb = 1 ton
1000 kg = 1 metric ton (t)	
Temperature	**Temperature**
Degrees Celsius (°C)	**Degrees Fahrenheit (°F)**
0°C = freezing point of water	32°F = freezing point of water
37°C = normal body temperature	98.6°F = normal body temperature
100°C = boiling point of water	212°F = boiling point of water

Area and Volume Formulas

Area of an equilateral triangle	Area $= \frac{\sqrt{3}}{4}s^2$ where s is the length of a side	
Volume and surface area of a right rectangular prism	Volume $= \ell wh$ where ℓ is the length, w is the width, and h is the height Surface area $= 2(\ell w + wh + \ell h)$	
Volume and surface area of a right cylinder	Volume $= \pi r^2 h$ where r is the base radius and h is the height Lateral surface area $= 2\pi rh$ Surface area $= 2\pi r^2 + 2\pi rh$	
Volume and surface area of a right regular pyramid	Volume $= \frac{1}{3}Bh$ where B is the area of the base and h is the height Lateral surface area $= \frac{1}{2}ns\ell$ where n is the number of sides of the base, s is the length of a side of the base, and ℓ is the slant height Surface area $= B + \frac{1}{2}ns\ell$	
Volume and surface area of a right circular cone	Volume $= \frac{1}{3}\pi r^2 h$ where r is the base radius and h is the height Lateral surface area $= \pi r\ell$ where ℓ is the slant height Surface area $= \pi r^2 + \pi r\ell$	
Volume and surface area of a sphere	Volume $= \frac{4}{3}\pi r^3$ where r is the radius Surface area $= 4\pi r^2$	

Other Formulas

Name of Formula	Statement of Formula	Page
Average rate of change formula	Average rate of change of f from x_1 to $x_2 = \dfrac{f(x_2) - f(x_1)}{x_2 - x_1}$	48
Quadratic formula	The solutions of $ax^2 + bx + c = 0$ are $$x = \frac{-b \pm \sqrt{b^2 - 4ac}}{2a}$$ where a, b, and c are real numbers such that $a \neq 0$.	91

Other Formulas (continued)

Name of Formula	Statement of Formula	Page
Discriminant of a quadratic equation	The expression $b^2 - 4ac$ is called the discriminant of the associated equation $ax^2 + bx + c = 0$. The value of the discriminant can be positive, zero, or negative, which corresponds to an equation having two real solutions, one real solution, or two imaginary solutions, respectively.	91
Explicit rule for an arithmetic sequence	The nth term of an arithmetic sequence with first term a_1 and common difference d is: $$a_n = a_1 + (n - 1)d$$	138
Sum of a finite arithmetic series	The sum of the first n terms of an arithmetic series is: $$S_n = n\left(\frac{a_1 + a_n}{2}\right)$$	138
Explicit rule for a geometric sequence	The nth term of a geometric sequence with first term a_1 and common ratio r is: $$a_n = a_1 r^{n-1}$$	143
Sum of a finite geometric series	The sum of the first n terms of a geometric series with common ratio $r \neq 1$ is: $$S_n = a_1\left(\frac{1 - r^n}{1 - r}\right)$$	143
Pythagorean Theorem	In a right triangle, $a^2 + b^2 = c^2$ where a and b are the lengths of the legs and c is the length of the hypotenuse.	150
Sides of a 45°-45°-90° triangle	Ratio of sides: $1 : 1 : \sqrt{2}$	151
Sides of a 30°-60°-90° triangle	Ratio of sides: $1 : \sqrt{3} : 2$	151
Trigonometric ratios	$\sin A = \dfrac{BC}{AB}$ $\sin^{-1}\dfrac{BC}{AB} = m\angle A$ $\cos A = \dfrac{AC}{AB}$ $\cos^{-1}\dfrac{AC}{AB} = m\angle A$ $\tan A = \dfrac{BC}{AC}$ $\tan^{-1}\dfrac{BC}{AC} = m\angle A$	157, 163, 172
Formulas for angle and segments formed by two chords	$m\angle 1 = \frac{1}{2}\left(m\overarc{CD} + m\overarc{AB}\right)$ $EA \cdot EC = EB \cdot ED$	212, 218

TABLES

Name of Formula	Statement of Formula	Page
Formulas for angle and segments formed by a tangent and a secant	$m\angle 2 = \frac{1}{2}(m\,\overset{\frown}{BC} - m\,\overset{\frown}{AB})$ $EB^2 = EA \cdot EC$	212, 218
Formulas for angle and segments formed by two tangents	$m\angle 3 = \frac{1}{2}(m\,\overset{\frown}{AQB} - m\,\overset{\frown}{AB})$ $EA = EB$	182, 212
Formulas for angle and segments formed by two secants	$m\angle 4 = \frac{1}{2}(m\,\overset{\frown}{CD} - m\,\overset{\frown}{AB})$ $EA \cdot EC = EB \cdot ED$	212, 218
Arc length formula	Arc length of $\overset{\frown}{AB} = \dfrac{m\,\overset{\frown}{AB}}{360°} \cdot 2\pi r$	224
Area of a sector formula	$A = \dfrac{m\,\overset{\frown}{AB}}{360°} \cdot \pi r^2$	230
Formula of mean of a data set	$\overline{x} = \dfrac{x_1 + x_2 + \cdots + x_n}{n}$ where $\overline{x}$ (read "x-bar") is the mean of the data $x_1, x_2, \cdots, x_n$.	259
Formula of standard deviation of a data set	$\sigma = \sqrt{\dfrac{(x_1 - \overline{x})^2 + (x_2 - \overline{x})^2 + \cdots + (x_n - \overline{x})^2}{n}}$ where σ (read "sigma") is the standard deviation of the data $x_1, x_2, \ldots, x_n$.	259
Areas under a normal curve	A normal distribution with mean $\overline{x}$ and standard deviation σ has these properties: • The total area under the related normal curve is 1. • About 68% of the area lies within 1 standard deviation of the mean. • About 95% of the area lies within 2 standard deviations of the mean. • About 99.7% of the area lies within 3 standard deviations of the mean.	264
z-score formula	$z = \dfrac{x - \overline{x}}{\sigma}$ where is x a data value, $\overline{x}$ is the mean, and σ is the standard deviation	264

TABLES

Postulates

Postulate	Statement of Postulate	Page
Angle-Angle (AA) Similarity Postulate	If two angles of one triangle are congruent to two angles of another triangle, then the two triangles are similar.	185
Arc Addition Postulate	The measure of an arc formed by two adjacent arcs is the sum of the measures of the two arcs.	191

Theorems

Theorem or Corollary		Statement of Theorem or Corollary	Page
5.1	45°-45°-90° Triangle Theorem	In a 45°-45°-90° triangle, the hypotenuse is $\sqrt{2}$ times as long as each leg.	151
5.2	30°-60°-90° Triangle Theorem	In a 30°-60°-90° triangle, the hypotenuse is twice as long as the shorter leg, and the longer leg is $\sqrt{3}$ times as long as the shorter leg.	151
6.1		In a plane, a line is tangent to a circle if and only if the line is perpendicular to a radius of the circle at its endpoint on the circle.	182
6.2		Tangent segments from a common external point are congruent.	182
6.3	Side-Side-Side (SSS) Similarity Theorem	If the corresponding side lengths of two triangles are proportional, then the triangles are similar.	185
6.4	Side-Angle-Side (SAS) Similarity Theorem	If an angle of one triangle is congruent to an angle of a second triangle and the lengths of the sides including these angles are proportional, then the triangles are similar.	185
6.5		In the same circle, or in congruent circles, two minor arcs are congruent if and only if their corresponding chords are congruent.	198
6.6		If one chord is a perpendicular bisector of another chord, then the first chord is a diameter.	198
6.7		If a diameter of a circle is perpendicular to a chord, then the diameter bisects the chord and its arc.	198
6.8		In the same circle, or in congruent circles, two chords are congruent if and only if they are equidistant from the center.	198
6.9	Measure of an Inscribed Angle Theorem	The measure of an inscribed angle is one half the measure of its intercepted arc.	205
6.10		If two inscribed angles of a circle intercept the same arc, then the angles are congruent.	205

TABLES

Theorem or Corollary	Statement of Theorem or Corollary	Page
6.11	If a right triangle is inscribed in a circle, then the hypotenuse is a diameter of the circle. Conversely, if one side of an inscribed triangle is a diameter of the circle, then the triangle is a right triangle and the angle opposite the diameter is the right angle.	205
6.12	A quadrilateral can be inscribed in a circle if and only if its opposite angles are supplementary.	205
6.13	If a tangent and a chord intersect at a point on a circle, then the measure of each angle formed is one half the measure of its intercepted arc.	212
6.14 Angles Inside the Circle	If two chords intersect inside a circle, then the measure of each angle is one half the sum of the measures of the arcs intercepted by the angle and its vertical angle.	212
6.15 Angles Outside the Circle	If a tangent and a secant, two tangents, or two secants intersect outside a circle, then the measure of the angle formed is one half the difference of the measures of the intercepted arcs.	212
6.16 Segments of Chords Theorem	If two chords intersect in the interior of a circle, then the product of the lengths of the segments of one chord is equal to the product of the lengths of the segments of the other chord.	218
6.17 Segments of Secants Theorem	If two secant segments share the same endpoint outside a circle, then the product of the lengths of one secant segment and its external segment equals the product of the lengths of the other secant segment and its external segment.	218
6.18 Segments of Secants and Tangents Theorem	If a secant segment and a tangent segment share an endpoint outside a circle, then the product of the lengths of the secant segment and its external segment equals the square of the length of the tangent segment.	218

TABLES

Properties of Exponents

Property	Statement of Property	Page
	Let a and b be real numbers, and let m and n be integers.	
Product of Powers Property	$a^m \cdot a^n = a^{m+n}$	107
Power of a Power Property	$(a^m)^n = a^{mn}$	107
Power of a Product Property	$(ab)^m = a^m b^m$	107
Negative Exponent Property	$a^{-m} = \dfrac{1}{a^m}$, $a \neq 0$	107
Zero Exponent Property	$a^0 = 1$, $a \neq 0$	107
Quotient of Powers Property	$\dfrac{a^m}{a^n} = a^{m-n}$, $a \neq 0$	107
Power of a Quotient Property	$\left(\dfrac{a}{b}\right)^m = \dfrac{a^m}{b^m}$, $b \neq 0$	107

Properties of Functions

Property	Statement of Property	Page
Operations on Functions	Let f and g be any two functions. A new function h can be defined using any of the following operations.	112
	Addition $\qquad h(x) = f(x) + g(x)$	
	Subtraction $\qquad h(x) = f(x) - g(x)$	
	Multiplication $\qquad h(x) = f(x) \cdot g(x)$	
	Division $\qquad h(x) = \dfrac{f(x)}{g(x)}$	
	Composition $\qquad h(x) = f(g(x))$	
	For addition, subtraction, multiplication, and division, the domain of h consists of the x-values that are in the domains of both f and g. Addditionally, the domain of the quotient does not include x-values for which $g(x) = 0$.	
	For composition, the domain of h is the set of all x-values such that x is in the domain of f and $f(x)$ is in the domain of g.	
Inverse Functions	Functions f and g are inverses of each other provided: $f(g(x)) = x$ and $g(f(x)) = x$	116

Table of Squares and Square Roots

No.	Square	Sq. Root	No.	Square	Sq. Root	No.	Square	Sq. Root
1	1	1.000	51	2601	7.141	101	10,201	10.050
2	4	1.414	52	2704	7.211	102	10,404	10.100
3	9	1.732	53	2809	7.280	103	10,609	10.149
4	16	2.000	54	2916	7.348	104	10,816	10.198
5	25	2.236	55	3025	7.416	105	11,025	10.247
6	36	2.449	56	3136	7.483	106	11,236	10.296
7	49	2.646	57	3249	7.550	107	11,449	10.344
8	64	2.828	58	3364	7.616	108	11,664	10.392
9	81	3.000	59	3481	7.681	109	11,881	10.440
10	100	3.162	60	3600	7.746	110	12,100	10.488
11	121	3.317	61	3721	7.810	111	12,321	10.536
12	144	3.464	62	3844	7.874	112	12,544	10.583
13	169	3.606	63	3969	7.937	113	12,769	10.630
14	196	3.742	64	4096	8.000	114	12,996	10.677
15	225	3.873	65	4225	8.062	115	13,225	10.724
16	256	4.000	66	4356	8.124	116	13,456	10.770
17	289	4.123	67	4489	8.185	117	13,689	10.817
18	324	4.243	68	4624	8.246	118	13,924	10.863
19	361	4.359	69	4761	8.307	119	14,161	10.909
20	400	4.472	70	4900	8.367	120	14,400	10.954
21	441	4.583	71	5041	8.426	121	14,641	11.000
22	484	4.690	72	5184	8.485	122	14,884	11.045
23	529	4.796	73	5329	8.544	123	15,129	11.091
24	576	4.899	74	5476	8.602	124	15,376	11.136
25	625	5.000	75	5625	8.660	125	15,625	11.180
26	676	5.099	76	5776	8.718	126	15,876	11.225
27	729	5.196	77	5929	8.775	127	16,129	11.269
28	784	5.292	78	6084	8.832	128	16,384	11.314
29	841	5.385	79	6241	8.888	129	16,641	11.358
30	900	5.477	80	6400	8.944	130	16,900	11.402
31	961	5.568	81	6561	9.000	131	17,161	11.446
32	1024	5.657	82	6724	9.055	132	17,424	11.489
33	1089	5.745	83	6889	9.110	133	17,689	11.533
34	1156	5.831	84	7056	9.165	134	17,956	11.576
35	1225	5.916	85	7225	9.220	135	18,225	11.619
36	1296	6.000	86	7396	9.274	136	18,496	11.662
37	1369	6.083	87	7569	9.327	137	18,769	11.705
38	1444	6.164	88	7744	9.381	138	19,044	11.747
39	1521	6.245	89	7921	9.434	139	19,321	11.790
40	1600	6.325	90	8100	9.487	140	19,600	11.832
41	1681	6.403	91	8281	9.539	141	19,881	11.874
42	1764	6.481	92	8464	9.592	142	20,164	11.916
43	1849	6.557	93	8649	9.644	143	20,449	11.958
44	1936	6.633	94	8836	9.695	144	20,736	12.000
45	2025	6.708	95	9025	9.747	145	21,025	12.042
46	2116	6.782	96	9216	9.798	146	21,316	12.083
47	2209	6.856	97	9409	9.849	147	21,609	12.124
48	2304	6.928	98	9604	9.899	148	21,904	12.166
49	2401	7.000	99	9801	9.950	149	22,201	12.207
50	2500	7.071	100	10,000	10.000	150	22,500	12.247

TABLES

Trigonometric Ratios

Angle	Sine	Cosine	Tangent	Angle	Sine	Cosine	Tangent
1°	.0175	.9998	.0175	46°	.7193	.6947	1.0355
2°	.0349	.9994	.0349	47°	.7314	.6820	1.0724
3°	.0523	.9986	.0524	48°	.7431	.6691	1.1106
4°	.0698	.9976	.0699	49°	.7547	.6561	1.1504
5°	.0872	.9962	.0875	50°	.7660	.6428	1.1918
6°	.1045	.9945	.1051	51°	.7771	.6293	1.2349
7°	.1219	.9925	.1228	52°	.7880	.6157	1.2799
8°	.1392	.9903	.1405	53°	.7986	.6018	1.3270
9°	.1564	.9877	.1584	54°	.8090	.5878	1.3764
10°	.1736	.9848	.1763	55°	.8192	.5736	1.4281
11°	.1908	.9816	.1944	56°	.8290	.5592	1.4826
12°	.2079	.9781	.2126	57°	.8387	.5446	1.5399
13°	.2250	.9744	.2309	58°	.8480	.5299	1.6003
14°	.2419	.9703	.2493	59°	.8572	.5150	1.6643
15°	.2588	.9659	.2679	60°	.8660	.5000	1.7321
16°	.2756	.9613	.2867	61°	.8746	.4848	1.8040
17°	.2924	.9563	.3057	62°	.8829	.4695	1.8807
18°	.3090	.9511	.3249	63°	.8910	.4540	1.9626
19°	.3256	.9455	.3443	64°	.8988	.4384	2.0503
20°	.3420	.9397	.3640	65°	.9063	.4226	2.1445
21°	.3584	.9336	.3839	66°	.9135	.4067	2.2460
22°	.3746	.9272	.4040	67°	.9205	.3907	2.3559
23°	.3907	.9205	.4245	68°	.9272	.3746	2.4751
24°	.4067	.9135	.4452	69°	.9336	.3584	2.6051
25°	.4226	.9063	.4663	70°	.9397	.3420	2.7475
26°	.4384	.8988	.4877	71°	.9455	.3256	2.9042
27°	.4540	.8910	.5095	72°	.9511	.3090	0.0777
28°	.4695	.8829	.5317	73°	.9563	.2924	3.2709
29°	.4848	.8746	.5543	74°	.9613	.2756	3.4874
30°	.5000	.8660	.5774	75°	.9659	.2588	3.7321
31°	.5150	.8572	.6009	76°	.9703	.2419	4.0108
32°	.5299	.8480	.6249	77°	.9744	.2250	4.3315
33°	.5446	.8387	.6494	78°	.9781	.2079	4.7046
34°	.5592	.8290	.6745	79°	.9816	.1908	5.1446
35°	.5736	.8192	.7002	80°	.9848	.1736	5.6713
36°	.5878	.8090	.7265	81°	.9877	.1564	6.3138
37°	.6018	.7986	.7536	82°	.9903	.1392	7.1154
38°	.6157	.7880	.7813	83°	.9925	.1219	8.1443
39°	.6293	.7771	.8098	84°	.9945	.1045	9.5144
40°	.6428	.7660	.8391	85°	.9962	.0872	11.4301
41°	.6561	.7547	.8693	86°	.9976	.0698	14.3007
42°	.6691	.7431	.9004	87°	.9986	.0523	19.0811
43°	.6820	.7314	.9325	88°	.9994	.0349	28.6363
44°	.6947	.7193	.9657	89°	.9998	.0175	52.2900
45°	.7071	.7071	1.0000				

TABLES

Standard Normal Table

If z is a randomly selected value from a standard normal distribution, you can use the table below to find the probability that z is less than or equal to some given value. For example, the table shows that $P(z \leq -0.6) = 0.2743$. You can find the value of $P(z \leq -0.6)$ in the table by finding the value where row -0 and column $.6$ intersect.

You can also use the standard normal table to find probabilities for any normal distribution by first converting values from the distribution to z-scores.

In the table, the value $.0000+$ means "slightly more than 0" and the value $1.0000-$ means "slightly less than 1."

z	.0	.1	.2	.3	.4	.5	.6	.7	.8	.9
−3	.0013	.0010	.0007	.0005	.0003	.0002	.0002	.0001	.0001	.0000+
−2	.0228	.0179	.0139	.0107	.0082	.0062	.0047	.0035	.0026	.0019
−1	.1587	.1357	.1151	.0968	.0808	.0668	.0548	.0446	.0359	.0287
−0	.5000	.4602	.4207	.3821	.3446	.3085	.2743	.2420	.2119	.1841
0	.5000	.5398	.5793	.6179	.6554	.6915	.7257	.7580	.7881	.8159
1	.8413	.8643	.8849	.9032	.9192	.9332	.9452	.9554	.9641	.9713
2	.9772	.9821	.9861	.9893	.9918	.9938	.9953	.9965	.9974	.9981
3	.9987	.9990	.9993	.9995	.9997	.9998	.9998	.9999	.9999	1.0000−

English-Spanish Glossary

A

absolute value function (p. 40) A function that contains an absolute value expression.

$y = |x|, y = |x - 3|$, and $y = 4|x + 8| - 9$ are absolute value functions.

función de valor absoluto (pág. 40) Función que contiene una expresión de valor absoluto.

$y = |x|, y = |x - 3|$ e $y = 4|x + 8| - 9$ son funciones de valor absoluto.

---

absolute value of a complex number (p. 17) If $z = a + bi$, then the absolute value of z, denoted $|z|$, is a nonnegative real number defined as $|z| = \sqrt{a^2 + b^2}$.

valor absoluto de un número complejo (pág. 17) Si $z = a + bi$, entonces el valor absoluto de z, denotado por $|z|$, es un número real no negativo definido como $|z| = \sqrt{a^2 + b^2}$.

$|-4 + 3i| = \sqrt{(-4)^2 + 3^2} = \sqrt{25} = 5$

---

algebraic model (p. 247) An expression, equation, or function that represents data or a real-world situation.

$h = -16t^2 + h_0$ is an algebraic model of the height h (in feet) of an object t seconds after being dropped from an initial height of h_0 (in feet).

modelo algebraico (pág. 247) Una expresión, ecuación o función que representa datos o una situación del mundo real.

$h = -16t^2 + h_0$ es un modelo algebraico de la altura h (en pies) de un objeto t segundos después de ser arrojado de una altura inicial de h_0 (en pies).

---

arc (p. 191) An unbroken part of a circle.

See major arc *and* minor arc.

arco (pág. 191) Una parte ininterrumpida de un círculo.

Ver arco mayor *and* arco menor.

---

arc length (p. 224) A portion of the circumference of a circle.

longitud de arco (pág. 224) Porción de la circunferencia de un círculo.

Arc length of $\widehat{AB} = \dfrac{m\widehat{AB}}{360°} \cdot 2\pi r$

Longitud de arco de $\widehat{AB} = \dfrac{m\widehat{AB}}{360°} \cdot 2\pi r$

arithmetic sequence (p. 138) A sequence in which the difference of consecutive terms is constant.

progresión aritmética (pág. 138) Progresión en la que la diferencia entre los términos consecutivos es constante.

−4, 1, 6, 11, 16, . . . is an arithmetic sequence with common difference 5.

−4, 1, 6, 11, 16, . . . es una progresión aritmética con una diferencia común de 5.

---

arithmetic series (p. 138) The expression formed by adding the terms of an arithmetic sequence.

serie aritmética (pág. 138) La expresión formada al sumar los términos de una progresión aritmética.

$$\sum_{i=1}^{5} 2i = 2 + 4 + 6 + 8 + 10$$

---

asymptote (p. 120) A line that a graph approaches more and more closely.

asíntota (pág. 120) Recta a la que se aproxima una gráfica cada vez más.

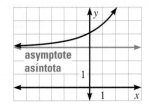

The asymptote for the graph shown is the line $y = 3$.

La asíntota para la gráfica que se muestra es la recta $y = 3$.

---

average rate of change for a function (p. 48) For a function, the average rate of change between any two points (x_1, y_1) and (x_2, y_2) is the slope of the line through the two points.

$$\text{Average rate of change} = \frac{y_2 - y_1}{x_2 - x_1}$$

tasa de cambio promedio de una función (pág. 48) Para un función, la tasa de cambio promedio entre dos puntos cualesquiera (x_1, y_1) y (x_2, y_2) es la pendiente de la recta que atraviesa los dos puntos.

$$\text{Tasa de cambio promedio} = \frac{y_2 - y_1}{x_2 - x_1}$$

The average rate of change of $y = -0.5x^2 + 4$ from $(-2, 2)$ to $(0, 4)$ is $\frac{4 - 2}{0 - (-2)}$, or 1.

La tasa de cambio promedio de $y = -0.5x^2 + 4$ de $(-2, 2)$ a $(0, 4)$ es $\frac{4 - 2}{0 - (-2)}$ ó 1.

---

axis of symmetry (p. 40) A vertical line that divides the graph of a function into mirror images.

eje de simetría (pág. 40) Una recta vertical que divide la gráfica de una función en imágenes espejo.

See parabola.

Ver parábola.

B

best-fitting line (p. 247) The line that lies as close as possible to all the data points in a scatter plot.

mejor recta de regresión (pág. 247) La recta que se ajusta lo más posible a todos los puntos de datos de un diagrama de dispersión.

best-fitting quadratic model (p. 255) The model given by using quadratic regression on a set of paired data.

modelo cuadrático con mejor ajuste (pág. 255) El modelo dado al realizar una regresión cuadrática sobre un conjunto de pares de datos.

biased sample (p. 268) A sample that overrepresents or underrepresents part of a population.

muestra sesgada (pág. 268) Muestra que representa de forma excesiva o insuficiente a parte de una población.

The members of a school's basketball team would form a biased sample for a survey about whether to build a new gym.

Los miembros del equipo de baloncesto de una escuela formarían una muestra sesgada si participaran en una encuesta sobre si quieren que se construya un nuevo gimnasio.

binomial (p. 74) The sum of two monomials.
binomio (pág. 74) La suma de dos monomios.

$3x - 1$ and $t^3 - 4t$ are binomials.
$3x - 1$ y $t^3 - 4t$ son binomios.

C

center of a circle (p. 182) *See* circle.
centro de un círculo (pág. 182) *Ver* círculo.

See circle.
Ver círculo.

center of a sphere (p. 237) *See* sphere.
centro de una esfera (pág. 237) *Ver* esfera.

See sphere.
Ver esfera.

central angle of a circle (p. 191) An angle whose vertex is the center of the circle.

ángulo central de un círculo (pág. 191) Ángulo cuyo vértice es el centro del círculo.

$\angle PCQ$ is a central angle of $\odot C$.
$\angle PCQ$ es un ángulo central de $\odot C$.

chord of a circle (p. 182) A segment whose endpoints are on a circle.

cuerda de un círculo (pág. 182) Segmento cuyos extremos están en un círculo.

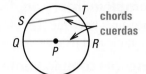

chords
cuerdas

---

chord of a sphere (p. 237) A segment whose endpoints are on a sphere.

cuerda de una esfera (pág. 237) Segmento cuyos extremos están en una esfera.

chord
cuerda

---

circle (p. 182) The set of all points in a plane that are equidistant from a given point called the center of the circle.

círculo (pág. 182) El conjunto de todos los puntos de un plano que son equidistantes de un punto dado, llamado centro del círculo.

Circle with center *P*, or ⊙*P*
Círculo con centro *P*, o ⊙*P*

---

circumference (p. 224) The distance around a circle.

circunferencia (pág. 224) La distancia por el contorno de un círculo.

---

circumscribed circle (p. 205) The circle that contains the vertices of an inscribed polygon.

círculo circunscrito (pág. 205) El círculo que contiene los vértices de un polígono inscrito.

circumscribed circles
círculos circunscritos

---

common difference (p. 138) The constant difference of consecutive terms of an arithmetic sequence.

diferencia común (pág. 138) La diferencia constante entre los términos consecutivos de una progresión aritmética.

See **arithmetic sequence.**

Ver **progresión aritmética.**

---

common ratio (p. 143) The constant ratio of consecutive terms of a geometric sequence.

razón común (pág. 143) La razón constante entre los términos consecutivos de una progresión geométrica.

See **geometric sequence.**

Ver **progresión geométrica.**

complementary angles (p. 157) Two angles whose measures have the sum 90°. The sum of the measures of an angle and its *complement* is 90°.

ángulos complementarios (pág. 157) Dos ángulos cuyas medidas suman 90°. La suma de las medidas de un ángulo y de su *complemento* es 90°.

completing the square (p. 86) The process of adding a term to a quadratic expression of the form $x^2 + bx$ to make it a perfect square trinomial.

completar el cuadrado (pág. 86) El proceso de sumar un término a una expresión cuadrática de la forma $x^2 + bx$, de modo que sea un trinomio cuadrado perfecto.

To complete the square for $x^2 + 16x$, add $\left(\frac{16}{2}\right)^2 = 64$:
$x^2 + 16x + 64 = (x + 8)^2$.

Para completar el cuadrado para $x^2 + 16x$, suma $\left(\frac{16}{2}\right)^2 = 64$:
$x^2 + 16x + 64 = (x + 8)^2$.

complex conjugates (p. 11) Two complex numbers of the form $a + bi$ and $a - bi$.

números complejos conjugados (pág. 11) Dos números complejos de la forma $a + bi$ y $a - bi$.

$2 + 4i, 2 - 4i$

complex number (p. 2) A number $a + bi$ where a and b are real numbers and i is the imaginary unit.

número complejo (pág. 2) Un número $a + bi$, donde a y b son números reales e i es la unidad imaginaria.

$0, 2.5, \sqrt{3}, \pi, 5i, 2 - i$

complex plane (p. 17) A coordinate plane in which each point (a, b) represents a complex number $a + bi$. The horizontal axis is the real axis and the vertical axis is the imaginary axis.

plano complejo (pág. 17) Plano de coordenadas en el que cada punto (a, b) representa un número complejo $a + bi$. El eje horizontal es el eje real, y el eje vertical es el eje imaginario.

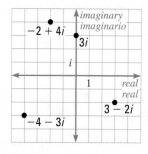

composition of functions (p. 112) The composition of a function g with a function f is $h(x) = g(f(x))$.

composición de funciones (pág. 112) La composición de una función g con una función f es $h(x) = g(f(x))$.

$$f(x) = 5x - 2, \ g(x) = 4x^{-1}$$
$$g(f(x)) = g(5x - 2)$$
$$= 4(5x - 2)^{-1}$$
$$= \frac{4}{5x - 2}, x \neq \frac{2}{5}$$

congruent arcs (p. 191) Two arcs that have the same measure and are arcs of the same circle or of congruent circles.

arcos congruentes (pág. 191) Dos arcos que tienen la misma medida y son arcos del mismo círculo o de círculos congruentes.

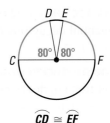

$$\overset{\frown}{CD} \cong \overset{\frown}{EF}$$

---

congruent circles (p. 191) Two circles that have the same radius.

círculos congruentes (pág. 191) Dos círculos que tienen el mismo radio.

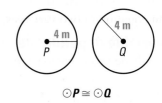

$$\odot P \cong \odot Q$$

---

conjugates (p. 82) The expressions $a + \sqrt{b}$ and $a - \sqrt{b}$ where a and b are rational numbers.

conjugados (pág. 82) Las expresiones $a + \sqrt{b}$ y $a - \sqrt{b}$ cuando a y b son números racionales.

The conjugate of $7 + \sqrt{2}$ **is** $7 - \sqrt{2}$.

El conjugado de $7 + \sqrt{2}$ **es** $7 - \sqrt{2}$.

---

correlation coefficient (p. 247) A measure, denoted by r where $-1 \leq r \leq 1$, of how well a line fits a set of data pairs (x, y).

coeficiente de correlación (pág. 247) Medida denotada por r, donde $-1 \leq r \leq 1$, y que describe el ajuste de una recta a un conjunto de pares de datos (x, y).

A data set that shows a strong positive correlation has a correlation coefficient of $r \approx 1$. *See also* **positive correlation** *and* **negative correlation.**

Un conjunto de datos que muestra una correlación positiva fuerte tiene un coeficiente de correlación de $r \approx 1$. *Ver también* **correlación positiva** *y* **correlación negativa.**

---

cosine (p. 163) A trigonometric ratio, abbreviated as *cos*. For a right triangle ABC, the cosine of the acute angle A is
$$\cos A = \frac{\text{length of leg adjacent to } \angle A}{\text{length of hypotenuse}} = \frac{AC}{AB}.$$

coseno (pág. 163) Razón trigonométrica, abreviada *cos*. Para un triángulo rectángulo ABC, el coseno del ángulo agudo A es
$$\cos A = \frac{\text{longitud del cateto adyacente a } \angle A}{\text{longitud de la hipotenusa}} = \frac{AC}{AB}.$$

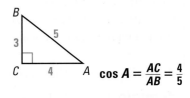

$$\cos A = \frac{AC}{AB} = \frac{4}{5}$$

---

curve fitting (p. 255) Finding a line or curve that matches a set of data points.

ajuste de curva (pág. 255) El proceso de hallar una recta o curva que coincide con un conjunto de puntos de datos.

See **quadratic regression.**

Ver **regresión cuadrática.**

exponential inequality in one variable
(p. 128) An inequality that can be written in the form $ab^x + k < 0$, $ab^x + k > 0$, $ab^x + k \leq 0$, or $ab^x + k \geq 0$, where $a \neq 0$, $b > 0$, and $b \neq 1$.

desigualdad exponencial con una variable
(pág. 128) Una desigualdad que puede escribirse en la forma $ab^x + k < 0$, $ab^x + k > 0$, $ab^x + k \leq 0$, ó $ab^x + k \geq 0$, donde $a \neq 0$, $b > 0$, y $b \neq 1$.

$3(2)^x - 5 \leq 0$ and $-5(0.8)^x + 2 > 0$ are exponential inequalities in one variable.

$3(2)^x - 5 \leq 0$ y $-5(0.8)^x + 2 > 0$ son desigualdades exponenciales con una variable.

---

external segment (p. 218) The part of a secant segment that is outside the circle.

segmento externo (pág. 218) La parte de un segmento secante que está en el exterior del círculo.

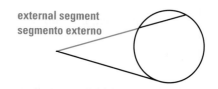
external segment
segmento externo

---

extraneous solution (p. 28) An apparent solution that must be rejected because it does not satisfy the original equation.

solución extraña (pág. 28) Solución aparente que debe rechazarse ya que no satisface la ecuación original.

Solving $|2x + 12| = 4x$ gives the apparent solutions $x = 6$ and $x = -2$. The apparent solution -2 is extraneous because it does not satisfy the original equation.

Al resolver $|2x + 12| = 4x$ se obtienen las soluciones aparentes $x = 6$ y $x = -2$. La solución aparente -2 es extraña ya no satisface la ecuación original.

---

extrema (p. 48) Maximums or minimums of a function. Extrema can be local (within a given part of the domain) or global (within the entire domain).

extremos (pág. 48) Máximos o mínimos de una función. Los extremos pueden ser locales (dentro de una parte dada del dominio) o globales (dentro de todo el dominio).

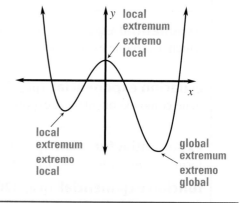
local extremum
extremo local
local extremum
extremo local
global extremum
extremo global

F

function (p. 33) A relation for which each input has exactly one output.

función (pág. 33) Relación para la que cada entrada tiene exactamente una salida.

The relation $(-4, 6)$, $(3, -9)$, and $(7, -9)$ is a function. The relation $(0, 3)$, $(0, 6)$, and $(10, 8)$ is not a function because the input 0 is mapped onto both 3 and 6.

La relación $(-4, 6)$, $(3, -9)$ y $(7, -9)$ es una función. La relación $(0, 3)$, $(0, 6)$ y $(10, 8)$ no es una función ya que la entrada 0 se hace corresponder tanto con 3 como con 6.

G

geometric sequence (p. 143) A sequence in which the ratio of any term to the previous term is constant.

progresión geométrica (pág. 143) Progresión en la que la razón entre cualquier término y el término precedente es constante.

$-19, 38, -76, 152$ is a geometric sequence with common ratio -2.

$-19, 38, -76, 152$ es una progresión geométrica con una razón común de -2.

---

geometric series (p. 143) The expression formed by adding the terms of a geometric sequence.

serie geométrica (pág. 143) La expresión formada al sumar los términos de una progresión geométrica.

$$\sum_{i=1}^{5} 4(3)^{i-1} = 4 + 12 + 36 + 108 + 324$$

---

graph of an equation in two variables (p. 33) The set of all points (x, y) that represent solutions of the equation.

gráfica de una ecuación con dos variables (pág. 33) El conjunto de todos los puntos (x, y) que representan soluciones de la ecuación.

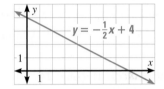

$y = -\frac{1}{2}x + 4$

---

great circle (p. 237) The intersection of a sphere and a plane that contains the center of the sphere.

círculo máximo (pág. 237) La intersección de una esfera y un plano que contiene el centro de la esfera.

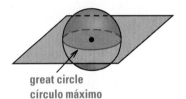

great circle
círculo máximo

---

growth factor (p. 120) The quantity b in the exponential growth function $y = ab^x$ with $a > 0$ and $b > 1$.

factor de crecimiento (pág. 120) La cantidad b de la función de crecimiento exponencial $y = ab^x$, con $a > 0$ y $b > 1$.

The growth factor for the function $y = 8(3.4)^x$ is 3.4.

El factor de crecimiento de la función $y = 8(3.4)^x$ es 3.4.

H

hemisphere (p. 237) Half of a sphere, formed when a great circle separates a sphere into two congruent halves.

hemisferio (pág. 237) Media esfera, formada cuando un círculo máximo divide a una esfera en dos mitades congruentes.

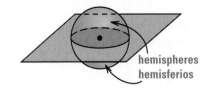

hemispheres
hemisferios

I

imaginary number (p. 2) A complex number $a + bi$ where $b \neq 0$.

número imaginario (pág. 2) Un número complejo $a + bi$, donde $b \neq 0$.

$5i$ and $2 - i$ are imaginary numbers.

$5i$ y $2 - i$ son números imaginarios.

imaginary unit *i* (p. 2) $i = \sqrt{-1}$, so $i^2 = -1$.

unidad imaginaria *i* (pág. 2) $i = \sqrt{-1}$, por lo que $i^2 = -1$.

$$\sqrt{-3} = i\sqrt{3}$$

---

independent variable (p. 33) The input variable in an equation in two variables.

variable independiente (pág. 33) La variable de entrada de una ecuación con dos variables.

In $y = 3x - 5$, the independent variable is x. The dependent variable is y because the value of y depends on the value of x.

En $y = 3x - 5$, la variable independiente es x. La variable dependiente es y ya que el valor de y depende del valor de x.

---

inference (p. 247) A logical conclusion derived from known data.

deducción (pág. 247) Una conclusión lógica obtenida a partir de datos conocidos.

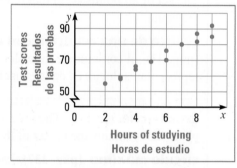

One inference that can be made from this scatter plot is that a person who spends 6.5 hours studying is likely to score between 70 and 80 on the test.

Una deducción que puede hacerse a partir de este diagrama de dispersión es que una persona que pasa 6.5 horas estudiando es probable que obtenga entre 70 y 80 puntos en la prueba.

---

inscribed angle (p. 205) An angle whose vertex is on a circle and whose sides contain chords of the circle.

ángulo inscrito (pág. 205) Ángulo cuyo vértice está en un círculo y cuyos lados contienen cuerdas del círculo.

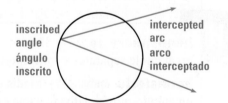

inscribed angle
ángulo inscrito

intercepted arc
arco interceptado

---

inscribed polygon (p. 205) A polygon whose vertices all lie on a circle.

polígono inscrito (pág. 205) Polígono que tiene todos los vértices en un círculo.

inscribed triangle
triángulo inscrito

inscribed quadrilateral
cuadrilátero inscrito

ENGLISH-SPANISH GLOSSARY

intercept form of a quadratic function
(p. 63) The form $y = a(x - p)(x - q)$, where
the x-intercepts of the graph are p and q.

forma de intercepto de una función
cuadrática (pág. 63) La forma $y = a(x - p)(x - q)$,
donde los interceptos en x de la gráfica son p y q.

The function $y = 2(x + 3)(x - 1)$ is
in intercept form.

La función $y = 2(x + 3)(x - 1)$ está
en la forma de intercepto.

---

intercepted arc (p. 205) The arc that lies in the
interior of an inscribed angle and has endpoints on
the angle.

arco interceptado (pág. 205) El arco situado en el
interior de un ángulo inscrito y que tiene los extremos en
el ángulo.

See inscribed angle.

Ver ángulo inscrito.

---

inverse cosine (p. 172) An inverse trigonometric
ratio, abbreviated as cos^{-1}. For acute angle A, if
$\cos A = z$, then $\cos^{-1} z = m\angle A$.

coseno inverso (pág. 172) Razón trigonométrica
inversa, abreviada cos^{-1}. Para el ángulo agudo A, si
$\cos A = z$, entonces $\cos^{-1} z = m\angle A$.

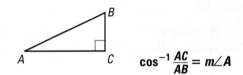

$$\cos^{-1} \frac{AC}{AB} = m\angle A$$

---

inverse function (p. 116) An inverse relation that is
a function. Functions f and g are inverses provided that
$f(g(x)) = x$ and $g(f(x)) = x$.

función inversa (pág. 116) Relación inversa que es
una función. Las funciones f y g son inversas siempre que
$f(g(x)) = x$ y $g(f(x)) = x$.

$$f(x) = x + 5; \; g(x) = x - 5$$
$$f(g(x)) = (x - 5) + 5 = x$$
$$g(f(x)) = (x + 5) - 5 = x$$

So, f and g are inverse functions.

Entonces, f y g son funciones
inversas.

---

inverse relation (p. 116) A relation that interchanges
the input and output values of the original relation. The
graph of an inverse relation is a reflection of the graph of
the original relation, with $y = x$ as the line of reflection.

relación inversa (pág. 116) Relación en la que se
intercambian los valores de entrada y de salida de la
relación original. La gráfica de una relación inversa es
una reflexión de la gráfica de la relación original, con
$y = x$ como eje de reflexión.

To find the inverse of $y = 3x - 5$,
switch x and y to obtain
$x = 3y - 5$. Then solve for y
to obtain the inverse relation
$y = \frac{1}{3}x + \frac{5}{3}$.

Para hallar la inversa de
$y = 3x - 5$, intercambia x e y para
obtener $x = 3y - 5$.
Luego resuelve para y para obtener
larelación inversa $y = \frac{1}{3}x + \frac{5}{3}$.

inverse sine (p. 172) An inverse trigonometric ratio, abbreviated as sin^{-1}. For acute angle A, if $\sin A = y$, then $\sin^{-1} y = m\angle A$.

seno inverso (pág. 172) Razón trigonométrica inversa, abreviada sen^{-1}. Para el ángulo agudo A, si $\operatorname{sen} A = y$, entonces $\operatorname{sen}^{-1} y = m\angle A$.

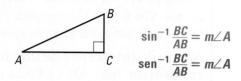

$$\sin^{-1} \frac{BC}{AB} = m\angle A$$
$$\operatorname{sen}^{-1} \frac{BC}{AB} = m\angle A$$

---

inverse tangent (p. 172) An inverse trigonometric ratio, abbreviated as tan^{-1}. For acute angle A, if $\tan A = x$, then $\tan^{-1} x = m\angle A$.

tangente inversa (pág. 172) Razón trigonométrica inversa, abreviada tan^{-1}. Para el ángulo agudo A, si $\tan A = x$, entonces $\tan^{-1} x = m\angle A$.

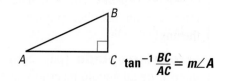

$$\tan^{-1} \frac{BC}{AC} = m\angle A$$

L

linear function (p. 33) A function that can be written in the form $y = mx + b$ where m and b are constants.

función lineal (pág. 33) Función que puede escribirse en la forma $y = mx + b$, donde m y b son constantes.

The function $y = -2x - 1$ is a linear function with $m = -2$ and $b = -1$.

La función $y = -2x - 1$ es una función lineal con $m = -2$ y $b = -1$.

---

linear regression (p. 247) The process of finding the best-fitting line to model a set of data.

regresión lineal (pág. 247) El proceso de hallar la mejor recta de regresión para representar un conjunto de datos.

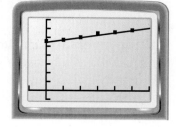

You can use a graphing calculator to perform linear regression on a data set.

Puedes usar una calculadora de gráficas para realizar una regresión lineal a un conjunto de datos.

M

major arc (p. 191) Part of a circle that measures between 180° and 360°.

arco mayor (pág. 191) Parte de un círculo que mide entre 180° y 360°.

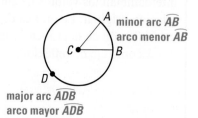

minor arc $\overset{\frown}{AB}$
arco menor $\overset{\frown}{AB}$

major arc $\overset{\frown}{ADB}$
arco mayor $\overset{\frown}{ADB}$

margin of error (p. 268) The margin of error gives a limit on how much the response of a sample would be expected to differ from the response of the population.

margen de error (pág. 268) El margen de error indica un límite acerca de cuánto se prevé que diferirían las respuestas obtenidas en una muestra de las obtenidas en la población.

If 40% of the people in a poll prefer candidate A, and the margin of error is ±4%, then it is expected that between 36% and 44% of the entire population prefer candidate A.

Si el 40% de los encuestados prefiere al candidato A y el margen de error es ±4%, entonces se prevé que entre el 36% y el 44% de la población total prefiere al candidato A.

---

maximum value of a quadratic function (p. 56) The y-coordinate of the vertex for $y = ax^2 + bx + c$ when $a < 0$.

valor máximo de una función cuadrática (pág. 56) La coordenada y del vértice para $y = ax^2 + bx + c$ cuando $a < 0$.

The maximum value of $y = -x^2 + 2x - 1$ is 0.

El valor máximo de $y = -x^2 + 2x - 1$ es 0.

---

mean (p. 259) For the data set $x_1, x_2, \ldots, x_n$, the mean is $\bar{x} = \dfrac{x_1 + x_2 + \ldots + x_n}{n}$. Also called average.

media (pág. 259) Para el conjunto de datos $x_1, x_2, \ldots, x_n$, la media es $\bar{x} = \dfrac{x_1 + x_2 + \ldots + x_n}{n}$. También se llama promedio.

See measure of central tendency.

Ver medida de tendencia central.

---

measure of central tendency (p. 259) A number used to represent the center or middle of a set of data values. Mean, median, and mode are three measures of central tendency.

medida de tendencia central (pág. 259) Número usado para representar el centro o la posición central de un conjunto de valores de datos. La media, la mediana y la moda son tres medidas de tendencia central.

14, 17, 18, 19, 20, 24, 24, 30, 32

The mean is
$$\frac{14 + 17 + 18 + \ldots + 32}{9} = \frac{198}{9} = 22.$$
The median is the middle number, 20.
The mode is 24 because 24 occurs the most frequently.

La media es
$$\frac{14 + 17 + 18 + \ldots + 32}{9} = \frac{198}{9} = 22.$$
La mediana es el número central, 20.
La moda es 24 ya que 24 ocurre más veces.

measure of dispersion (p. 259) A statistic that tells you how dispersed, or spread out, data values are. Range and standard deviation are measures of dispersion.

medida de dispersión (pág. 259) Estadística que te indica cómo se dispersan, o distribuyen, los valores de datos. El rango y la desviación típica son medidas de dispersión.

See **range** *and* **standard deviation.**

Ver **rango** *y* **desviación típica.**

---

measure of a major arc (p. 191) The difference between 360° and the measure of the related minor arc.

medida de un arco mayor (pág. 191) La diferencia entre 360° y la medida del arco menor relacionado.

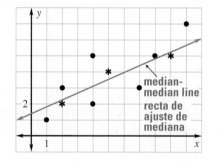

$m\widehat{ADB} = 360° - m\widehat{AB}$
$= 360° - 50°$
$= 310°$

---

measure of a minor arc (p. 191) The measure of the arc's central angle.

medida de un arco menor (pág. 191) La medida del ángulo central del arco.

See **measure of a major arc.**

Ver **medida de un arco mayor.**

---

median (p. 259) The median of n numbers is the middle number when the numbers are written in numerical order. If n is even, the median is the mean of the two middle numbers.

mediana (pág. 259) La mediana de n números es el número central cuando los números se escriben en orden numérico. Si n es par, la mediana es la media de los dos números centrales.

See **measure of central tendency.**

Ver **medida de tendencia central.**

---

median-median line (p. 247) A linear model used to fit a line to a data set. The line is fit only to summary points, key points calculated using medians.

recta de ajuste de mediana (pág. 247) Un modelo lineal usado para ajustar una recta a un conjunto de datos. La recta se ajusta solo a los puntos de resumen, puntos clave calculados usando medianas.

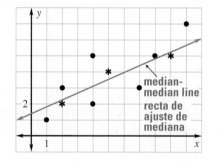

median-median line
recta de ajuste de mediana

---

minimum value of a quadratic function (p. 56) The y-coordinate of the vertex for $y = ax^2 + bx + c$ when $a > 0$.

valor mínimo de una función cuadrática (pág. 56) La coordenada y del vértice para $y = ax^2 + bx + c$ cuando $a > 0$.

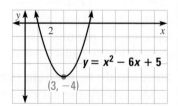

$y = x^2 - 6x + 5$

$(3, -4)$

The minimum value of $y = x^2 - 6x + 5$ is -4.

El valor mínimo de $y = x^2 - 6x + 5$ es -4.

minor arc (p. 191) Part of a circle that measures less than 180°.

See **major arc.**

arco menor (pág. 191) Parte de un círculo que mide menos de 180°.

Ver **arco mayor.**

---

mode (p. 259) The mode of *n* numbers is the number or numbers that occur most frequently.

See **measure of central tendency.**

moda (pág. 259) La moda de *n* números es el número o números que ocurren más veces.

Ver **medida de tendencia central.**

---

monomial (p. 74) An expression that is either a number, a variable, or the product of a number and one or more variables with whole number exponents.

6, $0.2x$, $\frac{1}{2}ab$, and $-5.7n^4$ are monomials.

monomio (pág. 74) Expresión que es un número, una variable o el producto de un número y una o más variables con exponentes naturales.

6, $0.2x$, $\frac{1}{2}ab$ y $-5.7n^4$ son monomios.

N

negative correlation (p. 247) The paired data (x, y) have a negative correlation if y tends to decrease as x increases.

correlación negativa (pág. 247) Los pares de datos (x, y) presentan una correlación negativa si y tiende a disminuir al aumentar x.

---

normal curve (p. 264) A smooth, symmetrical, bell-shaped curve that can model normal distributions.

See **normal distribution.**

curva normal (pág. 264) Curva lisa, simétrica y con forma de campana que puede representar distribuciones normales.

Ver **distribución normal.**

---

normal distribution (p. 264) A probability distribution with mean $\bar{x}$ and standard deviation σ modeled by a bell-shaped curve with the area properties shown at the right.

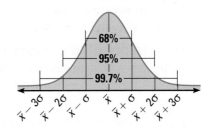

distribución normal (pág. 264) Una distribución de probabilidad con media $\bar{x}$ y desviación normal σ representada por una curva en forma de campana y que tiene las propiedades vistas a la derecha.

nth root of a (p. 116) For an integer n greater than 1, if $b^n = a$, then b is an nth root of a. Written as $\sqrt[n]{a}$.

raíz enésima de a (pág. 116) Para un número entero n mayor que 1, si $b^n = a$, entonces b es una raíz enésima de a. Se escribe $\sqrt[n]{a}$.

$\sqrt[3]{-216} = -6$ because $(-6)^3 = -216$.

$\sqrt[3]{-216} = -6$ ya que $(-6)^3 = -216$.

O

one-to-one function (p. 33) A function where no two different values in the domain have the same value in the range.

función uno a uno (pág. 33) Una función en la que no hay dos valores diferentes en el dominio con el mismo valor en el rango.

$(-4, 3), (-2, 1), (0, 2), (1, -2),$ and $(-3, -5)$ is a one-to-one function.

$(-4, 3), (-2, 1), (0, 2), (1, -2),$ y $(-3, -5)$ es una función uno a uno.

P

parabola (p. 56) The U-shaped graph of a quadratic function.

parábola (pág. 56) La gráfica en forma de U de una función cuadrática.

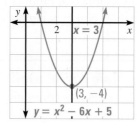

The graph of $y = x^2 - 6x + 5$ is a parabola. The axis of symmetry of the graph is $x = 3$. The vertex is $(3, -4)$.

La gráfica de $y = x^2 - 6x + 5$ es una parábola. El eje de simetría de la gráfica es $x = 3$. El vértice es $(3, -4)$.

---

piecewise function (p. 48) A function defined by at least two equations, each of which applies to a different part of the function's domain.

función definida a trozos (pág. 48) Función definida por al menos dos ecuaciones, cada una de las cuales se aplica a una parte diferente del dominio de la función.

$$g(x) = \begin{cases} 3x - 1, & \text{if } x < 1 \\ 0, & \text{if } x = 1 \\ -x + 4, & \text{if } x > 1 \end{cases}$$

$$g(x) = \begin{cases} 3x - 1, & \text{si } x < 1 \\ 0, & \text{si } x = 1 \\ -x + 4, & \text{si } x > 1 \end{cases}$$

---

point of discontinuity (p. 48) A point at which the graph of a function is broken.

punto de discontinuidad (pág. 48) Un punto en el que se interrumpe la gráfica de una función.

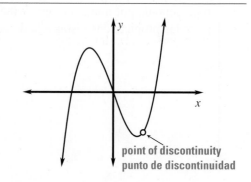

point of discontinuity
punto de discontinuidad

population (p. 268) A group of people or objects that you want information about.

población (pág. 268) Grupo de personas u objetos acerca del cual deseas informarte.

A sportswriter randomly selects 5% of college baseball coaches for a survey. The population is all college baseball coaches. The 5% of coaches selected is the sample.

Un periodista deportiva selecciona al azar al 5% de los entrenadores universitarios de béisbol para que participe en una encuesta. La población son todos los entrenadores universitarios de béisbol. El 5% de los entrenadores que resultó seleccionado es la muestra.

---

population mean (p. 273) The mean of a set of data values for the entire population under consideration.

media de la población (pág. 273) La media de un conjunto de valores de datos para la población total en consideración.

See mean.

Ver media.

---

positive correlation (p. 247) The paired data (x, y) have a positive correlation if y tends to increase as x increases.

correlacion positiva (pág. 247) Los pares de datos (x, y) presentan una correlación positiva si y tiende a aumentar al aumentar x.

---

power function (p. 112) A function of the form $y = ax^b$, where a is a real number and b is a rational number.

función potencial (pág. 112) Función de la forma $y = ax^b$, donde a es un número real y b es un número racional.

$f(x) = 4x^{3/2}$ is a power function.

$f(x) = 4x^{3/2}$ es una función potencial.

---

pure imaginary number (p. 2) A complex number $a + bi$ where $a = 0$ and $b \neq 0$.

número imaginario puro (pág. 2) Número complejo $a + bi$, donde $a = 0$ y $b \neq 0$.

$-4i$ and $1.2i$ are pure imaginary numbers.

$-4i$ y $1.2i$ son números imaginarios puros.

quadratic equation in one variable (p. 74)
An equation that can be written in the form
$ax^2 + bx + c = 0$ where $a \neq 0$.

ecuación cuadrática con una variable
(pág. 74) Ecuación que puede escribirse en la forma $ax^2 + bx + c = 0$, donde $a \neq 0$.

The equation $x^2 - 5x = 36$ is a quadratic equation in one variable because it can be written in the form $x^2 - 5x - 36 = 0$.

La ecuación $x^2 - 5x = 36$ es una ecuación cuadrática con una variable ya que puede escribirse en la forma $x^2 - 5x - 36 = 0$.

---

quadratic formula (p. 91) The formula
$x = \dfrac{-b \pm \sqrt{b^2 - 4ac}}{2a}$ used to find the solutions
of the quadratic equation $ax^2 + bx + c = 0$ when
a, b, and c are real numbers and $a \neq 0$.

fórmula cuadrática (pág. 91) La fórmula
$x = \dfrac{-b \pm \sqrt{b^2 - 4ac}}{2a}$ que se usa para hallar las soluciones
de la ecuación cuadrática $ax^2 + bx + c = 0$ cuando
a, b y c son números reales y $a \neq 0$.

To solve $3x^2 + 6x + 2 = 0$, substitute 3 for a, 6 for b, and 2 for c in the quadratic formula.

Para resolver $3x^2 + 6x + 2 = 0$, sustituye a por 3, b por 6 y c por 2 en la fórmula cuadrática.

$$x = \frac{-6 \pm \sqrt{6^2 - 4(3)(2)}}{2(3)} = \frac{-3 \pm \sqrt{3}}{3}$$

---

quadratic function (p. 56) A function that can be
written in the form $y = ax^2 + bx + c$ where $a \neq 0$.

función cuadrática (pág. 56) Función que puede
escribirse en la forma $y = ax^2 + bx + c$, donde $a \neq 0$.

The functions $y = 3x^2 - 5$ and $y = x^2 - 4x + 6$ are quadratic functions.

Las funciones $y = 3x^2 - 5$ e $y = x^2 - 4x + 6$ son funciones cuadráticas.

---

quadratic inequality in one variable (p. 96)
An inequality that can be written in the form
$ax^2 + bx + c < 0$, $ax^2 + bx + c \leq 0$, $ax^2 + bx + c > 0$,
or $ax^2 + bx + c \geq 0$.

desigualdad cuadrática con una variable
(pág. 96) Desigualdad que se puede escribir en la forma
$ax^2 + bx + c < 0$, $ax^2 + bx + c \leq 0$, $ax^2 + bx + c > 0$ ó
$ax^2 + bx + c \geq 0$.

$x^2 + x \leq 0$ and $2x^2 + x - 4 > 0$ are quadratic inequalities in one variable.

$x^2 + x \leq 0$ y $2x^2 + x - 4 > 0$ son desigualdades cuadráticas con una variable.

---

quadratic inequality in two variables (p. 96)
An inequality that can be written in the form
$y < ax^2 + bx + c$, $y \leq ax^2 + bx + c$, $y > ax^2 + bx + c$,
or $y \geq ax^2 + bx + c$.

desigualdad cuadrática con dos variables
(pág. 96) Desigualdad que se puede escribir en la forma
$y < ax^2 + bx + c$, $y \leq ax^2 + bx + c$, $y > ax^2 + bx + c$
ó $y \geq ax^2 + bx + c$.

$y > x^2 + 3x - 4$ is a quadratic inequality in two variables.

$y > x^2 + 3x - 4$ es una desigualdad cuadrática con dos variables.

quadratic regression (p. 255) The process of finding the best fitting quadratic model of a set of data.

regresión cuadrática (pág. 255) El proceso de hallar la mejor función cuadrática de regresión para representar un conjunto de datos.

You can use a graphing calculator to perform quadratic regression on a data set.

Puedes usar una calculadora científica para hacer la regresión cuadrática en un conjunto de datos.

R

radical (p. 2) An expression of the form $\sqrt{s}$ or $\sqrt[n]{s}$ where s is a number or an expression.

radical (pág. 2) Expresión de la forma $\sqrt{s}$ o $\sqrt[n]{s}$, donde s es un número o una expresión.

$$\sqrt{5}, \ \sqrt[3]{2x + 1}$$

---

radicand (p. 2) The number or expression beneath a radical sign.

radicando (pág. 2) El número o la expresión que aparece bajo el signo radical.

The radicand of $\sqrt{5}$ is 5, and the radicand of $\sqrt{8y^2}$ is $8y^2$.

El radicando de $\sqrt{5}$ es 5, y el radicando de $\sqrt{8y^2}$ es $8y^2$.

---

radius of a circle (p. 182) A segment whose endpoints are the center of the circle and a point on the circle. The distance from the center of a circle to any point on the circle. Plural is *radii*.

radio de un círculo (pág. 182) Un segmento cuyos extremos son el centro del círculo y un punto del círculo. La distancia desde el centro de un círculo a cualquier punto del círculo.

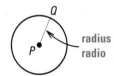

---

radius of a sphere (p. 237) A segment from the center of a sphere to a point on the sphere. The distance from the center of a sphere to any point on the sphere.

radio de una esfera (pág. 237) Segmento que va desde el centro de una esfera hasta un punto de la esfera. La distancia desde el centro de una esfera a cualquier punto de la esfera.

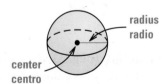

---

range of a relation (p. 33) The set of output values of a relation.

rango de una relación (pág. 33) El conjunto de los valores de salida de una relación.

See relation.

Ver relación.

range of data values (p. 259) A measure of dispersion equal to the difference between the greatest and least data values.

rango de valores de datos (pág. 259) Medida de dispersión igual a la diferencia entre el valor máximo y el valor mínimo de los datos.

14, 17, 18, 19, 20, 24, 24, 30, 32

The range of the data set above is $32 - 14 = 18$.

El rango del conjunto de datos de arriba es $32 - 14 = 18$.

---

rationalizing the denominator (p. 82) The process of eliminating a radical expression in the denominator of a fraction by multiplying both the numerator and denominator by an appropriate radical expression.

racionalizar el denominador (pág. 82) El proceso de eliminar una expresión radical del denominador de una fracción al multiplicar tanto el numerador como el denominador por una expresión radical adecuada.

To rationalize the denominator of $\frac{\sqrt{5}}{\sqrt{2}}$, multiply the numerator and denominator by $\sqrt{2}$.

Para racionalizar el denominador de $\frac{\sqrt{5}}{\sqrt{2}}$, multiplica el numerador y el denominador por $\sqrt{2}$.

---

reflection (p. 40) A transformation that flips a graph or figure in a line.

reflexión (pág. 40) Transformación que vuelca una gráfica o una figura en una recta.

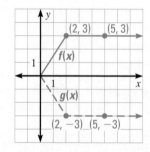

The graph of $g(x)$ is the reflection of the graph of $f(x)$ in the x-axis.

La gráfica de $g(x)$ es la reflexión de la gráfica de $f(x)$ en el eje de x.

---

relation (p. 33) A mapping, or pairing, of input values with output values.

relación (pág. 33) Correspondencia entre los valores de entrada y los valores de salida.

The ordered pairs $(-2, -2)$, $(-2, 2)$, $(0, 1)$, and $(3, 1)$ represent the relation with inputs (domain) of -2, 0, and 3 and outputs (range) of -2, 1, and 2.

Los pares ordenados $(-2, -2)$, $(-2, 2)$, $(0, 1)$ y $(3, 1)$ representan la relación con entradas (dominio) de -2, 0 y 3 y salidas (rango) de -2, 1 y 2.

root of an equation (p. 74) The solutions of a quadratic equation are its roots.

raíz de una ecuación (pág. 74) Las soluciones de una ecuación cuadrática son sus raíces.

The roots of the quadratic equation $x^2 - 5x - 36 = 0$ are 9 and -4.

Las raíces de la ecuación cuadrática $x^2 - 5x - 36 = 0$ son 9 y -4.

S

sample (p. 268) A subset of a population.

muestra (pág. 268) Subconjunto de una población.

See population.

Ver población.

---

scatter plot (p. 247) A graph of a set of data pairs (x, y) used to determine whether there is a relationship between the variables x and y.

diagrama de dispersión (pág. 247) Gráfica de un conjunto de pares de datos (x, y) que sirve para determinar si hay una relación entre las variables x e y.

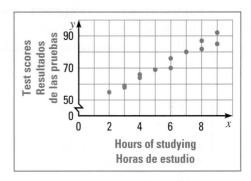

---

scientific notation (p. 107) The representation of a number in the form $c \times 10^n$ where $1 \leq c < 10$ and n is an integer.

notación científica (pág. 107) La representación de un número de la forma $c \times 10^n$, donde $1 \leq c < 10$ y n es un número entero.

0.693 is written in scientific notation as 6.93×10^{-1}.

0.693 escrito en notación científica es 6.93×10^{-1}.

---

secant line (p. 182) A line that intersects a circle in two points.

recta secante (pág. 182) Recta que corta a un círculo en dos puntos.

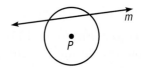

Line *m* is a secant.
La recta *m* es una secante.

---

secant segment (p. 218) A segment that contains a chord of a circle and has exactly one endpoint outside the circle.

segmento secante (pág. 218) Segmento que contiene una cuerda de un círculo y tiene sólo un extremo en el exterior del círculo.

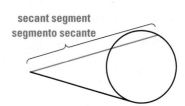

secant segment
segmento secante

sector of a circle (p. 230) The region bounded by two radii of the circle and their intercepted arc.

sector de un círculo (pág. 230) La región limitada por dos radios del círculo y su arco interceptado.

sector APB

---

segments of a chord (p. 218) When two chords intersect in the interior of a circle, each chord is divided into two segments called segments of the chord.

segmentos de una cuerda (pág. 218) Cuando dos cuerdas se cortan en el interior de un círculo, cada cuerda se divide en dos segmentos, llamados segmentos de la cuerda.

$\overline{EA}$ and $\overline{EB}$ are segments of chord $\overline{AB}$. $\overline{DE}$ and $\overline{EC}$ are segments of chord $\overline{DC}$.

$\overline{EA}$ y $\overline{EB}$ son segmentos de la cuerda $\overline{AB}$. $\overline{DE}$ y $\overline{EC}$ son segmentos de la cuerda $\overline{DC}$.

---

semicircle (p. 191) An arc with endpoints that are the endpoints of a diameter of a circle. The measure of a semicircle is 180°.

semicírculo (pág. 191) Arco cuyos extremos son los extremos de un diámetro de un círculo. Un semicírculo mide 180°.

$\overset{\frown}{QSR}$ is a semicircle.
$\overset{\frown}{QSR}$ es un semicírculo.

---

sequence (p. 133) A function whose domain is a set of consecutive integers. The domain gives the relative position of each term of the sequence. The range gives the terms of the sequence.

progresión (pág. 133) Función cuyo dominio es un conjunto de números enteros consecutivos. El dominio da la posición relativa de cada término de la secuencia. El rango da los términos de la secuencia.

For the domain $n = 1, 2, 3$, and 4, the sequence defined by $a_n = 2n$ has the terms 2, 4, 6, and 8.

Para el dominio $n = 1, 2, 3$ y 4, la secuencia definida por $a_n = 2n$ tiene los términos 2, 4, 6 y 8.

---

series (p. 133) The expression formed by adding the terms of a sequence. A series can be finite or infinite.

serie (pág. 133) La expresión formada al sumar los términos de una progresión. La serie puede ser finita o infinita.

Finite series: $2 + 4 + 6 + 8$
Infinite series: $2 + 4 + 6 + 8 + \cdots$

Serie finita: $2 + 4 + 6 + 8$
Serie infinita: $2 + 4 + 6 + 8 + \cdots$

---

sigma notation (p. 133) *See* summation notation.

notación sigma (pág. 133) *Ver* notación de sumatoria.

See summation notation.

Ver notación de sumatoria.

similar polygons (p. 182) Two polygons such that their corresponding angles are congruent and the lengths of corresponding sides are proportional.

polígonos semejantes (pág. 182) Dos polígonos tales que los ángulos correspondientes son congruentes y las longitudes de los lados correspondientes son proporcionales.

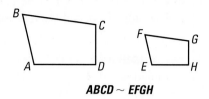

$$ABCD \sim EFGH$$

---

sine (p. 163) A trigonometric ratio, abbreviated as *sin*. For a right triangle ABC, the sine of the acute angle A is

$$\sin A = \frac{\text{length of leg opposite } \angle A}{\text{length of hypotenuse}} = \frac{BC}{AB}.$$

seno (pág. 163) Razón trigonométrica, abreviada *sen*. Para un triángulo rectángulo ABC, el seno del ángulo agudo A es

$$\text{sen } A = \frac{\text{longitud del cateto opuesto a } \angle A}{\text{longitud de la hipotenusa}} = \frac{BC}{AB}.$$

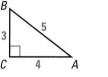

$$\sin A = \frac{BC}{AB} = \frac{3}{5}$$

$$\text{sen } A = \frac{BC}{AB} = \frac{3}{5}$$

---

solution of an equation in two variables (p. 33) An ordered pair (x, y) that produces a true statement when the values of x and y are substituted in the equation.

solución de una ecuación con dos variables (pág. 33) Par ordenado (x, y) que produce un enunciado verdadero al sustituir x e y por sus valores en la ecuación.

$(-2, 3)$ is a solution of $y = -2x - 1$.

$(-2, 3)$ es una solución de $y = -2x - 1$.

---

solve a right triangle (p. 172) To find the measures of all of the sides and angles of a right triangle.

resolver un triángulo rectángulo (pág. 172) Hallar las medidas de todos los lados y todos los ángulos de un triángulo rectángulo.

You can solve a right triangle if you know either of the following:
• Two side lengths
• One side length and the measure of one acute angle

Puedes resolver un triángulo rectángulo conociendo uno de estos grupos:
• Las longitudes de dos lados
• La longitud de un lado y la medida de un ángulo agudo

---

sphere (p. 237) The set of all points in space equidistant from a given point called the center of the sphere.

esfera (pág. 237) El conjunto de todos los puntos del espacio que son equidistantes de un punto dado, llamado centro de la esfera.

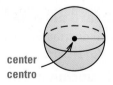

center
centro

square root (p. 2) If $b^2 = a$, then b is a square root of a. The radical symbol $\sqrt{\ }$ represents a nonnegative square root.

raíz cuadrada (pág. 2) Si $b^2 = a$, entonces b es una raíz cuadrada de a. El signo radical $\sqrt{\ }$ representa una raíz cuadrada no negativa.

The square roots of 9 are 3 and -3 because $3^2 = 9$ and $(-3)^2 = 9$. So, $\sqrt{9} = 3$ and $-\sqrt{9} = -3$.

Las raíces cuadradas de 9 son 3 y -3 ya que $3^2 = 9$ y $(-3)^2 = 9$. Así pues, $\sqrt{9} = 3$ y $-\sqrt{9} = -3$.

---

standard deviation (p. 259) The typical difference (or deviation) between a data value and the mean. The standard deviation σ of a numerical data set $x_1, x_2, \ldots, x_n$ is given by the following formula:

$$\sigma = \sqrt{\frac{(x_1 - \overline{x})^2 + (x_2 - \overline{x})^2 + \cdots + (x_n - \overline{x})^2}{n}}$$

desviación típica (pág. 259) La diferencia (o desviación) más común entre un valor de los datos y la media. La desviación típica σ de un conjunto de datos numéricos $x_1, x_2, \ldots, x_n$ viene dada por la siguiente fórmula:

$$\sigma = \sqrt{\frac{(x_1 - \overline{x})^2 + (x_2 - \overline{x})^2 + \cdots + (x_n - \overline{x})^2}{n}}$$

14, 17, 18, 19, 20, 24, 24, 30, 32

Because the mean of the data set is 22, the standard deviation is:

Como la media del conjunto de datos es 22, la desviación típica es:

$$\sigma =$$

$$\sqrt{\frac{(14 - 22)^2 + (17 - 22)^2 + \cdots + (32 - 22)^2}{9}}$$

$$= \sqrt{\frac{290}{9}} \approx 5.7$$

---

standard form of a quadratic equation in one variable (p. 74) The form $ax^2 + bx + c = 0$ where $a \neq 0$.

forma general de una ecuación cuadrática con una variable (pág. 74) La forma $ax^2 + bx + c = 0$, donde $a \neq 0$.

The quadratic equation $x^2 - 5x = 36$ can be written in standard form as $x^2 - 5x - 36 = 0$.

La ecuación cuadrática $x^2 - 5x = 36$ escrita en la forma general es $x^2 - 5x - 36 = 0$.

---

standard form of a quadratic function (p. 56) The form $y = ax^2 + bx + c$ where $a \neq 0$.

forma general de una función cuadrática (pág. 56) La forma $y = ax^2 + bx + c$, donde $a \neq 0$.

The quadratic function $y = 2(x + 3)(x - 1)$ can be written in standard form as $y = 2x^2 + 4x - 6$.

La función cuadrática $y = 2(x + 3)(x - 1)$ escrita en la forma general es $y = 2x^2 + 4x - 6$.

---

standard normal distribution (p. 264) The normal distribution with mean 0 and standard deviation 1. *See also* z-score.

distribución normal típica (pág. 264) La distribución normal con media 0 y desviación típica 1. *Ver también* puntuación z.

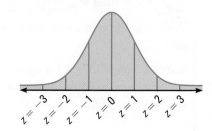

statistics (p. 259) Numerical values used to summarize and compare sets of data.

estadística (pág. 259) Valores numéricos utilizados para resumir y comparar conjuntos de datos.

See **mean, median, mode, range,** *and* **standard deviation.**

Ver **media, mediana, moda, rango** *y* **desviación típica.**

step function (p. 48) A piecewise function defined by a constant value over each part of its domain. Its graph resembles a series of stair steps.

$$f(x) = \begin{cases} 1, & \text{if } 0 \le x < 1 \\ 2, & \text{if } 1 \le x < 2 \\ 3, & \text{if } 2 \le x < 3 \end{cases}$$

función escalonada (pág. 48) Función definida a trozos y por un valor constante en cada parte de su dominio. Su gráfica parece un grupo de escalones.

$$f(x) = \begin{cases} 1, & \text{if } 0 \le x < 1 \\ 2, & \text{if } 1 \le x < 2 \\ 3, & \text{if } 2 \le x < 3 \end{cases}$$

summation notation (p. 133) Notation for a series that uses the uppercase Greek letter sigma, Σ. Also called sigma notation.

notación de sumatoria (pág. 133) Notación de una serie que usa la letra griega mayúscula sigma, Σ. También se llama notación sigma.

$$\sum_{i=1}^{5} 7i = 7(1) + 7(2) + 7(3) + 7(4) + 7(5)$$
$$= 7 + 14 + 21 + 28 + 35$$

tangent (p. 157) A trigonometric ratio, abbreviated as *tan*. For a right triangle *ABC*, the tangent of the acute angle *A* is

$$\tan A = \frac{\text{length of leg opposite } \angle A}{\text{length of leg adjacent to } \angle A} = \frac{BC}{AC}.$$

tangente (pág. 157) Razón trigonométrica, abreviada *tan*. Para un triángulo rectángulo *ABC*, la tangente del ángulo agudo *A* es

$$\tan A = \frac{\text{longitud del cateto opuesto a } \angle A}{\text{longitud del cateto adyacente a } \angle A} = \frac{BC}{AC}.$$

$$\tan A = \frac{BC}{AC} = \frac{3}{4}$$

tangent line (p. 182) A line in the plane of a circle that intersects the circle in exactly one point, the point of tangency.

recta tangente (pág. 182) Recta del plano de un círculo que corta al círculo en sólo un punto, el punto de tangencia.

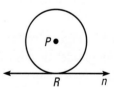

Line *n* is a tangent. *R* is the point of tangency.

La recta *n* es una tangente. *R* es el punto de tangencia.

terms of a sequence (p. 133) The values in the range of a sequence.

The first 4 terms of the sequence $1, -3, 9, -27, 81, -243, \ldots$ are $1, -3, 9,$ and -27.

términos de una progresión (pág. 133) Los valores del rango de una progresión.

Los 4 primeros términos de la progresión $1, -3, 9, -27, 81, -243, \ldots$ son $1, -3, 9$ y -27.

transformation (p. 40) A transformation changes a graph's size, shape, position, or orientation.

Translations, vertical stretches and shrinks, reflections, and rotations are transformations.

transformación (pág. 40) Una transformación cambia el tamaño, la forma, la posición o la orientación de una gráfica.

Las traslaciones, las expansiones y contracciones verticales, las reflexiones y las rotaciones son transformaciones.

translation (p. 40) A transformation that shifts a graph horizontally and/or vertically, but does not change its size, shape, or orientation.

traslación (pág. 40) Transformación que desplaza una gráfica horizontal o verticalmente, o de ambas maneras, pero que no cambia su tamaño, forma u orientación.

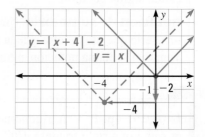

The graph of $y = |x + 4| - 2$ is the graph of $y = |x|$ translated down 2 units and left 4 units.

La gráfica de $y = |x + 4| - 2$ es la gráfica de $y = |x|$ al trasladar ésta 2 unidades hacia abajo y 4 unidades hacia la izquierda.

trigonometric ratio (p. 157) A ratio of the lengths of two sides in a right triangle. *See also* sine, cosine, *and* tangent.

Three common trigonometric ratios are sine, cosine, and tangent.

razón trigonométrica (pág. 157) Razón entre las longitudes de dos lados de un triángulo rectángulo. *Ver también* seno, coseno *y* tangente.

Tres razones trigonométricas comunes son el seno, el coseno y la tangente.

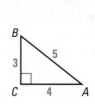

$$\tan A = \frac{BC}{AC} = \frac{3}{4}$$

$$\sin A = \frac{BC}{AB} = \frac{3}{5}$$

$$\cos A = \frac{AC}{AB} = \frac{4}{5}$$

$$\tan A = \frac{BC}{AC} = \frac{3}{4}$$

$$\text{sen } A = \frac{BC}{AB} = \frac{3}{5}$$

$$\cos A = \frac{AC}{AB} = \frac{4}{5}$$

trigonometry (p. 157) The branch of mathematics that deals with the relationships between the sides and angles at triangles and the calculations based on these relationships.

trigonometría (pág. 157) La rama de las matemáticas que trata las relaciones entre los lados y ángulos de los triángulos y los cálculos basados en estas relaciones.

See sine, cosine *and* tangent.

Ver seno, coseno *y* tangente.

---

trinomial (p. 74) The sum of three monomials.

trinomio (pág. 74) La suma de tres monomios.

$4x^2 + 3x - 1$ is a trinomial.

$4x^2 + 3x - 1$ es un trinomio.

---

unbiased sample (p. 268) A sample that is representative of the population you want information about.

muestra no sesgada (pág. 268) Muestra que es representativa de la población acerca de la cual deseas informarte.

You want to poll members of the senior class about where to hold the prom. If every senior has an equal chance of being polled, then the sample is unbiased.

Quieres encuestar a algunos estudiantes de último curso sobre el lugar donde organizar el baile de fin de año. Si cada estudiante de último curso tiene iguales posibilidades de ser encuestado, entonces es una muestra no sesgada.

---

verbal model (p. 24) A word equation that represents a real-life problem.

modelo verbal (pág. 24) Ecuación expresada mediante palabras que representa un problema de la vida real.

Distance =	Rate	·	Time
(miles)	(miles/hour)		(hours)

Distancia =	Velocidad	·	Tiempo
(millas)	(millas/hora)		(horas)

---

vertex form of a quadratic function (p. 63) The form $y = a(x - h)^2 + k$, where the vertex of the graph is (h, k) and the axis of symmetry is $x = h$.

forma de vértice de una función cuadrática (pág. 63) La forma $y = a(x - h)^2 + k$, donde el vértice de la gráfica es (h, k) y el eje de simetría es $x = h$.

The quadratic function
$y = -\frac{1}{4}(x + 2)^2 + 5$
is in vertex form.

La función cuadrática
$y = -\frac{1}{4}(x + 2)^2 + 5$
está en la forma de vértice.

---

vertex of a parabola (p. 56) The point on a parabola that lies on the axis of symmetry.

vértice de una parábola (pág. 56) El punto de una parábola que se encuentra en el eje de simetría.

See parabola.

Ver parábola.

vertex of an absolute value graph (p. 40) The highest or lowest point on the graph of an absolute value function.

vértice de una gráfica de valor absoluto (pág. 40) El punto más alto o más bajo de la gráfica de una función de valor absoluto.

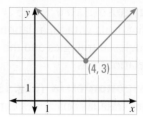

The vertex of the graph of $y = |x - 4| + 3$ is the point $(4, 3)$.

El vértice de la gráfica de $y = |x - 4| + 3$ es el punto $(4, 3)$.

---

zero of a function (p. 40) A number k is a zero of a function f if $f(k) = 0$.

cero de una función (pág. 40) Un número k es un cero de una función f si $f(k) = 0$.

The zeros of the function $f(x) = 2(x + 3)(x - 1)$ are -3 and 1.

Los ceros de la función $f(x) = 2(x + 3)(x - 1)$ son -3 y 1.

---

z-score (p. 264) The number z of standard deviations that a data value lies above or below the mean of the data set: $z = \frac{x - \bar{x}}{\sigma}$.

puntuación z (pág. 264) El número z de desviaciones típicas que un valor se encuentra por encima o por debajo de la media del conjunto de datos: $z = \frac{x - \bar{x}}{\sigma}$.

A normal distribution has a mean of 76 and a standard deviation of 9. The z-score for $x = 64$ is $z = \frac{x - \bar{x}}{\sigma} = \frac{64 - 76}{9} \approx -1.3$.

Una distribución normal tiene una media de 76 y una desviación típica de 9. La puntuación z para $x = 64$ es $z = \frac{x - \bar{x}}{\sigma} = \frac{64 - 76}{9} \approx -1.3$.

Index

using a graphing calculator,
254, 256–258, 280–282
identifying, 254–258, 280–282
predicting from, 254, 257, 258
Biased sample, 268
identifying, 269–271
Binomial, 74
square of a, 86–89

C

Calculator, *See* Graphing
calculator
Center
of a circle, 182
of a sphere, 237
Central angle
of a circle, 190, 191
relationship to arcs, 190–197
Checking
for extraneous solutions,
28–31
solutions
using a calculator, 142
by graphing, 256
using substitution, 129
Chord(s), 182, 198
perpendicular bisectors and,
199
properties of, 198
applying, 198–204
secant segments and, 218–223
segments of, 218–223
of a sphere, 237
tangent properties and,
182–189
triangle similarity and,
200–204
Circle(s), 182
angles formed by tangents and
chords, 211–217
arc length of, 224
finding measure of, 225–229
arc measures of, 190–204
area of, 230–235
center of, 182
central angle of, 190, 191
relationship to arcs, 190–197
chord of, 182, 198
using properties, 198–204
segments of, 218–223

circumference of, 224
arc length and, 224–229
finding measure of, 224–229
circumscribed, 205–210
congruent, 191
diameter of, 182
finding lengths in, 183–189,
198–204
inscribed angles and, 205–210
inscribed polygons and,
205–210
major arc of, 190, 191
minor arc of, 190, 191
perpendicular bisectors and,
199
radius of, 182
secant of, 182
secant segments and, 218–223
sector of, 230
area of, 230–235
special regions and, 236
tangent to, 182
applying properties, 182–189
theorems about, 182
Circumference
of a circle, 224
arc length and, 224–229
formula for, 224
measure of, 224–229
**Circumference of a circle
theorem,** 224
applying, 224–229
Circumscribed circle, 205–210
Classifying
functions, 34, 36, 38
samples, 268–271
Common difference, for an
arithmetic sequence, 137, 138
Common internal tangent, 185
Common ratio
of a geometric sequence, 143
to write a rule, 144–146
Common tangents, 183, 185–189
Communication, describing in
words, *Throughout. See for
example* 4, 8, 13, 26, 30, 42,
45, 60, 72, 85, 98
Comparing
average rates of change of a
function, 70–73
data sets, 260–262

exercises, 27, 106, 159, 170
families of graphs of absolute
value functions, 39, 40
statistics and parameters,
274–278
Complementary angles, 157
cosine ratios and, 163–169
sine ratios and, 163–169
tangent ratios and, 157–162
Completing the square, 86
to solve quadratic equations,
86–89
Complex conjugate(s), 11
Complex number(s), 2
absolute value of, 16–20
adding, 6–10
on a graphing calculator, 15
complex conjugates, 11
dividing, 11–14
on a graphing calculator, 15
multiplying, 11–14
on a graphing calculator, 15
plotting in the complex plane,
9, 16, 17, 19, 20
relationship among, 2
as solutions to quadratic
equations, 83–85, 87–89,
92–94
standard form of, 2, 11
subtracting, 6–10
on a graphing calculator, 15
Complex plane, 9, 16, 17
absolute value of a complex
number in, 16, 17
to add complex numbers, 9
imaginary axis, 9, 16, 17
plotting complex numbers in,
9, 16, 17, 19, 20
real axis, 9, 16, 17
Complex solution(s), to quadratic
equations, 83–85, 87–89,
92–94
Composition of a function,
112
finding, 113–115
Congruent arcs, 191
identifying, 192–196
Congruent circles, 191
Conjugates, 82
complex, 11
Convenience sample, 268

Visual thinking, *See also*
Geometry; Graphing; Indirect
measurement; Logical
reasoning; Measurement
exercises, 61, 66, 119
Vocabulary, lesson introduction,
Throughout. See for example
2, 6, 11, 17, 24, 28, 33, 40, 48,
56, 63
Volume
of a sphere, 237–242
effect of changing radius,
238, 240, 242
Volume of a sphere theorem, 237
applying, 238–242

W

Writing, *See also* Communication;
Verbal model
absolute value functions,
41–45
complex numbers, 2–5
in standard form, 3–5
equations for best-fitting lines,
246, 248–253
exercises, 62, 106, 137, 211,
246, 254
exponential expressions in
expanded form, 106
numbers in scientific notation,
107–111
piecewise functions, 49–52
quadratic functions
in intercept form, 255, 257,
258
in standard form, 64, 66, 68,
256–258
in vertex form, 255, 257, 258
terms of a sequence, 133, 135,
136

X

x-intercept
graphs of absolute value
functions and, 40–42, 44
graphs of quadratic functions
and, 53–68

Y

y-intercept
graphs of absolute value
functions and, 40–42, 44
graphs of quadratic functions
and, 56, 60

Z

Zero(s)
of a function, 40
graphs of absolute value
functions and, 40, 42, 44
graphs of quadratic functions
and, 63–68
of a quadratic function, 63
finding, 75–77, 80
Zero exponent property, 107
using to simplify expressions,
107–111
z-score, 264
z-value, 264

Selected Answers

UNIT 1

1.1 Exercise Set A (p. 4)

1. $10\sqrt{5}$ **3.** $11\sqrt{2}$ **5.** $5\sqrt{5}$ **7.** $\dfrac{5}{13}$ **9.** $\dfrac{\sqrt{23}}{11}$

11. $\dfrac{3\sqrt{3}}{2}$ **17.** $8i$ **19.** $4i\sqrt{2}$ **21.** $5i\sqrt{3}$ **23.** $\dfrac{6\sqrt{3}}{7}i$

25. $3 + i\sqrt{2}$ **27.** $9 + 9i$ **29.** -11 **31.** $6 + i\sqrt{11}$

33. 1 **35.** You can't add the real part to the imaginary part; The correct answer is $3 + 2i\sqrt{2}$.

37. $x = 2, y = 1$ **39.** $x = -7, y = -4$

41. $x = 11, y = -2$ **43.** $x = -1, y = -12$

45. $x = -3, y = 2$

1.1 Exercise Set B (p. 5)

1. $2\sqrt{13}$ **3.** $5\sqrt{7}$ **5.** $5\sqrt{15}$ **7.** $\dfrac{2\sqrt{19}}{15}$ **9.** $\dfrac{9\sqrt{5}}{2}$

11. $\dfrac{6\sqrt{6}}{25}$ **17.** $13i$ **19.** $i\sqrt{78}$ **21.** $\dfrac{4\sqrt{13}}{5}i$

23. $8\sqrt{2}$ **25.** $8 + 2i\sqrt{2}$ **27.** $1 - 20i$

29. $4 - 4i\sqrt{2}$ **31.** $-4 + i\sqrt{161}$ **33.** $29 + \dfrac{2\sqrt{30}}{13}i$

35. $x = -4, y = 9$ **37.** $x = \dfrac{1}{2}, y = -7$

39. $x = \dfrac{3}{8}, y = -\dfrac{5}{2}$ **41.** $x = -13, y = -12$

43. $x = -2, y = -2$

1.2 Exercise Set A (p. 8)

7. $10 - i$ **9.** $1 + 2i$ **11.** $-4 + i$

13. $-9 + 17i$ **15.** $-32 + 6i$ **17.** $17 - 9i$

19. $13 - 18i$ **21.** $8 + 20i$ **23.** $15 + 8i$

25. $-14 - 22i$ **27.** $-19 + 9i$

29. The negative sign needs to be distributed through the quantity $(3 + 4i)$ first; $3 - 8i$

1.2 Exercise Set B (p. 9)

7. $33 + 39i$ **9.** $-42 - 19i$ **11.** $-5 + 9i$

13. $3 + 21i$ **15.** $16 + 24i$ **17.** $-16 - 13i$

19. $2.7 - 6.8i$ **21.** $-2.1 + 13.1i$ **23.** $-10 - 32i$

25. $-24 + 8i$ **27.** $-38 + 28i$

1.3 Exercise Set A (p. 13)

1. $a + bi$ **5.** $-48 + 12i$ **7.** $42 - 18i$

9. $28 - 4i$ **11.** $3 + i$ **13.** $65 - 55i$

15. $-46 - 30i$ **17.** $-12 - 14i$ **19.** $-28 - 21i$

21. $-21 + 20i$ **23.** $-13 + 19i$ **25.** $-66 - 34i$

27. $\dfrac{20}{29} + \dfrac{8}{29}i$ **29.** $\dfrac{2}{25} - \dfrac{11}{25}i$ **31.** $-\dfrac{2}{3} - \dfrac{7}{6}i$

33. $-\dfrac{1}{2} - \dfrac{1}{2}i$ **35.** $\dfrac{2 + \sqrt{2}}{3} + \dfrac{2\sqrt{2} - 1}{3}i$

37. $\dfrac{24}{13} - \dfrac{10}{13}i$

39.

Powers of i	i^1	i^2	i^3	i^4
Simplified	i	-1	$-i$	1
Powers of i	i^5	i^6	i^7	i^8
Simplified	i	-1	$-i$	1

The pattern repeats every four powers of i; $i^9 = i$; $i^{10} = -1$; $i^{11} = -i$; $i^{12} = 1$

1.3 Exercise Set B (p. 14)

5. $13 + 18i$ **7.** $58i$ **9.** $50i$ **11.** $-25i$

13. $10 - 80i$ **15.** $-42 - 35i$ **17.** $-4 - 16i$

19. $17 - 19i$ **21.** $4 + 2i$ **23.** $\dfrac{40}{29} + \dfrac{16}{29}i$

25. $\dfrac{16}{5} - \dfrac{2}{5}i$ **27.** $-\dfrac{5}{2} + \dfrac{1}{2}i$ **29.** $-\dfrac{2}{3} - 3i$

31. $\dfrac{\sqrt{3}}{2} + \dfrac{1}{2}i$ **33.** $\dfrac{11}{13} + \dfrac{3}{13}i$ **35.** $-\dfrac{63}{50} - \dfrac{9}{50}i$

37. $-\dfrac{54}{17} + \dfrac{80}{17}i$

39. The product of the complex numbers is $(a_1 + b_1i)(a_2 + b_2i) = a_1a_2 + a_1b_2i + a_2b_1i + b_1b_2i^2 = (a_1a_2 - b_1b_2) + (a_1b_2 + a_2b_1)i$. So, the complex conjugate of the product is $(a_1a_2 - b_1b_2) - (a_1b_2 + a_2b_1)i$. The product of their complex conjugates is $(a_1 - b_1i)(a_2 - b_2i) = a_1a_2 - a_1b_2i - a_2b_1i + b_1b_2i^2 = (a_1a_2 - b_1b_2) - (a_1b_2 + a_2b_1)i$, which is equal to the complex conjugate of the original product.

1.4 Exercise Set A (p. 19)

9. $\sqrt{29}$ **11.** 5 **13.** $2\sqrt{10}$ **15.** $\sqrt{5}$ **17.** 5

19. $2\sqrt{13}$ **21.** $\sqrt{5}$ **23.** $\sqrt{130}$ **25.** $\sqrt{29}$

27. $\sqrt{53}$ **29.** $\sqrt{41}$ **31.** 3 **33.** 5

35. $|a - bi| = \sqrt{a^2 + (-b)^2} = \sqrt{a^2 + b^2}$

1.4 Exercise Set B (p. 20)

9. 26   **11.** 3   **13.** $\sqrt{74}$ **15.** $2\sqrt{13}$ **17.** $\sqrt{85}$

19. $2\sqrt{2}$ **21.** $2\sqrt{5}$ **23.** 2   **25.** $\dfrac{\sqrt{67}}{4}$

27. $a > 0, b > 0$ **29.** $a < 0, b < 0$ **31.** $a < 0, b = 0$

UNIT 2

2.1 Exercise Set A (p. 26)

1. 165 mi   **3.** 69 mi/h   **5.** 18 ft^2 **7.** 7 m

9. $y = 5x + 5$ **11.** $y = 17 - x$

13. The pattern shows the output is decreased by 10 each time the input is increased by 1 and the equation shows the output is increased by 65 each time the input is increased by 1; an equation that represents the table is $y = 65 - 10x$.

15. 6 premium channels   **17.** 5 buckets

2.1 Exercise Set B (p. 27)

1. $y = 8x + 18$ **3. a.** $22.50; $37.50; $52.50; $67.50; $82.50; *Sample Answer:* 20 songs
b. $y = 0.75x + 7.5$; 22 songs   **c.** yes; 22 rounded to the nearest 10 is 20.   **5.** $525,300

7. 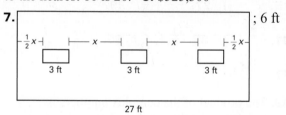 ; 6 ft

2.2 Exercise Set A (p. 30)

1. yes   **3.** yes   **5.** no   **7.** $-2, 8$ **9.** $-\dfrac{5}{3}, \dfrac{11}{3}$

11. -3 **13.** $0, 3$ **15.** $-\dfrac{1}{3}, 2$ **17.** $-5 < x < 11$

19. $0 \le x \le 6$ **21.** $-\dfrac{1}{2} < x < 4$ **23.** $x < -15$ or

$x > -9$ **25.** $x \le \dfrac{4}{9}$ or $x \ge \dfrac{8}{9}$ **27.** $|x - 88| \le 42$

2.2 Exercise Set B (p. 31)

1. $-5, 1$ **3.** $-1, \dfrac{11}{5}$ **5.** $\dfrac{2}{5}, \dfrac{8}{5}$ **7.** $-\dfrac{5}{3}, \dfrac{1}{3}$ **9.** $-1, 9$

11. $b - a, -b - a$ **13.** $\dfrac{b}{a}, -\dfrac{b}{a}$ **15.** $2a, 0$

17. $x \le -1$ or $x \ge 5$ **19.** no solution

21. all real numbers   **23.** no solution

25. $\dfrac{-v - u}{t} < x < \dfrac{v - u}{t}$ **27.** $\dfrac{-v - u}{t} \le x \le \dfrac{v - u}{t}$

29. $|x - 238{,}850| \le 13{,}150$

2.3 Exercise Set A (pp. 35–36)

1. domain: 0, 1, 2, 3, 4; range: 1, 2, 3, 4; function; *not* one-to-one   **3.** domain: 1, 2, 3, 4, 5; range: $-5, -4, 0, 1, 2$; function; one-to-one
5. domain: $-5, -3, 1, 2, 4$; range: $-5, -4, -1, 3, 6$; function; one-to-one   **7.** function
9. function

15. 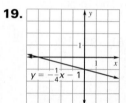   **17.**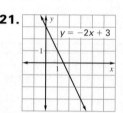

19. 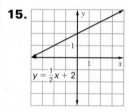   **21.**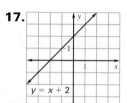

23. linear; 3; 7   **25.** linear; 3; -3

27. *not* linear; $-1; \dfrac{1}{2}$ **29.** domain: 2, 3, 5, 6

31. no   **33.** domain: $0 \le t \le 8$; range: $18 \le n \le 42$
35. a. domain: 11,400,000, 12,300,000, 12,400,000, 19,000,000, 33,900,000; range: 20, 21, 31, 55   **b.** yes; Each input p has exactly one output.
c. no; The input 21 has more than one output.

2.3 Exercise Set B (p. 37–38)

1. domain: $-5, -4, -3, -2, -1$; range: 0, 1, 2, 4, 5; function; one-to-one

3. domain: 1.1, 2.5, 3.6, 4.8; range: 1.1, 2.5, 3.6; function; *not* one-to-one

5. domain: $-\dfrac{2}{3}, \dfrac{1}{4}, \dfrac{2}{3}, \dfrac{3}{4}$; range: $\dfrac{1}{4}, \dfrac{1}{3}, \dfrac{2}{3}, \dfrac{3}{4}$; function; one-to-one

7. *not* a function   **9.** *not* a function

15.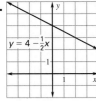
$y = 4 - \frac{1}{2}x$

17.
$y = 0.6x + 0.7$

15.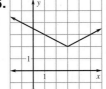

19.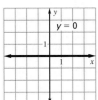
$y = 0$

21.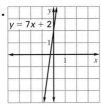
$y = 7x + 2$

17. $y = |x + 1| + 2$; x-intercepts (zeros): none; y-intercept: 3; increasing when $x > -1$; decreasing when $x < -1$

19. $y = \frac{1}{2}|x + 2| - 3$; x-intercepts (zeros): 4, −8; y-intercept: −2; increasing when $x > -2$; decreasing when $x < -2$

23. linear; 11; −1 **25.** *not* linear; 2; 2

27. *not* linear; $\frac{1}{2}$; $\frac{3}{2}$

29. domain: $0 \le t \le 5$, range: $138.5 \le w(t) \le 170$; over the years 1999–2004 the watermelon acreage ranged from a low of about 138,500 in 2004 to a high of 170,000 in 1999.

23.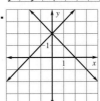

25.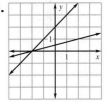

31.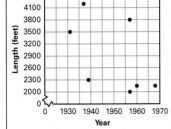

27.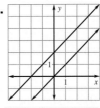

33. Yes, the postage rate is a function of the package weight because for each weight, there is one and only one corresponding rate.

29.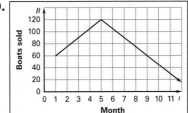

31. The minimum sold is 15 in December.

2.4 Exercise Set A (pp. 42–43)

1. a. down **b.** $(-1, 0)$ **c.** same

3. a. down **b.** $(-2, 2)$ **c.** narrower

5. a. down **b.** $(-1, 0)$ **c.** wider

7. a. up **b.** $(-9, -1)$ **c.** narrower

9. a. down **b.** $(1, 1)$ **c.** narrower

11.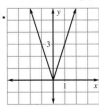

13.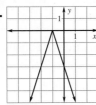

2.4 Exercise Set B (pp. 44–45)

1. a. down **b.** $(4, 0)$ **c.** narrower

3. a. down **b.** $(10, 2)$ **c.** same

5. a. down **b.** $(4, 8)$ **c.** wider

7. a. down **b.** $(-4, -3)$ **c.** wider

9. a. down **b.** $(7, 14)$ **c.** narrower

13.

15.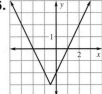

17.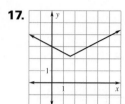

19. $y = -|x| + 3$; x-intercepts (zeros): $-3, 3$; y-intercept: 3; increasing when $x < 0$; decreasing when $x > 0$ **21.** $y = 2|x - 4| + 1$; x-intercepts (zeros): none; y-intercept: 9; increasing when $x > 4$; decreasing when $x < 4$

23.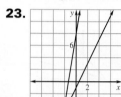

27. Yes. *Sample answer:* $(-10, 0)$ satisfies the equation in Exercise 26.

29. The maximum sold is 80 in March.

31. $y = -1.56|x| + 587.4$

2.5 Exercise Set A (p. 51)

1. a. -4 **b.** 2 **c.** 5 **3. a.** 1 **b.** 0 **c.** 1

5. ; none

7. ; $x = 2, x = 4$

9.
$$f(x) = \begin{cases} 0, & \text{if } 0 < x \le 2 \\ 1, & \text{if } 2 < x \le 4 \\ 2, & \text{if } 4 < x \le 6 \end{cases}$$

The function is constant on the intervals $0 < x \le 2$, $2 < x \le 4$, and $4 < x \le 6$.

11.
$$f(x) = \begin{cases} -2, & \text{if } 0 < x \le 1 \\ -1, & \text{if } 1 < x \le 2 \\ 0, & \text{if } 2 < x \le 4 \end{cases}$$

The function is constant on the intervals $0 < x \le 1$, $1 < x \le 2$, and $2 < x \le 4$.

13.
$$f(x) = \begin{cases} -x + 6, & \text{if } x < 3 \\ x, & \text{if } x \ge 3 \end{cases}$$

minimum: $(3, 3)$; rate of change: -1 when $x < 3$, 1 when $x > 3$

15.
$$f(x) = \begin{cases} -4, & \text{if } -4 \le x < -3 \\ -3, & \text{if } -3 \le x < -2 \\ -2, & \text{if } -2 \le x < -1 \\ -1, & \text{if } -1 \le x < 0 \\ 0, & \text{if } 0 \le x < 1 \\ 1, & \text{if } 1 \le x < 2 \\ 2, & \text{if } 2 \le x < 3 \\ 3, & \text{if } 3 \le x < 4 \\ 4, & \text{if } x = 4 \end{cases}$$

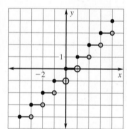

2.5 Exercise Set B (p. 52)

1. a. 1 **b.** 1 **c.** 0

3. ; $x = 2, x = 4$

5.
$$f(x) = \begin{cases} -1, & \text{if } 0 \le x < 1 \\ 0, & \text{if } 1 \le x < 2 \\ 1, & \text{if } 2 \le x < 3 \end{cases}$$

The function is constant on the intervals $0 \le x < 1$, $1 \le x < 2$, and $2 \le x < 3$.

7.
$$f(x) = \begin{cases} -3, & \text{if } 0 < x \le 1 \\ 0, & \text{if } 1 < x \le 3 \\ 2, & \text{if } 3 < x \le 6 \end{cases}$$

The function is constant on the intervals $0 < x \le 1$, $1 < x \le 3$, and $3 < x \le 6$.

9.
$$f(x) = \begin{cases} 2x + 6, & \text{if } x < -2 \\ -2x - 2, & \text{if } x \ge -2 \end{cases}$$

maximum: $(-2, 2)$; rate of change: 2 when $x < -2$, -2 when $x > -2$

11. 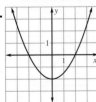 ; $25.50

Cost (dollars) vs Weight (ounces)

UNIT 3

3.1 Exercise Set A (pp. 58–59)

1. 8, 2, 0, 2, 8   **3.** $-8, -2, 0, -2, -8$

5. a. opens down **b.** $(0, 1)$ **c.** $x = 0$

7. a. opens up **b.** $\left(\frac{1}{3}, -\frac{1}{3}\right)$ **c.** $x = \frac{1}{3}$

9. a. opens up **b.** $\left(\frac{1}{2}, \frac{23}{4}\right)$ **c.** $x = \frac{1}{2}$

17.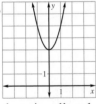
domain: all real numbers; range: $y \ge 3$

19.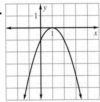
domain: all real numbers; range: $y \le 0$

21.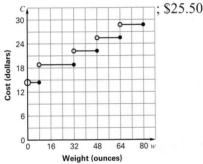
domain: all real numbers; range: $y \ge -2$

23.
domain: all real numbers; range: $y \ge -3$
$(0, -3)$

25.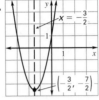

27.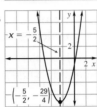

29.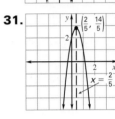

31.

33.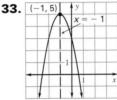

35. $R = -25x^2 + 300x + 2700$

37. $(12, 78)$; $x = 12$ **39.** 12 **41.** $160

3.1 Exercise Set B (pp. 60–61)

1. $-27, -9, -3, -9, -27$

3. $-15, -3, 1, -3, -15$

5. a. opens up **b.** $(0, 1)$ **c.** $x = 0$

7. a. opens down **b.** $(0, -4)$ **c.** $x = 0$

9. a. opens up **b.** $\left(-1, -\frac{5}{2}\right)$ **c.** $x = -1$

15. $c = -4$; The y-intercept of the graph is the value of c, which is -4.

17.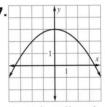
domain: all real numbers; range: $y \le 3$

19.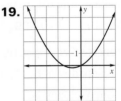
domain: all real numbers; range: $y \ge -\frac{3}{16}$

21.

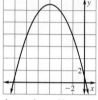

domain: all real numbers; range: $y \le 13$

23.

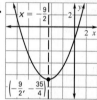

$x = -1$
$(-1, -1)$

25.

$\left(\frac{5}{4}, -\frac{1}{8}\right)$
$x = \frac{5}{4}$

27.

$x = -\frac{9}{2}$
$\left(-\frac{9}{2}, -\frac{35}{4}\right)$

29.

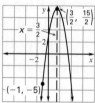

$(-4, 2)$
$x = -4$

31.

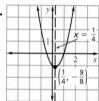

$x = \frac{1}{4}$
$\left(\frac{1}{4}, -\frac{9}{8}\right)$

33. $a = -2$, $b = 6$, $c = 3$;

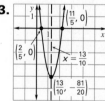

$x = \frac{3}{2}$
$\left(\frac{3}{2}, \frac{15}{2}\right)$
$(-1, -5)$

35. Yes, the store should raise the price of bubble gum to maximize revenue. Even though the store will sell less packs, the increased price will more than make up the difference.

37. $(20, 90)$; $x = 20$ **39.** 20

3.2 Exercise Set A (pp. 65–66)

1. a. opens down **b.** $(1, 4)$ **c.** $x = 1$

3. a. opens down **b.** $(-1, 50)$ **c.** $x = -1$

5. a. opens up **b.** $(-5, -1)$ **c.** $x = -5$

13.

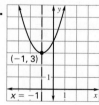

$(-1, 3)$
$x = -1$

15.

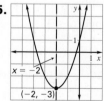

$x = -2$
$(-2, -3)$

17.

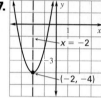

$x = -2$
$(-2, -4)$

19.

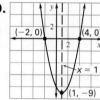

$(-2, 0)$ $(4, 0)$
$x = 1$
$(1, -9)$

21.

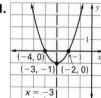

$(-4, 0)$
$(-3, -1)$ $(-2, 0)$
$x = -3$

23.

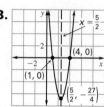

$x = \frac{5}{2}$
$(4, 0)$
$(1, 0)$
$\left(\frac{5}{2}, -\frac{27}{4}\right)$

25. $y = x^2 - 4x + 10$ **27.** $y = 3x^2 - 18x + 15$

29. $y = 4x^2 + 12x + 8$ **31.** minimum, 3

33. minimum, -3 **35.** minimum, -2

37. As a increases, the graph becomes more narrow and the vertex moves down. **39.** 260

3.2 Exercise Set B (pp. 67–68)

1. a. opens up **b.** $(4, -9)$ **c.** $x = 4$

3. a. opens down **b.** $(3, 0)$ **c.** $x = 3$

11.

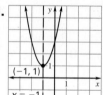

$(-1, 1)$
$x = -1$

13.

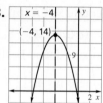

$x = -4$
$(-4, 14)$
9

15.

$\left(2, -\frac{5}{3}\right)$
$x = 2$

17.

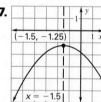

$(-1.5, -1.25)$
$x = -1.5$

19.

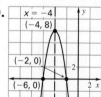

$x = -4$
$(-4, 8)$
$(-2, 0)$
$(-6, 0)$

21.

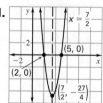

$x = \frac{7}{2}$
$(5, 0)$
$(2, 0)$
$\left(\frac{7}{2}, -\frac{27}{4}\right)$

23.

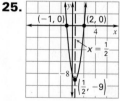

$\left(\frac{11}{5}, 0\right)$
$\left(\frac{2}{5}, 0\right)$
$x = \frac{13}{10}$
$\left(\frac{13}{10}, -\frac{81}{20}\right)$

25.

$(-1, 0)$ $(2, 0)$
$x = \frac{1}{2}$
-8
$\left(\frac{1}{2}, -9\right)$

27. $y = 3x^2 - 6x + 8$ **29.** $y = \frac{4}{3}x^2 - \frac{16}{3}x + \frac{1}{3}$

31. $y = 3x^2 + \frac{11}{2}x + \frac{3}{2}$ **33.** minimum, -3

35. minimum, $-\frac{4}{5}$ **37.** minimum, -9

39. $p = 4\left(n + \frac{1}{2}\right)\left(n + \frac{3}{2}\right)$ **41.** higher

3.3 Exercise Set A (p. 72)

1. increases over the interval $x > \frac{5}{4}$ and decreases over the interval $x < \frac{5}{4}$

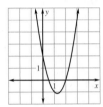

3. increases over the interval $x < 1$ and decreases over the interval $x > 1$

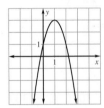

5. decrease   **7.** increase   **9.** -4 **11.** -8 **13.** 2

15. The average rate of change of $y = -x^2 - 5x - 2$ is -7 on the interval $0 \le x \le 2$. The average rate of change of $y = -\frac{1}{4}x^2 + 2$ is $-\frac{1}{2}$ on the interval $0 \le x \le 2$. The average rate of change of the first function is 14 times as great as the average rate of change of the second function on the given interval.

17. $0 \le x \le 22.5$; 0.5625

3.3 Exercise Set B (p. 73)

1. increases over the interval $x < 1$ and decreases over the interval $x > 1$

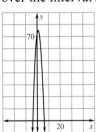

3. increase   **5.** increase   **7.** 5   **9.** -3 **11.** 3

13. The average rate of change of $y = \frac{1}{2}x^2 - 2$ is $-\frac{5}{2}$ on the interval $-5 \le x \le 0$. The average rate of change of $y = \frac{1}{10}x^2 + x - 2$ is $\frac{1}{2}$ on the interval $-5 \le x \le 0$. The average rate of change of the first function is negative and represents an interval of decrease. The average rate of change of the second function is positive and represents an interval of increase.

15. a.

x	0	400	800	1200	1600	2000
y	250	142	98	118	202	350

b.

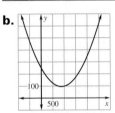

c. As the 200 unit interval moves to the right, the average rate of change increases.

3.4 Exercise Set A (p. 76)

1. $(x - 3)(x + 7)$ **3.** $(x + 2)(x + 4)$
5. $(x - 4)(x + 3)$ **7.** $(x - 4)(x - 5)$
9. $(x - 3)(x + 3)$ **11.** $(x - 4)(x - 7)$
13. $(x - 4)(x + 8)$ **15.** $(x - 5)(x + 5)$
17. $(x - 10)(x + 10)$ **19.** $-3, 2$ **21.** $2, 3$
23. $-4, -3$ **25.** $-6, 6$ **27.** $2, 9$ **29.** $1, 6$
31. $-5, -3$ **33.** $-5, 7$ **35.** $-9, -1$ **37.** $3, 9$
39. -8 **41.** 10 ft

3.4 Exercise Set B (p. 77)

1. $(x - 3)(x + 4)$ **3.** $(x - 7)(x - 5)$
5. $(x + 3)(x + 3)$ **7.** $(x - 4)(x + 6)$
9. $(x - 13)(x + 13)$ **11.** $(x + 7)(x + 14)$
13. $2, 8$ **15.** $-9, 8$ **17.** $9, 11$ **19.** $-7, 3$
21. $-5, 4$ **23.** $3, 6$ **25.** $-3, -1$ **27.** -8
29. $-7, -1$ **31.** $-7, 11$ **33.** $-17, 17$
35. $4x(x - 5)(x + 5)$ **37.** \$340

39. a. $x^2 + 6x + 5$ **b.** $(x + 5)(x + 1)$; each factor represents the length of a side of the rectangle

c.

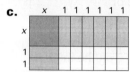

3.5 Exercise Set A (p. 80)

1. $(3x - 2)(x + 4)$ **3.** $(2x + 1)(2x + 1)$

5. $(4x - 3)(x + 2)$ **7.** $(3x + 2)(3x + 2)$

9. $2(3x - 1)(3x + 1)$ **11.** $(5x - 4)(3x + 4)$

13. $3(4x - 1)(x - 3)$ **15.** $2(5x - 6)(2x - 3)$

17. $(-12x + 11)(x + 1)$ **19.** $-2, \dfrac{1}{2}$ **21.** $\dfrac{1}{2}, \dfrac{3}{2}$

23. $\dfrac{1}{4}, \dfrac{1}{2}$ **25.** $-\dfrac{5}{3}, -\dfrac{2}{3}$ **27.** $0, \dfrac{3}{7}$ **29.** $-\dfrac{2}{3}, 0$

31. $2, 3$ **33.** $-\dfrac{8}{11}, 1$ **35.** 2 **37.** 0.375 ft

3.5 Exercise Set B (p. 81)

1. $(4x - 3)(x - 3)$ **3.** $(5x + 2)(2x + 5)$

5. $-3(2x - 3)(2x + 3)$ **7.** $-3(5x + 4)(x - 1)$

9. cannot factor **11.** $3x^2(4x - 3)(2x + 3)$

13. $(x^2 + 9)(x - 3)(x + 3)$

15. $3(2x^2 - 1)(x - 1)(x + 1)$

17. $1, \dfrac{5}{2}$ **19.** $-1, \dfrac{1}{6}$ **21.** $-\dfrac{3}{2}, \dfrac{7}{9}$ **23.** $-\dfrac{3}{4}, \dfrac{5}{7}$

25. $1, 2$ **27.** $\dfrac{2}{3}, \dfrac{7}{5}$ **29.** 10

3.6 Exercise Set A (p. 84)

1. $\dfrac{\sqrt{66}}{11}$ **3.** $\dfrac{2\sqrt{39}}{13}$ **5.** $8\sqrt{3}$ **7.** $\dfrac{\sqrt{14}}{7}$ **9.** $\sqrt{10}$

11. $\dfrac{-15 - 3\sqrt{11}}{7}$ **13.** ±17 **15.** ±16 **17.** $\pm4\sqrt{3}$

19. $\pm\sqrt{14}$ **21.** ±2 **23.** $3 \pm 2\sqrt{2}$ **25.** $-\dfrac{3}{4}, \dfrac{13}{4}$

27. $-8 \pm 3\sqrt{11}$ **29.** 4.33 sec **31.** 6.57 sec

33. 10 sec **35.** 6.63

3.6 Exercise Set B (p. 85)

1. $\dfrac{\sqrt{210}}{21}$ **3.** $\sqrt{5}$ **5.** $\dfrac{7\sqrt{10}}{20}$ **7.** $\dfrac{1}{3}$ **9.** $\dfrac{\sqrt{55}}{3}$

11. $\dfrac{-29 + 11\sqrt{7}}{3}$ **13.** ±18 **15.** $\pm13i$ **17.** $\pm3\sqrt{2}$

19. $\pm3i$ **21.** $-5 \pm 4i$ **23.** $\dfrac{9 \pm \sqrt{5}}{9}$ **25.** $\dfrac{2}{9} \pm \dfrac{\sqrt{2}}{2}$

27. $-3 \pm \dfrac{\sqrt{42}}{6}$ **29.** $a > -3$ **31.** $a < 4$ **33.** $a < 0$

35. The equation has two solutions; $x^2 = 64$, $x = \pm8$.

3.7 Exercise Set A (p. 88)

1. $-7, -1$ **3.** $-1, 13$ **5.** $-\dfrac{5}{2}, \dfrac{7}{2}$ **7.** $-\dfrac{2}{3}, \dfrac{4}{3}$

9. $-\dfrac{2}{3} \pm \dfrac{\sqrt{5}}{3}$ **11.** $121; (x - 11)^2$ **13.** $\dfrac{9}{4}; \left(x + \dfrac{3}{2}\right)^2$

15. $4; (3x - 2)^2$ **17.** $5 \pm \sqrt{15}$ **19.** $-3 \pm i$

21. $-6 \pm \sqrt{22}$ **23.** $-\dfrac{5}{2}$ **25.** $-1, 3$

27. $y = (x - 4)^2 - 6; (4, -6)$

29. $y = 3\left(x - \dfrac{3}{2}\right)^2 + \dfrac{45}{4}; \left(\dfrac{3}{2}, \dfrac{45}{4}\right)$ **31.** 8

3.7 Exercise Set B (p. 89)

1. $-\dfrac{2}{3}, 2$ **3.** $\dfrac{3}{5}, -\dfrac{11}{15}$ **5.** $-0.7 \pm \sqrt{3}$

7. $-4 \pm \sqrt{17}$ **9.** $\dfrac{3}{2} \pm \dfrac{\sqrt{37}}{2}$ **11.** -2

13. $4 \pm \sqrt{7}$ **15.** $-\dfrac{5}{2} \pm \dfrac{3}{2}i$

17. $1 \pm \dfrac{\sqrt{34}}{2}i$ **19.** $y = (x + 6)^2 - 30; (-6, -30)$

21. $y = -2\left(x - \dfrac{3}{2}\right)^2 + \dfrac{3}{2}; \left(\dfrac{3}{2}, \dfrac{3}{2}\right)$

23. a. $y = -0.025(x - 9)^2 + 4.025$

b.

x	0	2	4	6	8	10	12
y	2	2.8	3.4	3.8	4	4	3.8

x	14	16	18	20
y	3.4	2.8	2	1

c.

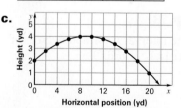

The maximum height is 4.025 yards and the distance traveled is about 22 yds.

25. -160 ft/sec

3.8 Exercise Set A (p. 93)

1. 4; two real   **3.** 0; one real

5. -15; two imaginary   **7.** $-2 \pm \sqrt{6}$

9. 0, 2   **11.** $\frac{1}{2}$ **13.** $-0.13, 1.25$

15. $-4, 6$ **17.** $\frac{3}{2}, 3$ **19.** $-\frac{1}{2}, \frac{2}{5}$

21. No. The area of the room is $x(10 - x)$ and can be expressed as $x(10 - x) = 28$ which has no real solutions.   **23.** 2 sec   **25.** 5 sec

3.8 Exercise Set B (p. 94)

1. 20; two real   **3.** 1; two real   **5.** 33; two real

7. $-\frac{5}{2} \pm \frac{\sqrt{33}}{2}$ **9.** $-10 \pm 2\sqrt{29}$ **11.** $-\frac{1}{2}, 3$

13. $-\frac{1}{10} \pm \frac{\sqrt{19}}{10}i$ **15.** $0.44, -1.36$

17. $-0.34, 1.08$ **19.** $b = \pm 4$ **21.** no solution

23. $c < \frac{25}{8}$ **25.** 45 mi/h   **27.** $h = -16t^2 + 220$

29. 1st object: 4.57 sec; 2nd object: 3.71 sec; 3rd object: 3.27 sec

3.9 Exercise Set A (pp. 98–99)

1. not a solution   **3.** solution

11. 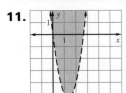   **13.**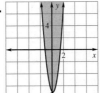

15.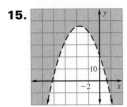

17. The parabola should be a solid line.

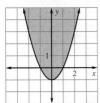

23. 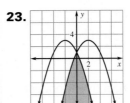   **25.**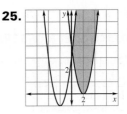

27.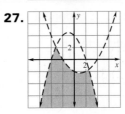

29. $x < -\frac{2}{3}$ or $x > 5$ **31.** $x \le -5$ or $x \ge 6$

33. $-3 \le x \le 6$ **35.** $2.92 < x < 57.08$

3.9 Exercise Set B (pp. 100–101)

5. 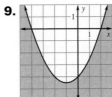   **7.**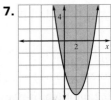

9. 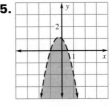   **11.**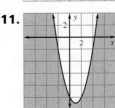

19. 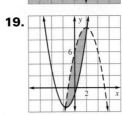   **21.**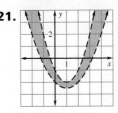

23. all real numbers   **25.** no solution

27. $\frac{5}{3} < x < 10$ **29.** $-\frac{2}{3} \le x \le \frac{7}{5}$ **31.** $\frac{3}{4} < x < \frac{6}{5}$

33. $3 \le x \le 8$ **35.** $x < 3$ or $x > 4$

37.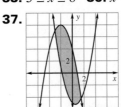

39. $4\sqrt{6}$ square units

UNIT 4

4.1 Exercise Set A (p. 110)

1. 256; product of powers

3. $\dfrac{1}{16,384}$; product of powers, negative exponent

5. $\dfrac{1}{256}$; quotient of powers, negative exponent

7. The exponents should be subtracted, not divided; x^8.

9. 1.342×10^{12} **11.** 1.054×10^{-2}

13. 2.025×10^9 **15.** 3.73248×10^{-7}

17. 3.5×10^{-15} **19.** y^{11}; quotient of powers

21. $\dfrac{1}{w^{10}}$; power of a product, power of a power, zero exponent, negative exponent

23. $\dfrac{16m^7}{n^3}$; product of powers, negative exponent

25. $\dfrac{h^9}{125g^{12}}$; power of a product, power of a power, negative exponent

27. $4q^3r$; quotient of powers

29. $\dfrac{4f^3}{9e^5}$; quotient of powers, negative exponent

31. $V = \dfrac{4}{3}\pi x^4$ **33.** 1.032×10^{11}

4.1 Exercise Set B (p. 111)

1. 25; product of powers

3. 1024; power of a power, quotient of powers

5. $\dfrac{64}{27}$; power of a quotient, negative exponent

7. $\dfrac{512}{19,683}$; zero exponent, quotient of powers, power of a quotient

9. 2.139×10^5 **11.** 1.6×10^5 **13.** 1.0×10^{-6}

15. x^6; product of powers, quotient of powers, zero exponent

17. $\dfrac{45c^{13}}{d^5}$; power of a power, quotient of powers, negative exponent

19. $\dfrac{9}{x^{14}y^2}$; quotient of powers, power of a quotient, power of a power, negative exponent

21. $\dfrac{1}{z^{12}}$; power of a power, negative exponent

23. *Sample answer:* $a^4b^4c^5$

25. *Sample answer:* $16m^6n^{17}$ **27. a.** $\dfrac{2}{3}$ **b.** $\dfrac{\pi}{6}$

c. *Sample answer:* The designer should choose the package shaped like a cube. There is more empty air space around the ornament to offer more protection from damage. Also, the cubes would fit more efficiently in a box for shipping.

4.2 Exercise Set A (p. 114)

1. $6x^5 + 2$ **3.** $-5x^5 + 5$ **5.** $-11x^5 + 3$

7. $-12x^6$ **9.** $-3x^7$ **11.** $\dfrac{x}{4}$ **13.** $\dfrac{3x + 9}{x + 1}$

15. $x + 8$ **17.** $x + 4$ **19.** all real numbers

21. all real numbers except $x = -3$

23. all real numbers **25.** $f(x) = x - 200$

27. $g(f(x)) = 0.8x - 160$

29. pay less with discount first

4.2 Exercise Set B (p. 115)

1. $2x^3 - x^2 + x - 4$ **3.** $4x^3 - 5x^2 + x + 1$

5. $-\dfrac{3}{x} - \dfrac{3}{x^3}$ **7.** -3 **9.** $\dfrac{2}{x^4} - \dfrac{1}{x^2}$; all real numbers except $x = 0$ **11.** $\dfrac{2x^2 - 7x + 5}{9}$; all real numbers

13. true **15.** true **17.** *Sample answer:* $f(x) = \sqrt{x}$, $g(x) = x + 1$

19. *Sample answer:* $f(x) = \dfrac{x + 1}{x^2}$, $g(x) = x - 1$

4.3 Exercise Set A (p. 118)

1. $y = \dfrac{1}{2}x - \dfrac{1}{2}$ **3.** $y = \dfrac{1}{6}x + \dfrac{1}{2}$ **5.** $y = \dfrac{3}{4} - \dfrac{3}{2}x$

7. Each term must be divided by 4; $x + 12 = 4y$, $\dfrac{x + 12}{4} = y$.

15.

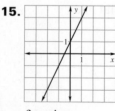

function

17.

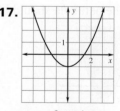

not a function

19.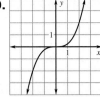

function

21. $C = \frac{5}{9}(F - 32)$; about 34.4°C

4.3 Exercise Set B (p. 119)

7. $f^{-1}(x) = \frac{3}{2} - \frac{1}{2}x$ **9.** $f^{-1}(x) = x^2 + 3, x \geq 0$

11. $f^{-1}(x) = \sqrt{\dfrac{x}{4}}$ **13.** $f^{-1}(x) = \dfrac{4}{3x + 1}$

15. $f^{-1}(x) = \dfrac{1}{2x}$

17.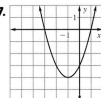

not a function

19. 548.64 U.S. dollars

21. $f(f(x)) = f\left(\dfrac{1}{x}\right) = \dfrac{1}{\left(\dfrac{1}{x}\right)} = x$

4.4 Exercise Set A (p. 122)

5. ; domain: all real numbers; range: $y > 1$

7. 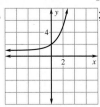 ; domain: all real numbers; range: $y > -3$

9. 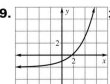 ; domain: all real numbers; range: $y > -2$

11. $f(x) \to 0$ as $x \to -\infty$ and $f(x) \to +\infty$ as $x \to +\infty$; y-intercept: $(0, 1)$; $\dfrac{65}{144}$ **13.** $3587.50

15. $3588.51   **17.** 1.0128; 1.28%

4.4 Exercise Set B (p. 123)

1. 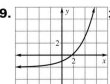 ; domain: all real numbers; range: $y > -3$

3. 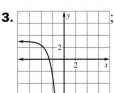 ; domain: all real numbers; range: $y < 3$

5. 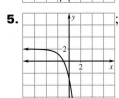 ; domain: all real numbers; range: $y < 2$

7. $\dfrac{255}{32}$

9. The power of $(x - 2)$ translates the graph 2 units to the right, not to the left.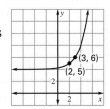

(3, 6)
(2, 5)

11. $8396.71   **13.** 2.13%   **15.** 19,726,093

4.5 Exercise Set A (p. 126)

1. exponential decay **3.** exponential decay

7. 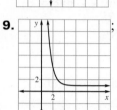 ; domain: all real numbers; range: $y > 2$

9. ; domain: all real numbers; range: $y > 1$

11. 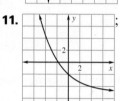 ; domain: all real numbers; range: $y > -5$

13. $f(x) \to 0$ as $x \to +\infty$ and $f(x) \to +\infty$ as $x \to -\infty$; y-intercept: $(0, 1)$; $-\dfrac{65}{144}$

15. $f(x) \to 0$ as $x \to +\infty$ and $f(x) \to -\infty$ as $x \to -\infty$; y-intercept: $(0, -2)$; $\dfrac{40}{9}$

17. \$9492.19 **19.** 5 years

4.5 Exercise Set B (p. 127)

1. exponential decay **3.** exponential growth
5. exponential decay

7. 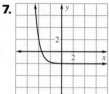 ; domain: all real numbers; range: $y > -2$

9. 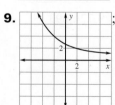 ; domain: all real numbers; range: $y > 1$

11. 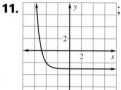 ; domain: all real numbers; range: $y > -3$

13. *Sample answer:* $y = (0.3)^x + 1$
15. $f(x) \to 0$ as $x \to +\infty$ and $f(x) \to +\infty$ as $x \to -\infty$; y-intercept: $(0, 1)$; $-\dfrac{2385}{784}$
17. The decay factor is $1 - r$, not r; $y = 100(0.96)^t$.
19. \$24,053.41 **21.** $V = 1600(0.80)^t$

4.6 Exercise Set A (p. 130)

1. 3 **3.** 2 **5.** 4 **7.** 2.5 **9.** $5\dfrac{1}{3}$

11. $x \le 5$ **13.** $x \ge 4$ **15.** $x \le 4$ **17.** 27

19. The solution is the x-coordinate 2, not 4.
21. *Sample answer:* $2^{3x} = 2^{2x + 4}$ **23.** 1999–2003

4.6 Exercise Set B (p. 131)

1. -3 **3.** $-\dfrac{8}{5}$ **5.** -2 **7.** 1 **9.** $-\dfrac{7}{5}$

11. $x \ge 7$ **13.** $x \le 2$ **15.** $x \ge \dfrac{19}{6}$ **17.** -9

19. 2 **21.** $x > -3$

23. a. **b.** 1 month **c.** $x = 1$

4.7 Exercise Set A (p. 135)

1. 7, 10, 15, 22, 31, 42 **3.** 9, 27, 81, 243, 729, 2187

5. $-\dfrac{4}{3}, -\dfrac{2}{3}, -\dfrac{4}{9}, -\dfrac{1}{3}, -\dfrac{4}{15}, -\dfrac{2}{9}$

7. $2^1, 2^2, 2^3, 2^4, \ldots; 32; a_n = 2^n$

9. $\dfrac{1}{1^2}, \dfrac{1}{2^2}, \dfrac{1}{3^2}, \dfrac{1}{4^2}, \ldots; \dfrac{1}{25}; a_n = \dfrac{1}{n^2}$

11. $2(1) + 1, 2(2) + 1, 2(3) + 1, 2(4) + 1, \ldots;$
11; $a_n = 2n + 1$ **13.** $0.6(1) + 0.1, 0.6(2) + 0.1,$
$0.6(3) + 0.1, 0.6(4) + 0.1, \ldots; 3.1; a_n = 0.6n + 0.1$

15. 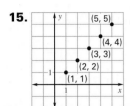 **17.**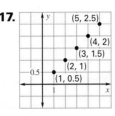

19. $\displaystyle\sum_{i=1}^{4}\frac{2i}{i+3}$ **21.** $\displaystyle\sum_{i=1}^{\infty}(5i-2)$ **23.** 50

25. The lower limit is zero, so the first term should be 4; $4 + 7 + 10 + 13 + 16 = 50$.

4.7 Exercise Set B (p. 136)

1. 4, 9, 16, 25, 36, 49 **3.** $\dfrac{1}{4}, \dfrac{4}{11}, \dfrac{3}{7}, \dfrac{8}{17}, \dfrac{1}{2}, \dfrac{12}{23}$

5. $7.7 - 1.1(1)$, $7.7 - 1.1(2)$, $7.7 - 1.1(3)$, $7.7 - 1.1(4)$, . . .; 2.2; $a_n = 7.7 - 1.1n$

7. 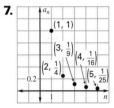 **9.**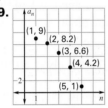

11. $\displaystyle\sum_{i=1}^{\infty}(-3)^i$ **13.** $\displaystyle\sum_{i=1}^{5}(2^i+1)$ **15.** $\displaystyle\sum_{i=1}^{4}\frac{2^i}{3^i}$ **17.** $\dfrac{1523}{630}$

19. true; $\displaystyle\sum_{i=1}^{n}(a_i + k) = (a_1 + k) + (a_2 + k) +$
$(a_3 + k) + \cdots + (a_n + k) =$
$(a_1 + a_2 + a_3 + \cdots + a_n) + nk = nk + \displaystyle\sum_{i=1}^{n} a_i$

21. a. $a_n = 60(0.9)^n$ **b.** 5 **c.** $60 + 2\displaystyle\sum_{i=1}^{\infty}60(0.9)^n$

4.8 Exercise Set A (p. 140)

1. yes; Each difference is -7.

3. no; Differences are not constant.

5. no; Differences are not constant.

7. $a_n = 6n - 10$; 50 **9.** $a_n = \dfrac{1}{2} - \dfrac{1}{4}n$; -2

11. $a_n = 14n - 40$ **13.** $a_n = -5 - n$

15. $a_n = \dfrac{n}{4} + 2$ **17.** 100 **19.** -210

21. $a_n = n - 2$ **23.** $a_n = -\dfrac{n}{2} + 5$

4.8 Exercise Set B (p. 141)

1. no; Differences are not constant.

3. yes; Each difference is -35.

5. $a_n = 59 - 14n$; -249 **7.** $a_n = 242 - 11n$; 0

9. $a_n = 46 + 3.8n$; 129.6 **11.** $a_n = 47 - 13n$

13. $a_n = -0.2 + 7.2n$ **15.** $a_n = \dfrac{3}{5} + \dfrac{2}{5}n$

17. yes; Each pair of terms yields a common difference of 3. **19.** 112 **21.** 28 **23.** -45
25. 9 **27.** 11

4.9 Exercise Set A (p. 145)

1. no; The ratios are different.

3. yes; Each ratio is $\dfrac{1}{2}$. **5.** yes; Each ratio is $\dfrac{3}{1}$.

7. $a_n = 2(3)^{n-1}$; 486;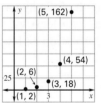

9. $a_n = 32\left(-\dfrac{1}{2}\right)^{n-1}$; -1;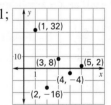

11. r and a_1 are switched around in the formula; $a_n = a_1 r^{n-1}$, $a_n = 4(3)^{n-1}$. **13.** $a_n = 6(2)^{n-1}$

15. $a_n = 4\left(\dfrac{1}{2}\right)^{n-1}$ **17.** $a_n = -3\left(\dfrac{2}{3}\right)^{n-1}$

19. $\dfrac{32{,}800}{243}$ **21.** 236,192 **23.** $\dfrac{255{,}875}{64}$

4.9 Exercise Set B (p. 146)

1. no; Ratios are not constant.

3. no; Ratios are not constant.

5. $a_n = 3.125(3.2)^{n-1}$; 1048.576

7. $a_n = 35\left(-\dfrac{1}{5}\right)^{n-1}$; $-\dfrac{7}{625}$

9. $a_n = -\dfrac{34}{3}\left(-\dfrac{2}{3}\right)^{n-1}$; $\dfrac{1088}{729}$

11. $a_n = \dfrac{3}{8}(-2)^{n-1}$; 6 **13.** $a_n = \dfrac{1}{64}\left(\dfrac{4}{3}\right)^{n-1}$; $\dfrac{4}{81}$

15. $a_n = -\frac{36}{7}\left(\frac{7}{3}\right)^{n-1}; -\frac{1372}{9}$

17. $a_n = -459\left(\frac{1}{3}\right)^{n-1}$ **19.** $a_n = \frac{1}{20}(10)^{n-1}$

21. $a_n = -\frac{64}{27}\left(-\frac{3}{2}\right)^{n-1}$ **23.** 9831

25. $\frac{1093}{9}$ **27.** -294.752

29. $a_n = 66(0.8)^n$; about 17.3 in.

UNIT 5

5.1 Exercise Set A (pp. 153–154)

1. $6\sqrt{2}$ **3.** 9   **5.** $4\sqrt{2}$ **7.** $x = 10\sqrt{3}, y = 15$
9. $x = 6\sqrt{3}, y = 12\sqrt{3}$

11. The length of the hypotenuse was incorrectly calculated as leg $\cdot$ leg $\cdot \sqrt{2} = \sqrt{7} \cdot \sqrt{7} \cdot \sqrt{2} = 7\sqrt{2}$. The correct solution is: Hypotenuse = leg $\cdot \sqrt{2} = \sqrt{7} \cdot \sqrt{2} = \sqrt{14}$

13.

a	9	$3\sqrt{3}$	5	11	8
b	$9\sqrt{3}$	9	$5\sqrt{3}$	$11\sqrt{3}$	$8\sqrt{3}$
c	18	$6\sqrt{3}$	10	22	16

15. $n = 30, p = 15, q = 15\sqrt{3}$
17. $a = 4\sqrt{3}, b = 2\sqrt{3}$
19. $f = 8\sqrt{3}, g = 8, h = 8\sqrt{2}$
21. neither   **23. a.** $x = y = 12\sqrt{2}$ ft   **b.** 1188 ft^2

5.1 Exercise Set B (pp. 155–156)

1. $x = 8\sqrt{3}, y = 12$ **3.** $x = \frac{15}{2}, y = \frac{5\sqrt{3}}{2}$

5. $x = 5\sqrt{3}, y = 10$ **7.** $x = 24\sqrt{3}, y = 36$

9. $x = \frac{16\sqrt{3}}{3}, y = \frac{32\sqrt{3}}{3}$ **11.** $x = 9\sqrt{2}, y = 9$

15. 72 in.^{2} **17.** 13.0 m   **19.** 5600.3 ft
21. more   **23.** 39.0 ft

5.2 Exercise Set A (pp. 159–160)

1. $\tan A \approx 1.6071, \tan B \approx 0.6222$
3. $\tan A = 0.75, \tan B \approx 1.3333$ **5.** 20.2

7. Smaller triangle: $\tan X = \frac{4}{3}, \tan Y = \frac{3}{4}$;

Larger triangle: $\tan X = \frac{8}{6} = \frac{4}{3}, \tan Y = \frac{6}{8} = \frac{3}{4}$;

The $\tan X$ and $\tan Y$ of the similar triangles are equivalent.

9. 12; 12; They are the same.   **11.** 8.3   **13.** 22.5
15. 180.0 ft^2 **17.** 145.2 in.   **19.** 215.5 ft   **21.** 80 ft

5.2 Exercise Set B (pp. 161–162)

1. 10.2   **3.** 17.1   **5.** 64.2

7. Smaller triangle: $\tan X = \frac{12}{9} = \frac{4}{3}, \tan Y = \frac{9}{12} = \frac{3}{4}$;

Larger triangle: $\tan X = \frac{36}{27} = \frac{4}{3}, \tan Y = \frac{27}{36} = \frac{3}{4}$;

The $\tan X$ and $\tan Y$ of the similar triangles are equivalent.

9. $4\sqrt{6}; 4\sqrt{6}$; They are the same.   **11.** 12.7
13. 17.7   **15.** about 51.96 in.

17. a. $\tan 30° = \frac{\text{opp.}}{\text{adj.}}; \tan 30° = \frac{5\sqrt{3}}{x}$;

$x = \frac{5\sqrt{3}}{\tan 30°}; x \approx \frac{5\sqrt{3}}{0.5774}; x \approx 15.0$ **b.** longer leg =

shorter leg $\cdot \sqrt{3}; x = 5\sqrt{3} \cdot \sqrt{3}; x = 15$
19. 84.5 ft   **21.** $h = x(\tan 62°)$;
$h = (x + 16)(\tan 45°)$ **23.** 875 ft

5.3 Exercise Set A (pp. 166–167)

1. $\sin R = \frac{3}{5} = 0.6, \sin S = \frac{4}{5} = 0.8$

3. $\sin R = \frac{8}{17} \approx 0.4706, \sin S = \frac{15}{17} \approx 0.8824$

5. $\sin R = \frac{28}{53} \approx 0.5283, \sin S = \frac{45}{53} \approx 0.8491$

7. $\cos A = \frac{12}{13} \approx 0.9231, \cos B = \frac{5}{13} \approx 0.3846$

9. $\cos A = \frac{4}{5} = 0.8, \cos B = \frac{3}{5} = 0.6$

11. $\cos A = \frac{48}{73} \approx 0.6575, \cos B = \frac{55}{73} \approx 0.7534$

13. $\sin X = \dfrac{28}{53}$, $\sin Y = \dfrac{45}{53}$, $\cos X = \dfrac{45}{53}$, $\cos Y = \dfrac{28}{53}$;

$\sin X = \cos Y$ and $\cos X = \sin Y$

15. $a \approx 9.1$, $b \approx 16.7$ **17.** $r \approx 28.9$, $s \approx 35.7$

19. $\sin 45° = \dfrac{\sqrt{2}}{2}$, $\cos 45° = \dfrac{\sqrt{2}}{2}$

21. $AB = 65$, $\sin A = \dfrac{33}{65} \approx 0.5077$,

$\cos A = \dfrac{56}{65} \approx 0.8615$

23. $AB = 8$, $\sin A = \dfrac{\sqrt{7}}{4} \approx 0.6614$,

$\cos A = \dfrac{3}{4} = 0.75$

25. 2178 ft

5.3 Exercise Set B (pp. 168–169)

1. $\sin R = \dfrac{72}{97} \approx 0.7423$, $\sin S = \dfrac{65}{97} \approx 0.6701$

3. $\sin R = \dfrac{91}{109} \approx 0.8349$, $\sin S = \dfrac{60}{109} \approx 0.5505$

5. $\cos A = \dfrac{51}{149} \approx 0.3423$, $\cos B = \dfrac{140}{149} \approx 0.9396$

7. $\sin X = \dfrac{14}{50} = \dfrac{7}{25}$, $\sin Y = \dfrac{48}{50} = \dfrac{24}{25}$,

$\cos X = \dfrac{48}{50} = \dfrac{24}{25}$, $\cos Y = \dfrac{14}{50} = \dfrac{7}{25}$,

$\sin X = \cos Y$ and $\sin Y = \cos X$

9. $a \approx 16.6$, $b \approx 27.5$ **11.** $e \approx 3.1$, $f \approx 4.3$

15. $AC = 20$, $\sin A = \dfrac{6\sqrt{61}}{61} \approx 0.7682$,

$\cos A = \dfrac{5\sqrt{61}}{61} \approx 0.6402$

17. $a \sin B$ **19. a.** about 16.5 ft   **b.** 12 ft   **c.** 31 ft

5.4 Exercise Set A (pp. 174–175)

1. 16.6   **3.** 25°   **5.** $m\angle P \approx 58.6°$, $m\angle N \approx 31.4°$,
$PN \approx 21.1$ **7.** $m\angle V = 39°$, $DM \approx 11.3$, $DV \approx 18.0$
9. $UM \approx 20.6$, $m\angle U \approx 42.7°$, $m\angle E \approx 47.3°$
11. $m\angle V = 70°$, $VW \approx 4.1$, $WX \approx 11.3$
13. The student incorrectly used WY, the length of the opposite side, in place of the length of the hypotenuse in the inverse sine ratio. The correct statement is $\sin^{-1} \dfrac{6}{WX} = 36°$.

15. 21.1°   **17.** 15.7°   **19.** 22.8°
21. 70.1°   **23.** about 84.02 ft

25. about 191.5 in. or about 15 ft 11.5 in.;
about 4.2°; Yes, the angle is less than 4.78°.

27. about 1648.5 ft

5.4 Exercise Set B (pp. 176–177)

1. $m\angle A = 51.9°$

3. $m\angle A = 11.5°$

5. $m\angle P \approx 59.7°$, $m\angle N \approx 30.3°$, $PN \approx 13.9$

7. $m\angle V = 73°$, $WX \approx 32.5$, $WV \approx 9.9$

9. $UM \approx 17.2$, $m\angle U \approx 17.1°$, $m\angle E \approx 72.9°$

11. $MD \approx 20.6$, $VD \approx 23.2$, $m\angle V = 62.8°$

13. $m\angle A \approx 9.2°$ **15.** $m\angle A \approx 75.9°$

17. $m\angle A \approx 83.2°$ **19.** $m\angle A \approx 26.1°$

21. $m\angle A = 45°$ **23.** $m\angle A \approx 5.2°$ **25.** 33 yd

27. 463 ft   **29.** 400 ft

UNIT 6

6.1 Exercise Set A (pp. 186–187)

1. a. chord   **b.** tangent   **c.** radius   **d.** diameter
e. secant   **f.** tangent

3. *Sample answer:*

5. true   **7.** false

9. *Sample answer:*

11. *Sample answer:*

13. 117   **15.** 24   **17.** 16   **19.** 3, –3
21. 14 ft   **23.** 60 ft

25.

$\overline{SR} \perp \overline{SP}$ and $\overline{TR} \perp \overline{TQ}$	Theorem 6.1
$m\angle PSR = 90°$ and $m\angle QTR = 90°$	Defn. $\perp$
$\angle PSR \cong \angle QTR$	Defn. $\cong \angle$
$\angle PRS \cong \angle QRT$	Reflexive
$\triangle PSR \cong \triangle QTR$	AA Similarity
$\dfrac{QT}{PS} = \dfrac{RT}{RS}$	Corresp. side lengths are proportional

6.1 Exercise Set B (pp. 188–189)

1. point of tangency **3.** radius **5.** center

7. secant **9.** All three circles have a diameter of 4 and radius of 2. **11.** the lines $y = 4$, $x = 2$, $x = 6$

13. *Sample answer:*

15. *Sample answer:*

17. no; $\overline{AB}$ is not $\perp$ to $\overline{BC}$.

19. no; By the Converse of the Pythagorean Thm., $\overline{AB}$ is *not* $\perp$ to $\overline{BC}$. **21.** $4\sqrt{5} - 4$ **23.** 4 **25.** 11.25

27. a. *Sample answer:* Because a tangent line is perpendicular to the radius drawn to the point of tangency, $\overline{QR} \perp \overline{RS}$ and $\overline{RS} \perp \overline{SP}$. Because $\overline{QT} \perp \overline{SP}$ is given, $\overline{QT} \parallel \overline{RS}$ (in a plane, 2 lines perpendicular to the same line are parallel), which implies $\overline{QT} \perp \overline{QR}$ (if a transversal is $\perp$ to one of two parallel lines, then it is $\perp$ to the other). So, $QRST$ has four right angles. Therefore, by the Rectangle Corollary, $QRST$ is a rectangle. **b.** $6\sqrt{3}$ in. **c.** $60°$

6.2 Exercise Set A (pp. 193–194)

1. minor arc **3.** semicircle **5.** major arc

7. minor arc **9.** $42°$ **11.** $286°$ **13.** $318°$

15. $222°$ **17.** $138°$ **19.** $7\sqrt{2}$ **21.** $135°$ **23.** $225°$

25. $325°$ **27.** $215°$ **29.** $180°$ **31.** $345°$ **33.** yes

35. no **37.** $15°$ **39.** $170°$

6.2 Exercise Set B (pp. 195–196)

1. minor arc; $73°$ **3.** semicircle; $180°$

5. minor arc; $81°$ **7.** minor arc; $73°$

9. major arc; $287°$ **11.** major arc; $279°$

13. $154°$ **15.** $120°$ **17.** 2 **19.** $44°$ **21.** $224°$

23. $136°$ **25.** $133°$ **27.** $227°$ **29.** $227°$

31. You can tell that the circles are congruent because they have the same radius $\overline{AB}$.

33. no; One circle is smaller than the other, so the arcs cannot be $\cong$. **35.** yes; Because $m\overset{\frown}{AC} = m\overset{\frown}{BD}$, you can use the Addition Prop. of Equality to deduce that $\overset{\frown}{AB} \cong \overset{\frown}{CD}$.

37. no; One circle is smaller than the other, so the arcs cannot be $\cong$. **39.** $327.3°$ **41.** $196.4°$

6.3 Exercise Set A (pp. 201–202)

1. $122°$ **3.** 22 **5.** $80°$ **7.** 1 **9.** 4 **11.** 4

13. $\overline{PQ}$ and $\overline{RS}$ are equidistant from the center of the circle so they are congruent by Theorem 6.8. Because they are congruent, they must have the same length.

15. Given; $\overline{PT} \cong \overline{QS}$; Definition of radius; SSS Congruence Postulate

17. *Sample answer:* Yes, the two points are the same. Because X, Y, and Z are noncollinear, there is only one point that is equidistant from them which is the center of the circle that contains X, Y, and Z.

6.3 Exercise Set B (pp. 203–204)

1. $\overset{\frown}{AB} \cong \overset{\frown}{DC}$; In the same circle, two minor arcs are $\cong$ if their corresponding chords are $\cong$.

3. $\overline{AD} \cong \overline{BD}$; If a diameter of a circle is $\perp$ to a chord, then it bisects the chord.

5. 5 **7.** $60°$ **9.** $105°$ **11.** $106°$ **13.** $48°$ **15.** $70°$

23. *Sample answer:* Because three points determine a plane, let P be the plane that contains X, Y, and Z. Let line j be the perpendicular bisector of $\overline{XY}$ in P, and let line k be the perpendicular bisector of $\overline{YZ}$ in P. Because X, Y, and Z are noncollinear points, $\overline{XY}$ and $\overline{YZ}$ are not collinear nor parallel. Then j and k are not parallel either, which means that j and k intersect in some point C. By the Perpendicular Bisector Thm., $CX = CY$, and $CY = CZ$. Therefore, the circle centered at C with radius $\overline{CY}$ contains X, Y, and Z.

25. no; The top board bisects the two boards it rests on whose inside edges form $\cong$ 10-foot chords. However, the top board is not perpendicular to the other boards, so it does not lie on a diameter of the pool. Therefore, the center of the top board is not the center of the pool.

6.4 Exercise Set A (pp. 207–208)

3. $140°$ **5.** $63°$ **7.** $123°$ **9.** $42°$ **11.** $48°$

13. $42°$ **15.** $180°$ **17.** $x = 58$, $y = 29$

19. $x = 39$, $y = 29$ **21.** $x = 6$, $y = 36.5$

23. $\angle AED \cong \angle BEC$; Theorem 6.10; Angle-Angle Similarity Postulate

6.4 Exercise Set B (pp. 209–210)

1. $74°$ **3.** $126°$ **5.** $132°$ **7.** $32°$ **9.** $120°$

11. $42.5°$ **13.** $42.5°$ **15.** $48.5°$ **17.** $180°$

19. no **21.** $x = 7$ **23.** $x = 23.25$

25. $w = 65$, $x = 66$, $y = 115$, $z = 114$

27. *Sample answer:* Draw $\overline{DG}$. Because $\overline{DF}$ is a diameter, $\angle DGF$ is a right angle inscribed in $\odot C$. Then $\overline{DG} \perp \overline{FG}$ and $\angle DGF \cong \angle DGE$, because perpendicular lines intersect to form four right angles. It is given that $\overline{FG} \cong \overline{GE}$ and by the Reflexive Property, $\overline{DG} \cong \overline{DG}$. Then by SAS, $\triangle DGF \cong \triangle DGE$, and corresponding parts of $\cong$ triangles are $\cong$, so $\overline{DF} \cong \overline{DE}$. Therefore, $\triangle DEF$ is isosceles by definition.

29. The measures of the arcs add up to 370°; change the measure of $\angle A$ to 45° or change the measure of $\overset{\frown}{AC}$ to 80°.

6.5 Exercise Set A (pp. 214–215)

1. $202°$ **3.** $240°$ **5.** $128°$ **7.** $63°$ **9.** $133°$

11. $42°$ **13.** 67 **15.** 61 **17.** 7

19. $m\angle 1 = 97°$, $m\angle 2 = 83°$, $m\angle 3 = 63°$, $m\angle 4 = 117°$

21. $30°$ **23.** $60°$ **25.** $60°$ **27.** 43 **29.** about $5.6°$

6.5 Exercise Set B (pp. 216–217)

1. $57.5°$ **3.** $40°$ **5.** $63°$ **7.** $180°$

9. $56°$ **11.** 37 **13.** 8 **15.** $20°$

17. *Sample answer:* Because it is given that m is tangent to both circles at T, $m\overset{\frown}{TU} = 2m\angle KTU = m\overset{\frown}{TV}$. Then $m\overset{\frown}{TWU} = 360° - 2m\angle KTU = m\overset{\frown}{TXV}$. Because $m\angle TJU = \frac{1}{2}\left(m\overset{\frown}{TWU} - m\overset{\frown}{TU}\right)$ and $m\angle TKV = \frac{1}{2}\left(m\overset{\frown}{TXV} - m\overset{\frown}{TV}\right)$, the Substitution and Transitive Properties of Equality can be used to show $m\angle TJU = m\angle TKV$.

19. a.

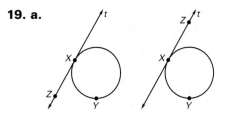

b. $m\overset{\frown}{XY} = 2m\angle YXZ$; $m\overset{\frown}{XY} = 2(180 - m\angle YXZ)$

c. when $\overset{\frown}{XY}$ is perpendicular to line t at point X

6.6 Exercise Set A (pp. 220–221)

1. 15 **3.** 4 **5.** $AB = 21$, $DE = 23$ **7.** 5

9. 7 **11.** $RT = 35$, $TV = 45$ **13.** 15 **15.** 4

17. 30 **19.** 4 **21.** 10 **23.** 4

25. $\angle MPN \cong \angle SPR$ by the Vertical Angles Theorem. Use Theorem 6.18 to find $QS = 2$. Use Theorem 6.16 to find $PR = 2\sqrt{30}$. Then $\frac{MP}{SP} = \frac{6}{12} = \frac{1}{2}$ and $\frac{NP}{RP} = \frac{\sqrt{30}}{2\sqrt{30}} = \frac{1}{2}$. Therefore, $\triangle MNP \sim \triangle SRP$ by the Side-Angle-Side Triangle Similarity Theorem.

27. 140 in.

6.6 Exercise Set B (pp. 222–223)

1. 3.7 **3.** 7.4 **5.** 1 **7.** 14.3 **9.** 10 **11.** 6

13. Yes. First you must find the lengths of unlabeled segments of the shorter and longer chords, 4 and 3 respectively; $x = 26$ and $y = 39$. Note that the figure is not drawn to scale. **15.** 90°

17. *Sample answer:* By the Segments of Secants and Tangents Thm., $OP(OQ) = (OT)^2$ and $OR(OS) = (OT)^2$. Therefore, $OP(OQ) = OR(OS)$ by the Transitive Prop. of Equality.

19. a.

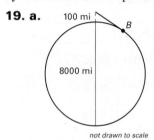

100 mi
B
8000 mi
not drawn to scale

b. The segment is the tangent from the satellite to Earth. **c.** 900 mi

6.7 Exercise Set A (pp. 226–227)

1. 50.27 ft **3.** 10.50 cm **5.** $\dfrac{39}{\pi}$ cm **7.** 54π ft

9. 47.12 in. **11.** 160° **13.** 19.55 m **15.** 280°

17. 114.02° **19.** 20.53 cm **21.** 138.56 in.

23. a. about 35.61 in. **b.** about 71 teeth

6.7 Exercise Set B (pp. 228–229)

1. about 35.81 cm **3.** about 14.96 in. **5.** $\dfrac{58}{\pi}$

7. 63.8π **9.** about 34.94 cm **11.** 259°

13. about 112.56 m **15.** 230.5°

17. about 50.82 cm **19.** about 36.25 ft

21. about 87.96 in. **23.** 17.1, 13.6, 79°, 143°, 12.04, 111.83 **25.** about 71.42 m; about 96.55 m

27. about 26.85 in.

6.8 Exercise Set A (pp. 232–233)

1. 36π in.²; 113.10 in.²

3. 153.76π cm²; 483.05 cm²

5. 9.61 m **7.** 20.88 yd **9.** 25.93 ft

11. 827.02 cm² and 1463.20 cm² **13.** 107.06 ft²

15. 6.83 m **17.** 60.94 in. **19.** 11.34 in.

21. 69.01 in. **23.** 199.11 in.² **25.** 37.70 ft²

27. 117.92 cm² **29. a.** 301.59 ft² **b.** 117.81 ft²

6.8 Exercise Set B (pp. 234–235)

1. $\dfrac{9\pi}{64}$ in.²; 0.44 in.² **3.** $\dfrac{529\pi}{16}$ in.²; 103.87 in.²

5. about 11.14 m **7.** about 15.39 yd

9. about 30.16 ft **11.** about 21.21 in.²

13. about 223.88 cm²

15. about 11.50 ft **17.** about 88.59 m

19. about 9.11 m **21.** about 107.68 m

23. about 114.16 m² **25.** about 110.01 in.²

27. about 12.57 cm²

29. The numerator should be 120°, not 240°. Area of sector $RST = \dfrac{120°}{360°} \times \pi \times 5^2 \approx 26.2$ m².

6.9 Exercise Set A (pp. 239–240)

1. 201.06 cm² **3.** 615.75 m² **5.** $\dfrac{7}{2}$ cm

7. 76.97 cm² **9.** 1436.76 ft³ **11.** 2144.66 m³

13. 4.83 cm

17. The surface area decreases by a factor of $\dfrac{1}{4}$ from about 452 cm² to about 113 cm² and the volume decreases by a factor of $\dfrac{1}{8}$ from about 905 cm³ to about 113 cm³.

19. 24π mm; 576π mm²; 2304π mm³

21. $\dfrac{7}{2}$ ft; 7π ft; $\dfrac{343}{6}\pi$ ft³ **23.** 18 cm **25.** 2.48 in.³

6.9 Exercise Set B (pp. 241–242)

1. 172.03 m² **3.** 79,422.6 mm³ **5.** 226.19 in.²

7. 2.1 m **9.** 0.6 ft **11.** 2352.07 cm³

13. 124,185.41 in.³ **15.** 21.77 mm³

17. $S = 104.72$ m², $V = 77.57$ m³

19. $S = 6597.34$ cm², $V = 38,788.74$ cm³

21. 16π in.² **23.** 58.43 ft, 1086.87 ft², 3369.28 ft³

25. 29 yd, 182.21 yd, 102,160.4 yd³

27. The surface area decreases by a factor of $\dfrac{1}{4}$ from about 2827 ft² to about 707 ft² and the volume decreases by a factor of $\dfrac{1}{8}$ from about 14,137 ft³ to about 1767 ft³.

UNIT 7

7.1 Exercise Set A (pp. 250–251)

1. 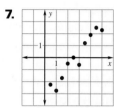 ; positive correlation; $r \approx 1$

5. *Sample answer:* $y = -\dfrac{2}{3}x + \dfrac{9}{4}$

7.

Sample answer:
$y = 1.2x - 3.33$

9.

Sample answer:
$y = 2$

11. *Sample answer:* $y = -10x + 165.8$

13. $y = 2x - 6$

7.1 Exercise Set B (pp. 252–253)

1. yes; More time spent studying results in more complete knowledge of the subject.

3. *Sample answer:* $y = 4.2x - 3.6$

5.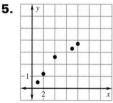

Sample answer: $y = 0.4x + 0.33$

7. Organize one of the data sets in increasing order in the table. Observe the pattern of the corresponding values of the second data set as the values of the first data set increase.

9. 20.14 million

11. *Sample answer:* $y = 19.89x + 1006.16$

13. negative correlation

7.2 Exercise Set A (p. 257)

1. $y = x^2$ **3.** $y = (x - 2)^2 - 4$

5. $y = (x - 3)(x - 2)$ **7.** $y = (x + 5)(x - 5)$

9. $y = 4x(x - 4)$ **11.** $y = x^2 - 3$

13. $y = x^2 - x + 1$ **15.** $y = -x^2 + 2x - 4$

17. $P = -0.2t^2 + 2.1t + 23$

19. $C = 0.07t^2 + 0.16t + 2.3$

7.2 Exercise Set B (p. 258)

1. $y = 2(x - 1)^2 + 2$ **3.** $y = 2\left(x - \dfrac{3}{4}\right)^2 + 2$

5. $y = (x + 3)(x - 7)$ **7.** $y = 0.5(x + 2)(x - 1.5)$

9. $y = -\dfrac{3}{8}(x + 2)\left(x - \dfrac{5}{4}\right)$ **11.** $y = -2x^2 - 3x + 7$

13. $y = \dfrac{1}{2}x^2 + 2x - 3$ **15.** $y = 3x^2 - \dfrac{7}{2}x - \dfrac{3}{2}$

17. a. $y = -0.037x^2 - 0.083x + 10.02$;
$y = -0.05x^2 - 0.01x + 10.01$ **b.** 2013

7.3 Exercise Set A (p. 261)

1. 11.4; 9; 8 **3.** 50; 48; 44

5. about 0.48; 0.36, 0.36 **7.** 47; 18.56

9. 8; about 2.6 **11.** 18; 6.1

13. The numbers need to be written in increasing order prior to choosing the median; 11

15. 44; 44; 40; 12; 3.8 **17.** 114.4; 110; 110; 35; 10.1

7.3 Exercise Set B (p. 262)

1. 12.25; 13; 14 **3.** 103.2; 103.5; 109

5. 5.2375; 5.9; 7.6 **7.** 9; about 3.0

9. 1.6; about 0.5 **11.** 380; about 119.6

13. about 26.1; 25.85; none; 6.8; about 1.9

15. about 0.0018; about 0.0015 **17.** Machine 2

7.4 Exercise Set A (p. 266)

1. 0.16 **3.** 0.9985 **5.** 0.3% **7.** 0.4985 **9.** 0.84

11. 0.84 **13.** 0.0107 **15.** 0.9821 **17.** 0.9990

19. The z-value was calculated incorrectly;
$z = \dfrac{6.5 - 7}{1} = -0.5$, $P(z \le -0.5) = 0.3085$

7.4 Exercise Set B (p. 267)

1. 0.0015 **3.** 0.975 **5.** 18.35% **7.** 0.8385

9. 0.16 **11.** 0.975 **13.** 0.0007 **15.** 0.5506

17. 0.1586 **19.** 0.7

7.5 Exercise Set A (pp. 270)

1. random sample; unbiased; The sample is representative of the population (car owners).

3. systematic; biased; Students in the math club are more likely to prefer math than other students.

5. ±5.3% **7.** ±2.0% **9.** ±4.5% **11.** ±1.1%

13. 625 people **15.** 1372 people

17. 40,000 people **19.** 178 people

21. between 6.5% and 15.5% **23.** 3.7%

25. 1600 kids

7.5 Exercise Set B (p. 271)

1. self-selected; unbiased; People visiting the team web site would not be biased toward any one particular player.

3. random; unbiased; Selecting employees at random would eliminate any chances of bias.

5. ±3.5% **7.** ±3.9% **9.** ±1.1% **11.** ±0.9%

13. 384 people **15.** 6944 people **17.** 918 people

19. 20,408 people **21.** between 67.5% and 76.9%

23. 308 people

7.6 Exercise Set A (p. 275)

1. *Sample Answer:* 42, 125, 41, 107, 3

3. *Sample Answer:* 80, 95, 63, 71, 76

5. The sample is not representative of the entire school because it is biased because members of the football team are likely to name football as their favorite sport. *Sample Answer:* Ethan could assign a number to every student in the school (or use student identification numbers) and generate random numbers to select students for a sample.

7. The sample mean is greater than the population mean and the sample standard deviation is less than the population standard deviation.

9. The standard deviation of a sample is less than the standard deviation of the population.

11. The mean and standard deviation of Chandra's sample are less than the corresponding population parameters. The mean of Xavier's sample is greater than the population mean and the standard deviation of his sample is less than the population standard deviation.

7.6 Exercise Set B (p. 276)

1. No; members of the sailing club are more likely than other students to spend time sailing during the summer.

3. *Sample Answer:* 639, 603, 607, 587, 554, 529, 578, 566, 642, 544, 669, 583

5. The sample mean and the sample standard deviation are less than the corresponding population parameters.

7. The means of different samples from the same population vary and can be greater than the population mean or less than the population mean.

9. The mean and standard deviation of the store manager's sample are less than the corresponding population parameters. The mean of the cashier's sample is greater than the population mean and the standard deviation of the cashier's sample is less than the population standard deviation.

7.7 Exercise Set A (pp. 281)

1. quadratic; The graph is in the shape of a parabola.

3. exponential; The graph rises rapidly and begins several units above the origin.

7. $y = 0.4x + 58.4$; 106kg

7.7 Exercise Set B (p. 282)

1. cubic; The graph rises, levels off, and then rises again. **3.** quadratic; The graph is the shape of a parabola. **5.** $y = 1.81(2.13)^x$; Use an exponential model because the graph rises slowly at first and then rises rapidly.

7. $y = 2.78x + 33.87$

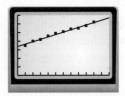